Workbook by **Monica Prieto**
Lab Manual by **Silvia Sobral**

Student Activities Manual

to Accompany

MOSAICOS

Spanish as a World Language

Fourth Edition

Matilde Olivella de Castells
Emerita, California State University, Los Angeles

Elizabeth Guzmán
College of Saint Benedict, St. John's University

Paloma Lapuerta
Central Connecticut State University

Carmen García
Arizona State University

PEARSON
Prentice Hall

Upper Saddle River, NJ 07458

Executive Editor: Bob Hemmer
Editorial Assistant: Debbie King
Executive Director of Market Development: Kristine Suárez
Director of Editorial Development: Julia Caballero
Production Supervision: Claudia Dukeshire
Project Manager: Amy Rose of Interactive Composition Corporation
Asst. Director of Production: Mary Rottino
Supplements Editor: Meriel Martínez Moctezuma
Media Editor: Samantha Alducin
Media Production Manager: Roberto Fernández
Prepress and Manufacturing Buyer: Christina Helder
Prepress and Manufacturing Assistant Manager: Mary Ann Gloriande
Cover Art Director: Jayne Conte
Cover Design: Bruce Kenselaar
Director, Image Resource Center: Melinda Reo
Manager, Rights and Permissions IRC: Zina Arabia
Manager, Visual Research: Beth Boyd Brenzel
Manager, Cover Visual Research & Permissions: Karen Sanatar
Cover Image: Antonio Gaudi y Coronet. Mosaics in Park Guell, Barcelona, Spain
Photographer: Charles Lenars
Sr. Marketing Manager: Jacquelyn Zautner
Marketing Assistant: William J. Bliss
Publisher: Phil Miller

© 2006 by Pearson Education, Inc.
Upper Saddle River, NJ 07458

Printed in the United States of America

10 9 8 7 6 5 4 3 2

ISBN: 0-13-192326-9

Pearson Education LTD., London
Pearson Education Australia PTY, Limited, Sydney
Pearson Education Singapore, Pte. Ltd.
Pearson Education North Asia Ltd., Hong Kong
Pearson Education Canada, Ltd., Toronto
Pearson Educación de México, S.A. de C.V.
Pearson Education—Japan, Tokyo
Pearson Education Malaysia, Pte. Ltd.
Pearson Education, Upper Saddle River

Contents

Lección preliminar

Bienvenidos

LAS PRESENTACIONES

P-1   Presentaciones. Mary is spending a month in Zihuatanejo, Mexico. She has just met a few people, but her Spanish is not very good, so she does not know how to respond. Help Mary choose the appropriate responses.

1. CARLOS: Me llamo Carlos González, ¿y tú?

    MARY: a. Mucho gusto.   b. Me llamo Mary Jones.

2.   ROSA: Mary, mi amigo Juan.

    MARY: a. Encantada.   b. ¿Cómo te llamas?

3. ANABEL: Hola, ¿cómo te llamas?

    MARY: Me llamo Mary Jones.

  ANABEL: Mucho gusto.

    MARY: a. Muy bien, gracias.   b. Igualmente.

P-2   ¡Qué lío! Your best friend is recounting a Spanish conversation to you, but his Spanish is not good, and he has mixed everything up. Help your friend order the sentences so that the conversation makes sense.

1. _____   a. Igualmente, Marina.

2. _____   b. Encantada, Carlos.

3. _____   c. Hola, ¿cómo se llama usted?

4. _____   d. Adela, mi amigo Carlos.

5. _____   e. Me llamo Adela Pérez.

6. _____   f. Mucho gusto, Adela.

7. _____   g. Soy Marina Camacho, ¿y usted?

8. _____   h. Mucho gusto.

SALUDOS, DESPEDIDAS, EXPRESIONES DE CORTESÍA

P-3 **Al teléfono.** You work for a company in Mexico, answering phones and directing calls to the appropriate person. How would you greet these people at the following times of day?

1. 9:00 a.m. _____

2. 3:00 p.m. _____

3. 10:30 a.m. _____

4. 12:10 p.m. _____

5. 10:00 p.m. _____

6. 7:00 p.m. (there is still daylight) _____

P-4 **¡Ayuda!** Mike has been invited to a Latin party by a girl he likes a lot. He knows that everyone at the party will be speaking Spanish. Help Mike rehearse the best response in the following situations.

1. CARLOS: Buenas noches, Mike.

   MIKE: a. Buenas noches.   b. ¿Cómo está usted?   c. ¿Cómo estás?

2. MIKE: Hola, Elena.

   ELENA: Hola, Mike.

   MIKE: a. ¿Qué tal?   b. Mucho gusto.   c. Igualmente.

3. MIKE: Hola.

   JUAN: Hola. ¿Qué tal?

   MIKE: a. Lo siento.   b. Bastante bien.   c. Gracias.

4. LINDA: Hasta luego, Mike.

   MIKE: a. Hola. ¿Qué tal?   b. Buenos días.   c. Adiós.

P-5   Formal o informal. As you already know, in Spanish there are formal and informal forms of introducing yourself and meeting people. Indicate whether the following introductions are formal or informal.

1.   SRA. GÓMEZ: Buenos días, señor González.   a. formal

      SR. GONZÁLEZ: Buenos días, señora Gómez. ¿Cómo está usted?   b. informal

      SRA. GÓMEZ: Bien, gracias. ¿Y usted?

      SR. GONZÁLEZ: Bastante bien, gracias.

2.   ROSA: Hola, ¿qué tal?   a. formal

      PEDRO: Regular.   b. informal

      ROSA: ¡Oh! Lo siento.

3.   ISABEL: Hola, ¿cómo se llama?   a. formal

      CARLOS: Me llamo Carlos Aguirre, ¿y usted?   b. informal

      ISABEL: Soy Isabel Carrasco. Encantada.

      CARLOS: Igualmente.

4.   JUANA: Marisol, mi amiga Inés.   a. formal

      MARISOL: Hola Inés. Mucho gusto.   b. informal

      INÉS: Mucho gusto. ¿Cómo estás?

      MARISOL: Bien, gracias. ¿Y tú?

      INÉS: Muy bien, gracias.

P-6   Situaciones. It is important to be polite even in a second language. Decide what Spanish expression you would use in these situations.

    a. perdón   b. de nada   c. por favor   d. gracias

_____ 1. You spilled a cup of coffee on your friend.

_____ 2. You want your friend to lend you her class notes.

_____ 3. You want your father to lend you money.

_____ 4. Your mother thanks you for helping her.

_____ 5. You greeted a stranger, thinking he was someone you knew.

_____ 6. You thank your brother for lending you his car.

EL ALFABETO

P-7   De viaje. You are planning to spend your spring break in Cancún. You call the hotel to get the address to give it to the cab driver when you are at the airport. The receptionist spells the address so that there are no mistakes. Write the address as he tells you.

1. pe, a, ese, e, o   ka, u, ka, u, ele, ce, a con acento, ene

_____

2. zeta, o, ene, a   hache, o, te, e, ele, e, ere, a

_____

3. ce, a, ene, ce, u con acento, ene

_____

4. eme, e con acento, equis, i, ce, o

_____

IDENTIFICACIÓN Y DESCRIPCIÓN DE PERSONAS

P-8   ¿De qué habla? Read the descriptions Montserrat wrote and decide to what person or object she is referring.

1. Es atractivo.
   a. el campus   b. los estudiantes   c. la chica

2. Eres valiente.
   a. yo   b. la profesora   c. tú

3. Soy responsable.
   a. el chico   b. yo   c. el estudiante

4. Es sentimental.
   a. tú   b. el actor   c. las profesoras

P-9 Sus opiniones. What do you think about the following people? Select the adjective that best describes how you feel about that person, and write a sentence expressing your opinion.

MODELO: El presidente de EE.UU.   a. responsable   b. tradicional   c. liberal
El presidente de EE.UU. es responsable.

1. Picasso   a. creativo   b. perfeccionista   c. romántico

_____.

2. Mi familia   a. cómica   b. sincera   c. optimista

_____.

3. Mi amigo   a. optimista   b. interesante   c. importante

_____.

4. Tú   a. dinámico/a   b. paciente   c. eficiente

_____.

5. Yo   a. extrovertido/a b. generoso/a   c. sincero/a

_____.

P-10 ¿Cómo son? Marcos's friend Teresa is giving a party (**una fiesta**), and Marcos is inviting Irene to come even though Irene does not know Teresa. Marcos calls Irene on the phone. Read their conversation and then indicate whether the statements below are cierto (**C**) or falso (**F**).

MARCOS: Hola, Irene, ¿qué tal?

IRENE: Muy bien, ¿y tú?

MARCOS: Muy bien, gracias. Mi amiga Teresa da (*is giving*) una fiesta. ¿Vienes? (*Are you coming?*)

IRENE: ¿Y cómo es Teresa?

MARCOS: Es muy interesante y popular.

IRENE: ¿Sí?

MARCOS: Sí, Teresa es optimista y cómica.

IRENE: Entonces (*So*) es divertida.

MARCOS: Sí, y es muy dinámica y atractiva.

IRENE: ¿Dinámica? Yo también (*too*) soy muy dinámica y atlética.

MARCOS: También (*Also*) eres muy atractiva.

IRENE: Gracias, Marcos.

1. _____ Irene está bien.

2. _____ La amiga de Marcos se llama Teresa.

3. _____ Teresa es muy amiga de Irene.

4. _____ Teresa es interesante y divertida.

5. _____ Irene es atractiva.

COGNADOS

P-11   Opuestos. Jorge and Luis are brothers, but they do not get along very well because they are complete opposites. Based on Jorge's description below, indicate what Luis is like. Note that there are more options than you will need.

a. introvertido	d. moderno	g. activo
b. competente	e. pesimista	h. serio
c. tranquilo	f. tradicional	i. religioso

Jorge   *Luis*

1. optimista   _____

2. liberal   _____

3. extrovertido   _____

4. pasivo   _____

5. cómico   _____

6. impaciente   _____

P-12   Los famosos. Decide whether the following sentences are **Cierto** or **Falso**, according to what most people would say about these famous people.

	Cierto	*Falso*
1. Madonna es introvertida y tímida.	_____	_____
2. Ellen Degeneres es cómica.	_____	_____
3. Laura Bush es elegante.	_____	_____
4. Steven Spielberg es creativo.	_____	_____
5. Mike Tyson es pasivo y tranquilo.	_____	_____
6. Michael Jordan es atlético.	_____	_____

¿QUÉ HAY EN EL SALÓN DE CLASE?

P-13   **En la clase.** Maricela has been asked to group items in a classroom, but she has done a terrible job. In each of the following groups of items, select the item that does not belong.

1. a. mesa   b. borrador   c. pupitre   d. escritorio

2. a. computadora   b. televisor   c. grabadora   d. cesto

3. a. bolígrafo   b. lápiz   c. cuaderno   d. tiza

4. a. silla   b. pizarra   c. tiza   d. borrador

5. a. libro   b. cuaderno   c. mochila   d. papel

P-14   **¿Qué tiene?** Identify the items Raúl has in his Spanish class.

1. _____

2. _____

3. _____

4. _____

5. _____

¿DÓNDE ESTÁ?

P-15   **El salón de clase.** Think about your Spanish class and use the phrases below to indicate the location of the following objects and persons.

enfrente de   al lado de   debajo de

sobre   detrás de   entre

1. el profesor/la profesora: _____.

2. el cesto: _____.

3. la ventana: _____.

4. tu mochila: _____.

5. el reloj: _____.

P-16   **La obra de teatro.** You are watching a play and talking on the phone with your boyfriend. Explain to your boyfriend where the actors are located on the stage.

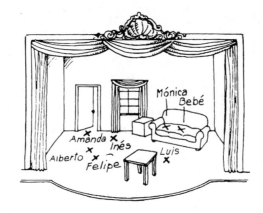

MODELO: Amanda: *Amanda está enfrente de la puerta.*

1. Alberto: _____

2. Luis: _____

3. El bebé: _____

4. Mónica: _____

5. Inés: _____

6. Felipe: _____

LOS NÚMEROS 0 A 99

P-17 Números de teléfono. Tonight is the first time María has gone out on a date with her husband since she had a baby. She is trying to write down all the important numbers for the babysitter in case of an emergency. The numbers are mixed up; help María match the numbers with the right people.

1. _____ pediatra: seis, sesenta y dos, noventa, quince   a. 843-2782

2. _____ abuela: ocho, cuarenta y tres, ochenta y uno, cincuenta y dos   b. 685-2213

3. _____ restaurante: seis, ochenta y cinco, veintidós, trece   c. 518-6339

4. _____ hospital: ocho, cuarenta y tres, veintisiete, ochenta y dos   d. 662-9015

5. _____ móvil: cinco, dieciocho, sesenta y tres, treinta y nueve   e. 843-8152

P-18 Obras y cortes. This city map shows the streets of Madrid undergoing repairs (**obras**) and the ones closed to traffic (**cortes**). You are living in Madrid and have been asked to give a report on the ongoing repairs to your local neighborhood association. Look at the map and give the information requested. Spell out the numbers required.

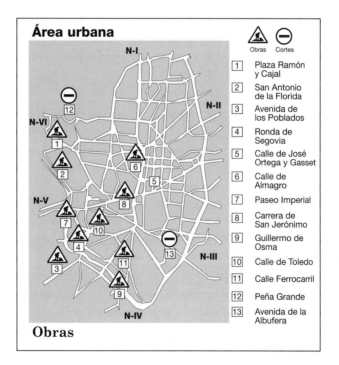

1. Número de obras: _____

2. Número de cortes: _____

3. ¿Dónde está la obra uno? _____

4. ¿Dónde está la obra diez? _____

5. ¿Dónde está el corte trece? _____

P-19   Problemas. Are you good with mathematics? Solve the following problems, spelling out the answer.

MODELO: 1 + 3 = *cuatro*

1. 10 + 1 = _____
2. 7 + 6 = _____
3. 35 – 12 = _____
4. 99 – 22 = _____

5. 50 + 15 = _____
6. 20 + 2 = _____
7. 15 + 21 = _____
8. 48 – 2 = _____

LOS DÍAS DE LA SEMANA Y LOS MESES DEL AÑO

P-20   Los días de la semana. Indicate which day of the week best corresponds to each statement.

1. The first day of the weekend.   _____
2. The first day of the week on calendars in most Hispanic countries. _____
3. The last day of the week on calendars in most Hispanic countries. _____
4. Thanksgiving is celebrated on this day.   _____
5. When the 13th falls on this day, some consider it bad luck.   _____

P-21   Los meses. Think of the holidays on the United States calendar, and match each holiday with the appropriate month.

1. _____ el Día del Trabajo (*Labor Day*)   a. julio
2. _____ el Día de Año Nuevo (*New Year's Day*)   b. septiembre
3. _____ el Día de San Patricio (*Saint Patrick's*)   c. diciembre
4. _____ el Día de Acción de Gracias (*Thanksgiving*)   d. febrero
5. _____ el Día de la Raza (*Columbus Day*)   e. enero
6. _____ el Día de la Independencia   f. noviembre
7. _____ el Día de Navidad (*Christmas*)   g. octubre
8. _____ el Día de los Presidentes   h. marzo

P-22   Secuencias. Look at the following sequences and complete them with the day or month that best completes them.

1. lunes, martes, _____

2. octubre, noviembre, _____

3. viernes, _____, domingo

4. junio, julio, _____

5. febrero, _____, abril

6. miércoles, _____, viernes

7. domingo, lunes, _____

8. noviembre, diciembre, _____

P-23   Calendario escolar. Cristina is a student from Spain who is coming to the United States to attend the university. She needs to know when some of the school events take place. Answer Cristina's questions, giving the appropriate months or days.

MODELO: ¿En qué mes son (*are*) las vacaciones de primavera (*spring*)? *marzo*

1. ¿En qué mes empieza (*starts*) el semestre de otoño (*autumn*)? _____

2. ¿En qué mes empieza el semestre de primavera (*spring*)? _____

3. ¿Qué día de la semana los estudiantes nunca (*never*) tienen (*have*) clase? _____

4. ¿Cuándo (*When*) es la orientación para (*for*) estudiantes nuevos (*new*)? _____

LA HORA

P-24   Los horarios de vuelo. Mario studies in Madrid and wants to go on a vacation with his friends. He calls Iberia, the major Spanish airline, to find out their domestic and international destinations (**destinos**) and flights (**vuelos**). You kindly assist Mario. Look at the schedule below and give Mario the information he requests. Do not use numerals to write the times, and do not forget to indicate morning (**de la mañana**), afternoon (**de la tarde**), or night (**de la noche**).

MODELO: ¿A qué hora sale el vuelo con destino a Barcelona?
A las doce y veinte de la mañana.

VUELOS INTERNACIONALES

CIUDAD DE SALIDA (*Departure city*)	DESTINO	NÚMERO DE VUELO	HORA DE SALIDA
Madrid	Buenos Aires	IB2527	1:10 p.m.
Madrid	Chicago	IB695	3:20 p.m.
Madrid	Londres	IB1287	8:30 a.m.
Madrid	Miami	IB496	7:45 a.m.
Madrid	Montreal	IB87	6:25 p.m.

VUELOS NACIONALES

CIUDAD DE SALIDA	DESTINO	NÚMERO DE VUELO	HORA DE SALIDA
Madrid	Barcelona	IB123	12:20 p.m.
Madrid	Bilbao	IB945	11:20 a.m.
Madrid	Sevilla	IB587	9:35 a.m.
Madrid	Mallorca	IB234	10:55 a.m.

Teléfonos de información:

Atención al cliente: (92) 636-1840, de lunes a viernes de 8:00 de la mañana a 5:00 de la tarde.

Iberia en el aeropuerto: (92) 525-8814, todos los días de 6:00 de la mañana a 11:00 de la noche.

---

1. ¿A qué hora es la salida del vuelo IB695 con destino a Chicago? _____

2. ¿A qué hora es la salida del vuelo con destino a Buenos Aires? _____

3. ¿A qué hora es la salida del vuelo con destino a Sevilla? _____

4. ¿A qué hora es la salida del vuelo con destino a Mallorca? _____

5. ¿A qué hora es la salida del vuelo con destino a Londres? _____

6. ¿A qué hora es el vuelo más temprano (*earliest*)? _____

7. ¿A qué hora es el vuelo más tarde (*latest*)? _____

P-25 **Las clases.** María and Susana have to take the same classes this semester: Spanish, communications, history, literature, and English. Susana does not like María and does not want to take any classes at the same time as María. Below you can see the possible class schedule and María's schedule. At what times does Susana have to take her classes to avoid María? Spell out the appropriate times, and remember to indicate morning (**de la mañana**) or afternoon (**de la tarde**).

Horario de clases:

ESPAÑOL	COMUNICACIÓN	HISTORIA	LITERATURA	INGLÉS
Sec. 1 9:30 a.m.	Sec. 1 11:00 a.m.	Sec. 1 12:30 p.m.	Sec. 1 9:30 a.m.	Sec. 1 10:40 a.m.
Sec. 2 1:00 a.m.	Sec. 2 2:30 p.m.	Sec. 2 4:45 p.m.	Sec. 2 11:00 a.m.	Sec. 2 2:15 p.m.

Clases de María:

Español, Sección 2   Historia, Sección 1   Comunicación, Sección 1

Literatura, Sección 1   Inglés, Sección 2

Clases de Susana:

1. Hora de la clase de español: _____

2. Hora de la clase de historia: _____

3. Hora de la clase de literatura: _____

4. Hora de la clase de comunicación: _____

5. Hora de la clase de inglés: _____

P-26 **Una graduación.** Your brother has received the following invitation to his friend's graduation from medical school. He is away for the weekend and calls to chat with you. You tell him about the invitation in the mail, and he asks you to open it and give him the information. Answer your brother's questions about the invitation.

Nombre: _____ Fecha: _____

El Presidente y Decano, La Facultad
y la Clase Graduada de la
Escuela Superior de Medicina de Ponce
tienen el placer de invitarle a la
Ceremonia de Graduación
que se celebrará el
Sábado, 26 de mayo de 2005
a las 10:00 de la mañana
en el Teatro La Perla (Ponce)
Le seguirá recepción
a las 11:45 de la mañana

1. ¿Qué día de la semana es la graduación? _____

2. ¿En qué mes es la graduación? _____

3. ¿A qué hora es la ceremonia? _____

4. ¿A qué hora es la recepción? _____

5. ¿Dónde es la ceremonia de graduación? _____

EXPRESIONES ÚTILES EN LA CLASE

P-27 ¿Qué dice usted? This is your first semester taking Spanish, and it is likely that your class is taught in Spanish. You will find situations in which you need to speak in Spanish. In the following situations indicate what you would say.

a. Otra vez. b. No sé. c. No comprendo. d. Más alto, por favor.

1. _____ Quiere (*you want*) que la profesora repita (*repeat*).
2. _____ No puede oír (*cannot hear*) bien.
3. _____ Tiene problemas de comprensión.
4. _____ Ignora la respuesta (*answer*).

P-28 ¿Quién lo dice? Indicate who would be most likely to say the following statements in a Spanish classroom, the student (**estudiante**) or the instructor (**profesor**).

	Estudiante	*Profesor*
1. ¿Comprenden?	_____	_____
2. ¿En qué página?	_____	_____
3. ¿Tienen alguna pregunta?	_____	_____
4. Más despacio, por favor.	_____	_____
5. Tengo una pregunta.	_____	_____
6. Presente.	_____	_____

LAS PRESENTACIONES Fecha: _____

P-29 **Presentaciones.** María and Isabel are meeting for the first time. Listen to María and choose the appropriate response for Isabel.

1. a. Mucho gusto.   b. Encantada.   c. Me llamo Isabel.

2. a. ¿Cómo te llamas?   b. Igualmente.   c. ¿Y tú?

3. a. ¿Y tú?   b. Mucho gusto.   c. Igualmente.

P-30 **¿Formal o informal?** Remember that in Spanish you can address someone in a formal or an informal manner. Listen to the introductions once and choose **formal** o **informal** to indicate how the speakers are addressing each other.

Conversación 1.   a. formal   b. informal

Conversación 2.   a. formal   b. informal

Conversación 3.   a. formal   b. informal

SALUDOS, DESPEDIDAS, EXPRESIONES DE CORTESÍA

P-31 **Saludos y despedidas.** Listen to the conversations and select the greeting and farewell expressions each speaker uses.

	MARÍA	CARLOS	SR. VÁZQUEZ	SRTA. ALONSO
Buenos días.				
Buenas tardes.				
Buenas noches.				
¡Hola!				
¿Qué tal?				
Hasta luego.				
Hasta mañana.				
Hasta pronto.				
Adiós.				

P-32   **¿Tú o usted?** Listen to the conversations in exercise P-31 again. This time indicate in which conversation you hear the following:

1. tú   a. Conversación 1   b. Conversación 2

2. usted   a. Conversación 1   b. Conversación 2

3. ¿Qué tal?   a. Conversación 1   b. Conversación 2

4. ¿Cómo estás?   a. Conversación 1   b. Conversación 2

5. ¿Cómo está usted?   a. Conversación 1   b. Conversación 2

6. Based on what you observed, which   a. Conversación 1   b. Conversación 2
   conversation is more formal?

P-33   **¿Cómo están?** Listen once to the conversation between Tomás, Pedro, and Ana to get the gist of it. Then listen again and fill in the blanks with words to describe how they are feeling. Answer the two questions that follow.

1. TOMÁS: ¡Hola Ana, Pedro! ¿Qué tal?

   ANA: _____, ¿y tú?

2. TOMÁS: Bastante _____.

   PEDRO: Lo siento, Tomás.

3. TOMÁS: ¿Y cómo estas tú, Pedro?

   PEDRO: Yo estoy _____, gracias.

4. Who is feeling best? _____

5. Who is feeling worst? _____

P-34   **Cortesía.** Listen to some statements and respond appropriately both orally and in writing below. By saying the answers out loud as well as writing them down, you practice pronunciation and reinforce the new vocabulary and forms, helping you remember them better later.

Por favor.	Buenos días.	Gracias.	Perdón.
Buenas tardes.	Adiós.	Bien, ¿y tú?	De nada.

1. _____   4. _____

2. _____   5. _____

3. _____

P-35   Más expresiones. Toni is studying Spanish in Mexico City. He is going to have lunch before the afternoon classes start, and he encounters the situations below. Read each situation and think of appropriate expressions he could use in each case. Then listen to Toni and place each expression he uses next to the appropriate situation.

1. Toni is going to lunch but will be coming back later. Toni says good-bye to his classmates. _____

2. Toni is trying to leave the classroom, but another student is blocking the door. Toni politely lets her know that he needs to move past her. _____

3. The student at the door moves aside and lets Toni walk out. Toni thanks her.
    _____

4. As he walks out, he bumps into his Spanish grammar teacher. Toni apologizes.
    _____

5. He says good-bye to her; they will see each other again tomorrow. _____

EL ALFABETO

P-36   Nombres hispanos. You and your friends are organizing a little party, and you are in charge of calling six of the guests. Look at the list of guests below. Listen to your friend as he spells the names of the six friends you have to call. Mark their names in the list below.

Gregorio	_____	Beatriz	_____
Yolanda	_____	Iñaki	_____
Rosana	_____	Francisco	_____
Jorge	_____	Luis Alfredo	_____
Ignacio	_____	Joaquín	_____
Roberto	_____		

P-37   Más nombres hispanos. One of your friends wants to invite some other people, and she asks you to add their names to the guest list. Listen to her as she spells their names, and write them in the spaces below. Be sure to use capital letters when necessary!

1. _____   _____

2. _____   _____

3. _____

4. _____   _____

IDENTIFICACIÓN Y DESCRIPCIÓN DE PERSONAS

 P-38   **¿Sí o no?** Felipe sees his friend Linda talking to another girl he does not know. Afterward he wants to find out more about her. Listen to their conversation and indicate whether each statement is **Cierto** or **Falso**. Do not worry if you do not understand every word.

	CIERTO	FALSO
1. Linda está muy mal.	_____	_____
2. La amiga de Linda se llama Carmen.	_____	_____
3. Carmen es muy amiga de Felipe.	_____	_____
4. Carmen es inteligente, activa y seria.	_____	_____

P-39   **¿Cómo son Felipe y Carmen?** Linda wants to arrange for Felipe and Carmen to meet because she thinks they are similar and would get along, but Carmen is not sure. Listen to their conversation and mark whether the following features are mentioned to describe Carmen, Felipe or both (*los dos*).

1. optimista   a. Felipe   b. Carmen   c. los dos

2. idealista   a. Felipe   b. Carmen   c. los dos

3. sentimental   a. Felipe   b. Carmen   c. los dos

4. realista   a. Felipe   b. Carmen   c. los dos

5. inteligente   a. Felipe   b. Carmen   c. los dos

PRONUNCIACIÓN

Las vocales

Read carefully the explanation of how Spanish vowels are pronounced. Listen to and repeat the words indicated.

Spanish has five simple vowel sounds, represented in writing by the letters **a**, **e**, **i**, **o**, and **u**. These vowels are tense and short and, for all practical purposes, constant in length. To avoid the glide sound of English stressed vowels (as in *no*, or *same*), do not move your tongue, lips, or jaw. Also, avoid the *uh* sound of English unstressed vowels (as in *opera* and *about*.)

a

The pronunciation of the Spanish **a** is similar to the English *a* in *father*, but shorter and tenser. Listen carefully and then repeat. Imitate the Spanish pronunciation as closely as possible. **Repitan las siguientes palabras** (*Repeat the following words*).

| llama | mañana | banana | Panamá | encantada |

e

The pronunciation of the Spanish **e** is similar to the English *e* in *they*, but without the glide sound. **Repitan las siguientes palabras.**

| sé | nene | este | Sánchez | bastante |

i

The pronunciation of the Spanish **i** is similar to the pronunciation of the English *i* in *machine*, but without the glide sound. **Repitan las siguientes palabras.**

| sí | ni | Mimí | Inés | Felipe |

o

The pronunciation of the Spanish **o** is similar to the English *o* in *no*, but without the glide sound. **Repitan las siguientes palabras.**

| no | con | Mónica | noches | profesor |

U

The pronunciation of the Spanish **u** is similar to the English *u* in *tuna,* but without the glide sound. **Repitan las siguientes palabras.**

su   tú   mucho   uno   usted

COGNADOS

P-40   Similares. There are many English cognates in Spanish. Although these words are often easy to recognize when we see them, the differences between English and Spanish pronunciation may make them more difficult to understand aurally. Look at the list of cognates below and read them out loud, being careful to use Spanish pronunciation. Now listen carefully and select any cognates you hear. Pay attention to how they are pronounced, and repeat the pronunciation.

popular	_____	perfeccionista	_____	creativo	_____
importante	_____	eficiente	_____	generoso	_____
religioso	_____	responsable	_____	imparcial	_____
serio	_____	valiente	_____	sincero	_____
elegante	_____	interesante	_____	pasivo	_____

P-41   Más cognados. Because cognates can be very helpful, it is important to be able to recognize them when you hear them. To practice this skill, listen to the following words, four of which are cognates. Write the cognates in the spaces below in the order you hear them (check your textbook, p. 10 for spelling). Practice pronouncing them as well.

1. _____

2. _____

3. _____

4. _____

¿QUÉ HAY EN EL SALÓN DE CLASE?

P-42   **En el salón de clase.** The classroom in this illustration may be similar to yours. Do you remember the names of people and objects usually found in classrooms? Listen to the recording, identify the object or person in the illustration, and write the corresponding letter in the space provided.

MODELO: You hear: a. una pizarra
You write: __a__

1. _____   4. _____   7. _____   10. _____

2. _____   5. _____   8. _____   11. _____

3. _____   6. _____   9. _____   12. _____

P-43   **¿Están en su salón de clase?** Dan is not sure about the names of these objects. Can you help him? Listen to his questions, and tell him what the right word is. Answer the questions orally and before you write them down.

MODELO: You hear: ¿Qué es esto, una tiza o un borrador?
You say and write: Es un borrador.

1. _____   4. _____

2. _____   5. _____

3. _____   6. _____

¿DÓNDE ESTÁ?

P-44   **¿Qué o quién está...?** You will hear some questions about the location of several people and objects. Look at the illustration and answer each question both orally and by writing in the spaces provided.

MODELO: You hear: ¿Qué está al lado de la pizarra?
You say and write: La puerta.

1. _____   3. _____

2. _____   4. _____

P-45   **¿Dónde está?** Look at the illustration in exercise P-44 again. You will be asked to locate persons and objects in the room. Answer each question orally and by writing in the spaces provided.

MODELO: You hear: ¿Dónde está la pizarra, detrás de la profesora o delante de la profesora?
You say and write: Está detrás de la profesora.

1. _____   3. _____

2. _____   4. _____

P-46   ¿Cómo se llaman? You already know all of your classmate's names except for four: three females and one male. You draw the seating chart to show Manuel, who is also in your class. Listen to him to find out the names of the four classmates. Then select the name of the student in each seat from the options that follow the chart.

1. Natalia	Pedro	Alberto	_____
2. Rosa	Pablo	_____	Irene
3. Carlos	Tomás	_____	Federico
4. _____	Marcela	Carmen	Manuel

a. Marta   b. Ana   c. Gabriela   d. Antonio

LOS NÚMEROS 0 A 99

P-47   Bingo. You are playing Bingo with your friends at the Spanish Club. Listen to the numbers and write them in the spaces provided. Then look at your card and say whether the numbers matched a line (write **línea**), the whole card (write **bingo**) or neither (write **nada**).

B	I	N	G	O
5	16	31	48	62
8	18	38	50	65
10	21		55	68
13	22	42	56	70
15	30	45	60	75

MODELO: You hear: tres
               You write: __3__

1. _____   6. _____
2. _____   7. _____
3. _____   8. _____
4. _____   9. ¿Bingo, línea o nada? _____
5. _____

P-48   Problemas de matemáticas. You are helping your little cousin practice addition. Listen to each math problem, write the problem, and give the correct answer both orally and by writing it in the spaces.

MODELO: You hear: dos más dos
           You write: 2 + 2 = 4
           You say: Dos más dos son cuatro.

1. _____ + _____ = _____   6. _____ + _____ = _____

2. _____ + _____ = _____   7. _____ + _____ = _____

3. _____ + _____ = _____   8. _____ + _____ = _____

4. _____ + _____ = _____   9. _____ + _____ = _____

5. _____ + _____ = _____

P-49   Agenda de teléfonos. You are going to form a study group for your chemistry class, so you write down the phone numbers of the classmates in the group. Listen to them as they say their phone numbers, and note them next to their names.

MODELO: Luis: 477-22-12

1. Amelia: _____   4. Beatriz: _____

2. Susana: _____   5. David: _____

3. Mateo: _____

LOS DÍAS DE LA SEMANA Y LOS MESES DEL AÑO

P-50   Días y meses. Mark is starting to learn Spanish and he is trying to clarify some things about the names of days of the weeks and months. You are going to help him out by marking whether what he is saying is correct (**Sí**) or incorrect (**No**).

	Sí	*No*
1.	_____	_____
2.	_____	_____
3.	_____	_____
4.	_____	_____
5.	_____	_____

5. _____   _____   (Note: la Navidad = *Christmas*)

P-51 **Más días y meses.** Mark is still having some trouble remembering the days of the week and months in Spanish. He is forgetting two days of the week and three months! Listen to him and write the days of the week and months he is forgetting in the spaces provided and in chronological order. Listen as many times as necessary.

Días de la semana: 1. _____   2. _____

Meses del año: 3. _____   4. _____   5. _____

 P-52 **¿Qué día es?** Look at the calendar. You will be asked on what days of the week certain dates fall. Answer each question by writing the appropriate day.

MODELO: You hear: ¿Qué día es el 15?
You answer: Es jueves.

Octubre						
L	M	M	J	V	S	D
			1	2	3	4
5	6	7	8	9	10	11
12	13	14	15	16	17	18
19	20	21	22	23	24	25
26	27	28	29	30	31	

1. _____

2. _____

3. _____

4. _____

5. _____

6. _____

7. _____

LA HORA

 P-53 **¿Qué hora es?** You will hear a time for each clock you see here. If the time you hear corresponds to the time shown on the clock, mark **Sí**. If it does not correspond, mark **No**.

	Sí	*No*
1.	_____	_____
2.	_____	_____
3.	_____	_____
4.	_____	_____
5.	_____	_____

P-54   **La hora del tren.** Your friend Cara is traveling in Spain and has asked you to pick her up at the station today. You know that she is arriving at 8:50 p.m., but you are unsure where she is coming from. Listen to the arrival times for tonight and write them down as in the *Modelo*. Do not worry if you do not understand everything you hear; just focus on the relevant information: city names and times. Finally, figure out what city she is coming from and write the name of the city in the last space.

MODELO: You hear: El tren de Madrid llega a las once y media. (llega = *arrives*)
                You write: Madrid: <u>11:30</u>

1. Valencia: _____   4. Málaga: _____

2. Sevilla: _____   5. Barcelona: _____

3. Toledo: _____   6. Cara llega de: _____

P-55   **¿A qué hora sale el autobús?** Cara has not even returned yet, and she is already planning her next trip! She cannot make up her mind, so she decides she will go wherever the earliest bus takes her. She asks you to find out for her so you call the station and listen to tomorrow's departure schedule. Take notes to help you remember. Then select the city where Cara will go. (**sale** = *departs*)

Málaga   _____   Valencia   _____

Madrid   _____   Toledo   _____

Barcelona   _____

EXPRESIONES ÚTILES EN LA CLASE

P-56   **En la clase.** You will hear several expressions that are frequently used in class. Write in the space provided the letter corresponding to the expression that describes each illustration.

a   b   c   d

1. _____   2. _____   3. _____   4. _____

P-57   ¡Escuche! You will hear additional class expressions. Choose the appropriate translation.

1. a. Open the book.   b. Close the book.

2. a. Stand up.   b. Sit down.

3. a. Answer.   b. Repeat.

4. a. Read.   b. Write.

PRONUNCIACIÓN

Las consonantes p, t, c, q, s, and z

In this section you will learn to pronounce Spanish consonants that are slightly different from their English counterparts. Carefully read the pronunciation explanations, and repeat after the speaker as indicated.

p

The Spanish **p** is pronounced like the English *p*, but it is never accompanied by the puff of air that often follows the English *p*. Listen to the pronunciation of these two words and note the differences.

Spanish	*English*
papá	papa

Now listen to and repeat the following words.

Pepe   pino   pan   peso   poco   popular

t

The Spanish **t** is pronounced by placing the tip of the tongue against the back of the upper teeth. It is never accompanied by a puff of air. The English *t*, in contrast, is pronounced by placing the tip of the tongue against the ridge of the upper gum, and it is often followed by a puff of air. **Repitan las siguientes palabras.**

te   tú   tomate tres   está   optimista

c, q, s, and z

The Spanish **c** before a consonant or **a, o,** or **u** is pronounced like an English *k*, but without the puff of air. The Spanish combination of the letters **qu** before **e** or **i** is pronounced like an English *k*, also without a puff of air. **Repitan las siguientes palabras.**

| como | café | cuna | típico | qué | quién |

The Spanish **c** before **e** or **i** is pronounced like the English *c* before *e* or *i*. **Repitan las siguientes palabras.**

| cena | cita | cesto | once | gracias | cinco |

s and z

The Spanish **s** and **z** are pronounced like the English *s* in *some*. Because of the influence of English, you may tend to pronounce the Spanish **s** as *z* when it occurs between vowels. This is never done in Spanish. **Repitan las siguientes palabras.**

| señora | está | ese | casa | zeta | tiza |

Lección 1

Nombre: _____

Fecha: _____

Los estudiantes y la universidad

A PRIMERA VISTA

1-1   El horario de clases. Laura and Chris are two exchange students at the Universidad Complutense in Madrid. They have mixed up their class schedules. Read the descriptions about the courses and indicate who is taking each class, Laura or Chris.

Laura:

a. Esta clase es difícil. Siempre (*Always*) practico mucho (*a lot*) con números y ecuaciones.

b. En esta clase usamos (*we use*) un telescopio para (*in order to*) mirar los planetas. Es fascinante.

c. En esta clase aprendemos sobre (*we learn about*) el pasado (*the past*) de los países. Mi período favorito es la época colonial.

Chris:

a. Ésta (*This*) es mi clase favorita. Trabajo con un mapa y aprendo sobre (*I learn about*) las realidades geofísicas del planeta.

b. En esta clase hablamos sobre la conducta (*behavior*) de las personas. Las teorías de Freud son muy interesantes.

c. En esta clase necesito un diccionario a veces. También (*Also*) visito el laboratorio de lenguas y escucho casetes.

	Laura	*Chris*
1. matemáticas	_____	_____
2. historia	_____	_____
3. geografía	_____	_____
4. español	_____	_____
5. astronomía	_____	_____
6. psicología	_____	_____

1-2   El mentiroso. Miguel is a student at the University of Valencia and is telling Marta about some of the classes offered at the university, but Miguel is lying about some of the classes. Help Marta determine which of Miguel's statements are **Cierto (C)** and which ones are **Falso (F)**.

1. C F   En la clase de biología hablamos de los animales y las plantas. A veces la clase es en el laboratorio y usamos microscopios.
2. C F   En la clase de educación física tocamos el piano y la guitarra.
3. C F   Todos los días en la clase de matemáticas necesito un mapa del mundo (*world*).
4. C F   A veces en la clase de economía necesitamos una calculadora.
5. C F   En la clase de informática usamos mucho las computadoras.

1-3   La vida estudiantil. Here are some activities that students do at the university. In each group, indicate the activity that does not belong.

1. a. mirar televisión   c. montar en bicicleta
   b. escuchar música   d. estudiar para un examen

2. a. comprar tus (*your*) CDs favoritos   c. practicar frisbi
   b. estudiar en la biblioteca   d. conversar en un café

3. a. caminar en el parque   c. estudiar
   b. tomar un examen   d. trabajar con computadoras

4. a. tomar apuntes   c. sacar buenas notas
   b. bailar en una fiesta   d. escuchar casetes en el laboratorio de lenguas

1-4   ¿Qué opina usted? Indicate your opinion about the following, using the adjectives provided.

grande	pequeño	bueno	interesante	aburrido
fácil	difícil	excelente	fascinante	regular

MODELO: su clase de español: *divertida*

1. sus clases: _____
2. sus amigos: _____
3. su casa: _____
4. montar en bicicleta: _____
5. bailar salsa: _____
6. las telenovelas (*soap operas*): _____
7. hablar por teléfono: _____
8. el cine: _____
9. la cafetería de la universidad: _____
10. la playa: _____

1-5   La universidad. Find in this word search the names of six items related to student life in a university.

m	e	b	g	i	m	n	a	s	i	o
a	r	a	r	m	i	e	s	t	l	e
o	i	r	a	n	o	i	c	c	i	d
b	l	e	b	s	t	c	a	s	e	l
i	c	e	a	ñ	g	o	h	f	m	e
b	t	i	d	m	n	c	u	i	f	r
l	h	i	o	c	h	j	i	a	l	a
i	c	a	r	p	s	o	a	m	r	a
o	ñ	e	a	l	i	b	r	e	r	s
t	u	a	d	e	r	n	p	c	o	n
e	u	n	i	v	e	r	o	l	a	p
c	a	l	c	u	l	a	d	o	r	a
a	f	i	l	o	s	o	g	o	n	a

EXPLICACIÓN Y EXPANSIÓN

Síntesis gramatical

1. Subject pronouns

SINGULAR		PLURAL	
yo	*I*	nosotros/as	*we*
tú	*you* (familiar)	vosotros/as	*you* (familiar)
usted	*you* (formal)	ustedes	*you* (formal)
él	*he*	ellos	*they*
ella	*she*	ellas	*they*

2. Present tense of regular -ar verbs

hablar *(to speak)*

	SINGULAR		PLURAL
yo	**hablo**	nosotros/as	**hablamos**
tú	**hablas**	vosotros/as	**habláis**
Ud., él, ella	**habla**	Uds., ellos, ellas	**hablan**

3. Articles and nouns: Gender and number

	SINGULAR			PLURAL		
	MASC.	FEM.		MASC.	FEM.	
DEFINITE ARTICLES	**el**	**la**	*the*	**los**	**las**	*the*
INDEFINITE ARTICLES	**un**	**una**	*a/an*	**unos**	**unas**	*some*

4. Present tense of the verb estar

yo	**estoy**	*I*	*am*
tú	**estás**	*you*	*are*
Ud., él, ella	**está**	*you, he/she*	*are, is*
nosotros/as	**estamos**	*we*	*are*
vosotros/as	**estáis**	*you*	*are*
Uds., ellos, ellas	**están**	*you, they*	*are*

5. Question words

cómo	*how/what*	**cuál(es)**	*which*
dónde	*where*	**quién(es)**	*who*
qué	*what*	**cuánto/a**	*how much*
cuándo	*when*	**cuántos/as**	*how many*
por qué	*why*		

1. Subject pronouns

1-6 **Ana y sus amigos.** Ana and her friends have a very active life at the university. Here are some of their activities. Indicate who does each of the following activities.

MODELO: Compra un diccionario.

(a.) Ana   b. Cristina y Luis   c. Jorge y yo   d. yo

1. Baila salsa en una fiesta.
   a. Ana   b. Ana y Jorge   c. Luis y yo   d. tú

2. Estudian en la biblioteca.
   a. yo   b. Laura y Cristina   c. Luis   d. Ana y yo

3. Escucho los casetes en el laboratorio de lenguas.
   a. Cristina   b. Luis y yo   c. tú   d. yo

4. Trabajas después de (*after*) las clases.
   a. Ana y Laura   b. Luis   c. Cristina   d. tú

5. Sacamos buenas notas.
   a. Ana   b. Luis   c. yo   d. Jorge y yo

1-7 **A conocernos.** Today is the first day of class, and Mario and Carolina have just met. Read their conversation and complete the sentences with the appropriate subject pronoun.

MARIO: Hola. ¿Qué tal? Me llamo Mario. ¿Y (1) _____, cómo te llamas?

CAROLINA: Hola, me llamo Carolina.

MARIO: ¿Qué estudias, Carolina?

CAROLINA: Estudio español, ¿y (2) _____, qué estudias?

MARIO: (3) _____ estudio ciencias sociales. ¿Tienes muchas clases?

CAROLINA: No, (4) _____ tengo cuatro clases este semestre. ¿Y tú?

MARIO: (5) _____ también tengo cuatro clases. ¿Son pocas, verdad?

CAROLINA: Sí, está muy bien. Mi amiga Susana estudia medicina, y (6) _____ tiene (*has*) siete clases este semestre.

MARIO: Sí, mis amigos Carlos y Julián estudian derecho, y (7) _____ también tienen siete clases este semestre.

CAROLINA: (8) _____ tenemos mucha suerte.

2. Present tense of regular *-ar* verbs

1-8   ¿Quién? Rubén and his friends attend the University of Granada and have a very busy life. Read the sentences about their life and indicate who does each of the following activities.

1. _____ Practica español en clase.

2. _____ Escucho música rock.

3. _____ Compran libros para (*for*) la clase de literatura americana.

4. _____ Comes (*eat*) en la cafetería.

5. _____ Preparamos la cena en el apartamento.

6. _____ Miro la televisión por la noche.

7. _____ Estudias en la biblioteca.

8. _____ Habla con su novia por teléfono todos los días.

9. _____ Trabajan en un restaurante.

a. yo

b. tú

c. él/ella

d. nosotros

e. ellos/as

1-9   Lucía. Lucía is a typical student attending the University of Salamanca. Complete the sentences, indicating what you think an average day is like for her.

1. Lucía _____ (llegar/caminar) a la universidad a las ocho de la mañana.

2. Todos los días _____ (estudiar/hablar con su amiga) en la biblioteca.

3. En clase, siempre _____ (conversar con amigos/escuchar al profesor).

4. Por la tarde todos los días _____ (trabajar/estudiar).

5. Por la noche muchas veces _____ (mirar la televisión/escuchar música).

6. Los fines de semana _____ (montar en bicicleta/bailar en una discoteca).

1-10   La vida de los estudiantes. Complete the following sentences, indicating the typical activities of you and your friends at the university.

1. Mis amigos y yo _____ (estudiar/no estudiar) en la biblioteca.

2. Mi amiga _____ (trabajar/no trabajar) después de las clases.

3. Mis amigos _____ (bailar/no bailar) en una fiesta los sábados por la noche.

4. Mi amigo _____ (tomar/no tomar) apuntes en sus clases.

5. Tú _____ (tomar/no tomar) café en la cafetería de la universidad.

6. Yo _____ (mirar/no mirar) la televisión por la noche.

7. Mis amigos y yo _____ (practicar/no practicar) voleibol los sábados.

3. Articles and nouns: Gender and number

1-11   ¡Qué lío! Here are some objects you can find in a university. Arrange the letters to find out what they are. Remember to write in the appropriate article: **el, la, los, las.**

MODELO: plizá   *el lápiz*

1. uardcnsoe _____

2. pama _____

3. rpfoearso _____

4. ppeturi _____

5. oblir _____

6. ssame _____

7. lsails _____

8. boalartioors _____

1-12   ¿Qué necesitan? These people wish to do (**quieren** + *infinitive*) several things but lack the necessary things to do them. Choose from the list the article that they need to complete their task. Remember to include the appropriate indefinite article: **un, una, unos, unas.**

MODELO: Ignacio quiere sacar un libro. ¿Qué necesita? *una biblioteca*

bolígrafos	grabadora	discoteca	diccionario
librería	mapas	televisor	calculadora

1. Irene quiere tomar apuntes. ¿Qué necesita? _____

2. Aurelia quiere buscar el significado (*meaning*) de *escritorio*. ¿Qué necesita?
   _____

3. Marcos quiere escuchar música. ¿Qué necesita? _____

4. Adelia quiere practicar las matemáticas. ¿Qué necesita? _____

5. Miranda quiere comprar un lápiz. ¿Qué necesita? _____

6. Sandra quiere bailar salsa. ¿Qué necesita? _____

7. Beatriz quiere buscar las naciones que limitan (*border*) Colombia. ¿Qué necesita?
   _____

8. Alain quiere mirar el programa *Friends*. ¿Qué necesita? _____

1-13   Una discusión. You have just had an argument with your boyfriend/girlfriend, and you are really upset. She/he is telling you about the things that you need to buy (**necesitas comprar**) when you go shopping. You are so upset that you disagree with him/her on everything. Select one of the options to tell him/her what you think you really need. Remember to include the appropriate article (**un, una, unos, unas**).

MODELO: TU NOVIO/A: Necesito comprar un libro.

                TÚ: No, yo necesito comprar *una mesa* (mesa, silla).

1. TU NOVIO/A: Necesito comprar unos libros.

          TÚ: No, necesitamos comprar _____ (computadora, pizarra).

2. TU NOVIO/A: Necesitamos una silla.

          TÚ: No, necesitamos _____ (sofá, sillón).

3. TU NOVIO/A: Necesito comprar un lápiz.

          TÚ: No, yo necesito comprar _____ (videocasetera, grabadora).

4. TU NOVIO/A: Necesito comprar una mesa.

          TÚ: No, yo necesito comprar _____ (pupitre, escritorio).

5. TU NOVIO/A: Necesitamos unas pizarras.

          TÚ: No, necesitamos _____ (bolígrafos, lápices).

1-14   De compras. Marisa and her son Ricardo are going shopping for Ricardo's back-to-school needs. Read Ricardo's shopping list and tell Marisa the number of items Ricardo needs.

MODELO: libro (6) *seis libros.*

1. lápiz (5) _____
2. bolígrafo (5) _____
3. mochila (2) _____
4. cuaderno (4) _____
5. mapa (3) _____

6. calculadora (2) _____
7. casete (6) _____
8. papel (25) _____
9. libro (8) _____
10. goma (3) _____

4.   Present tense of the verb *estar*

1-15   Una cita. Andrea and Jaime are really good friends. Andrea calls Jaime on his cell phone to see if he wants to meet with her. Complete their conversation with the correct form of **estar.**

ANDREA: Hola, Jaime, soy Andrea. ¿Cómo (1) _____?

JAIME: Hola, Andrea. (2) _____ muy bien, ¿y tú?

ANDREA: Yo, bien gracias. ¿Dónde (3) _____ ahora (*now*)?

JAIME: (4) _____ en casa, y miro la televisión. ¿Y tú?

ANDREA: (5) _____ en la universidad.

JAIME: ¿Laura (6) _____ en la universidad también (*too*)?

ANDREA: No, ella (7) _____ en la oficina, pero llega a las tres. ¿Quieres venir?

JAIME: Sí, nos vemos a las 3:30. ¿Dónde (8) _____ ustedes a las 3:30?

ANDREA: A las 3:30 Laura y yo (9) _____ en la cafetería.

JAIME: Perfecto. Hasta entonces (*Until then*).

1-16 **¿Dónde están?** Consider what the following people are doing to write sentences to indicate where they are. Be sure to conjugate the verb correctly.

MODELO: Juan nada: *Está en la playa.*

      estar en la biblioteca   estar en la librería   estar en el restaurante

      estar en el gimnasio   estar en la discoteca

1. Juan estudia: _____

2. María baila: _____

3. José y Maite comen (*eat*): _____

4. Laura y Roberto practican los aeróbicos: _____

5. Carlos y yo compramos un libro: _____

1-17 **Tu rutina y la de tus amigos.** Write sentences describing where you and your friends are at the following times. Remember to write out the time.

MODELO: El miércoles a las 8:00: *A las ocho de la mañana, estoy en el gimnasio.*

1. Tu amiga, el lunes a las 15:30: _____

2. Tú, los domingos a las 10:00: _____

3. Tus amigos, el martes a las 16:00: _____

4. Tú, el miércoles a las 19:00: _____

5. Tu amigo y tú, el sábado a las 22:00: _____

5. Question words

1-18   La universidad. You just returned home from the university, and your brother, a senior in high school who will start at your college in the fall, wants to know everything about your life at the university. Complete his questions with the appropriate question word.

1. ¿ _____ son los profesores? Los profesores son muy inteligentes.
   a. Cómo   b. Cuándo   c. Qué   d. Dónde

2. ¿ _____ es tu clase favorita? Mi clase favorita es español.
   a. Qué   b. Cómo   c. Por qué   d. Cuál

3. ¿ _____ amigos tienes? Tengo muchos amigos.
   a. Quiénes   b. Cuántos   c. Dónde   d. Cuáles

4. ¿ _____ comes (*eat*)? Como en la cafetería.
   a. Dónde   b. Cuándo   c. Cuál   d. Cuánto

5. ¿ _____ estudias? Estudio por las noches todas los días de la semana.
   a. Quién   b. Por qué   c. Cuándo   d. Cómo

6. ¿ _____ sacas buenas notas? Porque estudio mucho.
   a. Dónde   b. Cuáles   c. Cómo   d. Por qué

7. ¿ _____ es tu profesor favorito? Mi profesor favorito es el de historia.
   a. Quién   b. Cómo   c. Dónde   d. Cuánto

1-19   Interferencias. You are listening to an interview of an exchange student from Spain on the university radio station. However, although you can hear the student, static prevents you from hearing the interviewer. Choose the question that prompted each response.

1. Soy de Madrid.
   a. ¿De dónde eres?
   b. ¿Cómo eres?
   c. ¿Cuál eres?
   d. ¿Quién eres?

2. Me llamo Arturo.
   a. ¿Cuántos años tienes?
   b. ¿Cuál es tu nombre?
   c. ¿Quién es tu amigo?
   d. ¿Cómo se llama el profesor?

3. Tengo seis clases este semestre.
   a. ¿Qué clases tienes?
   b. ¿Cuántas clases tienes?
   c. ¿Cómo son tus clases?
   d. ¿Dónde son tus clases?

4. Trabajo en el periódico de la universidad.
   a. ¿Cuándo trabajas?
   b. ¿Dónde trabajas?
   c. ¿Con quién trabajas?
   d. ¿Cuánto trabajas?

5. Porque quiero aprender sobre la cultura americana.
   a. ¿Cuándo vienes a EE.UU.?
   b. ¿Por qué vienes a EE.UU.?
   c. ¿Cómo vienes a EE.UU.?
   d. ¿Cuánto vienes a EE.UU.?

6. Soy inteligente y divertido.
   a. ¿Qué eres?
   b. ¿Quién eres?
   c. ¿Cómo eres?
   d. ¿Cuál eres?

7. Estoy en EE.UU. por un año.
   a. ¿Cuándo llegas a EE.UU.?
   b. ¿Cómo estás en EE.UU.?
   c. ¿Dónde estás en EE.UU.?
   d. ¿Cuánto tiempo estás en EE.UU.?

8. Estudio en la residencia estudiantil.
   a. ¿Con quién estudias?
   b. ¿Cómo estudias?
   c. ¿Dónde estudias?
   d. ¿Por qué estudias en la residencia?

1-20   La entrevista. A reporter from the school newspaper is interviewing you about your experience at the university. Answer the reporter's questions so that he can write an article about you.

REPORTERO: Hola, ¿cómo estás?

TÚ: (1) _____

REPORTERO: ¿Cómo te llamas?

TÚ: (2) _____

REPORTERO: ¿De dónde eres?

TÚ: (3) _____

REPORTERO: ¿Dónde vives (*you live*) en el campus? (Answer: **Vivo...**)

TÚ: (4) _____

REPORTERO: ¿Cuántas clases tomas este semestre?

TÚ: (5) _____

REPORTERO: ¿Qué clases tomas este semestre?

TÚ: (6) _____

REPORTERO: ¿Cómo son tus clases?

TÚ: (7) _____

REPORTERO: ¿Dónde comes normalmente (*ordinarily*)?

TÚ: (8) _____

REPORTERO: ¿Qué notas sacas?

TÚ: (9) _____

REPORTERO: ¿Cuáles son tus materias favoritas?

TÚ: (10) _____

REPORTERO: Muchas gracias por tu tiempo.

TÚ: De nada. Hasta luego.

1-21   Los famosos. You are working for *People en Español* magazine, and you have to interview a famous person. Choose one of the famous people from the following list and write six questions you would like to ask him/her.

Jennifer Aniston   Shaquille O'Neal   Harrison Ford   Shakira

Oprah Winfrey   Carlos Santana   Britney Spears   Antonio Banderas

1. _____

2. _____

3. _____

4. _____

5. _____

6. _____

ALGO MÁS: SOME REGULAR *-ER* AND *-IR* VERBS

1-22   Mis amigos. Gonzalo is a freshman at the University of Santiago de Compostela and is telling you about his experience and about his new friends during the first year. Complete his description with the appropriate verb forms.

Mis amigos y yo (1) _____ (vivir) en un apartamento. Somos cuatro personas. Yo (2) _____ (estudiar) español. Mi amigo Raúl (3) _____ (estudiar) biología. Carlos y Javier (4) _____ (estudiar) medicina. Por la mañana, yo (5) _____ (preparar) café y los cuatro (6) _____ (desayunar). Más tarde, nosotros (7) _____ (asistir) a clase. A veces, yo (8) _____ (leer) en la biblioteca después de clase. Raúl y Javier (9) _____ (trabajar) después de las clases. Normalmente, Raúl y Javier (10) _____ (comer) en la cafetería. Carlos y yo (11) _____ (comer) en casa. Por la noche, mis amigos (12) _____ (escribir) la tarea. Los viernes por la noche todos (13) _____ (comer) pizza, y los sábados todos (14) _____ (asistir) a una fiesta. Me encanta la vida estudiantil.

1-23 **¿Los conoce bien?** Think of your friends and family. Do you know their routines? For each of the following people, write three sentences describing a typical day. Feel free to use verbs from the list.

comer	estudiar	asistir	escribir	vivir
leer	practicar	aprender	comprar	hablar por teléfono

Su mejor amigo:

1. _____

2. _____

3. _____

Sus padres:

1. _____

2. _____

3. _____

Usted:

1. _____

2. _____

3. _____

MOSAICOS

1-24. **Antes de leer. Programas de estudio.** Look at the list of courses in exercise 1-25, and indicate which of the following statements is more accurate.

a. Es un programa de estudios para estudiantes españoles.

b. Es un programa de estudios para estudiantes internacionales.

1-25 **A leer. Primera fase. La Universidad de Deusto.** Read the following announcement about the University of Deusto in Bilbao (Spain), and then indicate whether the following sentences are **Cierto (C)** or **Falso (F)**.

La Universidad de Deusto, un centro jesuita de enseñanza e investigación (*teaching and research*), y con larga (*long*) tradición, es una de las instituciones privadas más prestigiosas de España. Dos presidentes de España y varios congresistas son ex-alumnos (*alumni*) de esta universidad. Cada año llegan a la Universidad de Deusto estudiantes de todo el mundo. La universidad está en un lugar (*place*) excelente, enfrente del Museo Guggenheim-Bilbao, en el centro de la ciudad. La enseñanza allí utiliza tecnologías modernas.

La universidad ofrece (*offers*) muchos cursos para extranjeros:

SEMESTRE:	VERANO:
• Español 1, 2 y 3	• Español 1, 2 y 3
• Civilización y cultura española	• Civilización y cultura española
• Cultura y lengua vasca	• Literatura española: Siglo XX
• Español para negocios	• España en Europa
• Cine y literatura española	• Español académico
• Literatura española: Siglos XVI–XVII	
• Literatura española: Siglos XVIII–XIX	
• Literatura española: Siglo XX	
• Ficción española: Siglo XX	
• Composición y sintaxis española	
• Historia de España hasta el siglo XVIII	
• Variedades de español	
• Europa en el mundo	

Las Facultades de Derecho, Ingeniería, Economía y otras suplementan la oferta básica. Además, hay excursiones guiadas (*guided tours*) a Madrid, Segovia, Toledo, Burgos, la reserva de la biosfera Urdaibai, la bahía de Vizcaya, el sur de Francia y Pamplona para ver los Sanfermines.

1. C F En la Universidad de Deusto hay pocos (*few*) cursos de español para extranjeros.

2. C F La Universidad de Deusto es una institución nueva.

3. C F La Universidad de Deusto no usa tecnología.

4. C F En la Universidad de Deusto hay clases sobre muchos temas (*subjects*).

5. C F En el programa para extranjeros de la Universidad de Deusto hay sólo (*only*) clases de español.

Segunda fase. Más información. Look again at the description of programs for international students at the University of Deusto, and select the answer that best completes each of the following sentences.

1. La Universidad de Deusto está en...
   a. Segovia.
   b. Burgos.
   c. Bilbao.

2. Los programas de estudio ofrecen...
   a. cursos de diseño.
   b. cursos de geografía.
   c. cursos de los dialectos de español.

3. La universidad está...
   a. lejos del museo Guggenheim.
   b. en el centro de la ciudad.
   c. al lado de la casa del presidente de España.

4. El programa ofrece además (*also*)...
   a. visitas a ciudades (*cities*) de España.
   b. excursiones a Inglaterra.
   c. vacaciones en el mediterráneo.

1-26   Después de leer. Deseo solicitar. After reading the announcement for the University of Deusto and the Internet announcement for the University of Salamanca, you decide to go abroad for one year. Select a university and fill in the application (**la solicitud de admisión**) form with the necessary information.

Universidad de _____

Solicitud de Admisión

Curso académico 200_____ 200_____

Nombre: _____

Dirección: _____
            Calle y número

_____
Ciudad   Estado/Provincia (*State*)   País (*Country*)

¿Qué cursos desea (*wish to*) tomar? _____

¿En qué año de carrera (*year in college*) está usted? _____

Por la presente solicito la admisión al programa para estudiantes extranjeros de la Universidad de _____.

_____   _____
Firma   Fecha

1-27   Antes de escribir. Comparación. Look at the announcements in exercise 1-25 and in your textbook for the universities of Deusto and Salamanca, and indicate to what each of these statements refer: Salamanca, Deusto, or both.

1. Está situada en la costa norte de España.
   a. Salamanca
   b. Deusto
   c. Las dos

2. Puedes estudiar Bellas Artes y Farmacia.
   a. Salamanca
   b. Deusto
   c. Las dos

3. Es una institución muy antigua.
   a. Salamanca
   b. Deusto
   c. Las dos

4. Hay muchos cursos para estudiantes extranjeros.
   a. Salamanca
   b. Deusto
   c. Las dos

5. Esta institución tiene (*has*) más de un campus.
   a. Salamanca
   b. Deusto
   c. Las dos

6. La tecnología es parte de la enseñanza en esta institución.
   a. Salamanca
   b. Deusto
   c. Las dos

1-28   A escribir. Carta de presentación. You have decided to go abroad to Salamanca or to Deusto. Together with your application form, you need to send a letter talking about yourself. Write a letter to the admissions dean describing yourself. Mention your field of study, your other academic interests, hobbies, and so on. Remember to mention why you are interested in studying abroad and why you chose that particular university.

Estimado/a señor/a:

_____

_____

_____

_____

_____

_____

_____

Firma

1-29   Después de escribir. En el extranjero. You were accepted to study at the university you applied for and are now studying there for a semester. Your mother calls you and wants to know everything about your life in Spain. Answer your mother's questions.

1. ¿Cuántas clases tomas? ¿Cuándo son tus clases?

    _____

2. ¿Cómo son las clases?

    _____

3. ¿Cómo son los profesores?

    _____

4. ¿Cómo es la familia con quien (*with whom*) vives?

    _____

5. ¿Te gusta Salamanca/Bilbao? ¿Cómo es tu rutina?

    _____

6. ¿Tienes muchos amigos? ¿Cómo son tus amigos?

    _____

ENFOQUE CULTURAL

1-30   Read again the **Enfoque cultural** section on pages 51–56 in your textbook, and indicate whether the following statements are **Cierto (C)** or **Falso (F)**.

1. C   F   Todas las universidades en España son muy antiguas.

2. C   F   La universidad de Santo Tomás de Aquino en Santo Domingo es una de las primeras universidades de Hispanoamérica.

3. C   F   Son muy pocas (*few*) las universidades hispanas con programas de español para extranjeros.

4. C   F   Madrid es una ciudad española famosa por (*due to*) la celebración de la Feria de Abril.

5. C   F   El famoso Museo del Prado está en Madrid.

6. C   F   Una actividad típica de Sevilla es la corrida de toros.

7. C   F   Una persona es *maja* cuando (*when*) es antipática.

A PRIMERA VISTA

1-31 Mi vida de estudiante. Daniel is an American student in a study abroad program in Spain. Today, in his first Spanish class, he is introducing himself to his classmates. What topics do you think Daniel will mention? Listen to Daniel once, focusing on getting a general idea of the topics he mentions. Then look at the following statements about Daniel. Listen again and mark whether these statements are **Cierto** or **Falso** according to his description.

	Cierto	*Falso*
1. Daniel estudia en la Universidad de Salamanca.	_____	_____
2. Daniel no trabaja.	_____	_____
3. Daniel estudia matemáticas y psicología.	_____	_____
4. La clase de biología es fácil.	_____	_____
5. Daniel saca malas notas en biología.	_____	_____
6. La profesora de español es buena.	_____	_____
7. Daniel practica español en la oficina.	_____	_____
8. Daniel trabaja con personas norteamericanas.	_____	_____

1-32 Una conversación con Andrea. Daniel has met Andrea in their biology class. They want to start a study group, so now they are talking on the phone. Daniel is curious about his Spanish peers, and he asks a lot of questions. Can you guess some of his questions to Andrea? Then listen to some of Daniel's questions and match them with Andrea's answers.

MODELO: You see: A las nueve de la mañana.
You hear: a. ¿A qué hora llegas a la universidad?
You write: _a_

1. La clase de literatura. _____

2. Sí, trabajo en una librería. _____

3. Tomo historia, literatura y economía. _____

4. No, todas mis clases son interesantes. _____

5. Es muy fácil. _____

6. En la biblioteca. _____

Did you guess any questions correctly?

1-33 **¿Similar o diferente?** Student life in the United States and Spain involves many similar activities, but are there any differences? Daniel has now spent a few weeks in Spain, and he has learned some things about college life. Listen to Daniel once, focusing on the main idea: what is he talking about?

Daniel is talking about some of the differences between college life in the United States and in Spain. Now listen to Daniel again and complete the chart.

	ESTUDIANTES EN EE.UU.	ESTUDIANTES EN ESPAÑA
¿Cuándo toman clases?	por la mañana	
¿Cuándo trabajan?		
¿Qué hacen por las tardes?	Están en el gimnasio.	Toman algo en la cafetería.
¿Practican frisbi?		No.
¿Dónde estudian?		

Are any of these differences surprising to you?

 1-34 **Pedro y Gabriela.** Pedro and Gabriela are students, and one of them is not getting very good grades. Think about one or two reasons why someone might get bad grades. Now listen to the conversation and select whether the statement is true for Pedro, Gabriela, or both (**los dos**).

1. Toma tres clases.
   a. Pedro   b. Gabriela   c. Los dos

2. Saca malas notas.
   a. Pedro   b. Gabriela   c. Los dos

3. Monta en bicicleta por las tardes.
   a. Pedro   b. Gabriela   c. Los dos

4. Estudia en la biblioteca.
   a. Pedro   b. Gabriela   c. Los dos

5. Mira la televisión por las noches.
   a. Pedro   b. Gabriela   c. Los dos

6. Baila en discotecas los fines de semana.
   a. Pedro   b. Gabriela   c. Los dos

7. No estudia mucho.
   a. Pedro   b. Gabriela   c. Los dos

1-35   **De compras.** The semester has already started, and you still need a couple of books and school supplies. You only have 55 euros, so you call the bookstore to check for the prices of the items you need. Here is your shopping list:

1.	diccionario de español
2.	libro de historia
3.	lápiz
4.	bolígrafo
5.	calculadora
6.	cuaderno

Now you are on the phone with the bookstore information desk. Ask out loud for each item in the order it appears in your list. Then listen to the answer and note it down in the space provided.

MODELO: You ask: ¿Cuánto cuesta un diccionario de español?
            You hear: El diccionario de español cuesta 22 euros.
            You write: __22__ euros.

1. _____ euros.

2. _____ euros.

3. _____ euros.

4. _____ euros.

5. _____ euros.

6. _____ euros.

Add up the cost of the items in your shopping list and write the total in the space below.

7. Todas las cosas cuestan _____ euros en total.

Do you have enough money for everything?

EXPLICACIÓN EXPANSIÓN

1. Subject pronouns

 1-36   Los pronombres. Pick the appropriate pronoun for the person or people in the statements you hear.

1. yo   ella   él   tú

2. ellas   ustedes   nosotras   nosotros

3. ella   usted   tú   él

4. usted   tú   yo   ella

5. ellas   nosotros   ellos   nosotras

6. tú   yo   ella   usted

 1-37   ¿Tú o usted? It is important to remember that in Spanish, people address each other using different pronouns, depending on their relationship. Which pronouns are appropriate for formal or familiar situations?

Below is a list with people who are going to engage in conversations; how do you think they might address each other? Listen to their conversations, paying attention to the pronouns they use. Who are the speakers involved? Write the letter of the conversation (**a, b, c** or **d**) next to the corresponding speakers.

1. dos compañeros de clase   Conversación _____

2. un profesor, dos estudiantes   Conversación _____

3. un profesor, un estudiante   Conversación _____

4. el presidente de México, el presidente   Conversación _____
   del gobierno de España

2. Present tense of regular -*ar* verbs

 1-38 **¿Cómo estudiamos español?** You are just starting to learn Spanish, and you might feel like you are not learning very fast. Are there other things you could do to improve your Spanish skills?

Listen to the following activities and check the appropriate box in the chart to indicate how often you do them.

	SIEMPRE/TODOS LOS DÍAS	MUCHAS VECES	A VECES	NUNCA
1.	_____	_____	_____	_____
2.	_____	_____	_____	_____
3.	_____	_____	_____	_____
4.	_____	_____	_____	_____
5.	_____	_____	_____	_____
6.	_____	_____	_____	_____
7.	_____	_____	_____	_____
8.	_____	_____	_____	_____

After completing the chart, can you think of anything you could do differently to improve your skills faster? Can you think of other things that might help? Be ready to share your ideas and opinions in class.

1-39 **Un día típico.** Luis is a professor in Madrid, and many of his daily activities are similar to students' activities. Listen to Luis describe his day once, paying attention to the gist of the description and the activities you recognize. Then listen again and number his activities chronologically.

1. _____ tomar café

2. _____ tomar un sándwich

3. _____ mirar la televisión

4. _____ trabajar en la oficina

5. _____ montar en bicicleta

6. _____ caminar a casa

7. _____ revisar tareas de los estudiantes

8. _____ ir (*go*) a la universidad en autobús

3. Articles and nouns: Gender and number

1-40   Horas de oficina. Sonia is having some trouble with her economics class, so she wants to ask a few questions of her professor, señor Torres, during his office hours. She talks to his secretary, señor Marín.

First read their conversation, below, to get the gist of it. Then read the conversation again and fill in the spaces with **el, la, los, las** or null (Ø) if there should be no article. Remember that you must use articles differently, depending on whether you are talking about someone or addressing him/her directly.

Finally, listen to the conversation and check the use of articles. Change your answers below if you made any mistakes.

SONIA: Buenos días, (1) _____ señor Marín. ¿Está (2) _____
señor Torres en (3) _____ oficina?

SR. MARÍN: No, no está en este momento.

SONIA: ¡Ah! Y ¿cuándo tiene horas de oficina (4) _____ señor Torres?

SR. MARÍN: Todos (5) _____ días, a (6) _____ 10:30 de la mañana.

SONIA: ¡Gracias, (7) _____ señor Marín!

1-41   ¡Yo tengo dos! Pablito and Adriana are small children who play together. They get along well, but whenever Pablito says he has something, Adriana always says she has two of it! Listen to what Pablito says, and then write Adriana's response, saying she has two.

MODELO: You hear: Yo tengo un bolígrafo.
You write: *Yo tengo dos bolígrafos.*

1. _____

2. _____

3. _____

4. _____

5. _____

4. Present tense of the verb *estar*

 1-42 **¿Cuándo tomamos un café?** A group of your classmates and you want to meet for a Spanish conversation hour. You would like to meet on Tuesdays, but you all have busy schedules.

Listen to your classmates tell you about their activities for Tuesday, and complete the following agenda.

MARTES	
9:00.	*Yo estoy en la clase de matemáticas.*
10:00.	_____
11:00.	_____
12:00.	_____
1:00.	_____
2:00.	_____
3:00.	_____

Did you find any time when you can meet?

 1-43 **¿Dónde está la biblioteca?** Your Spanish conversation group is going to have its first meeting at the library, but you do not know where the library is! You have a campus map, but some buildings are not identified.

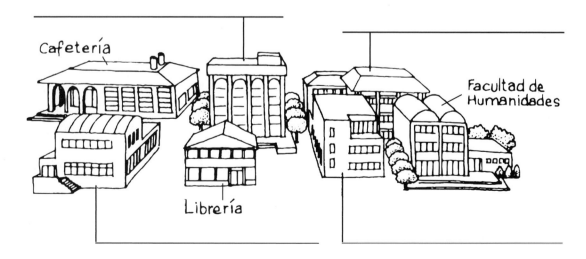

You call Maria and ask her for directions. As you listen to her, look at the campus map and note the names of the buildings she describes until you find the library. Write that down too, in case you forget!

1. _____

2. _____

3. _____

4. _____

5. Question words

1-44   En orden. Last week your Spanish teacher asked you to interview a Spanish friend for homework. You interviewed your friend Carlos about his studies and recorded his answers, but now you realize you did not ask the questions in the order you had written them. Luckily, you still have a list of your questions. Listen to the recording and match each answer to the appropriate question.

1. Tú eres español, ¿verdad?   _____

2. ¿Dónde estudias?   _____

3. ¿Por qué (*Why*) estudias allí?   _____

4. ¿Cuántas clases tomas?   _____

5. ¿Qué clases tomas?   _____

6. ¿Cuál es tu clase favorita?   _____

7. ¿Cómo es el profesor de esa clase?   _____

8. ¿Estudias inglés?   _____

1-45   Otra entrevista. This time you are the interviewee. Your classmate Sara wants to find out about your activities in your free time (**tiempo libre**). Can you anticipate some of the questions that she might ask you? Listen carefully to your friend's six questions, and answer them out loud.

ALGO MÁS: SOME REGULAR -ER AND -IR VERBS

1-46   Tu imaginación. You will hear the first half of five sentences about various people. Think about each person, and write a sentence about things they might do. Be creative, and use the verbs that follow.

comer	leer	escribir	escuchar
vivir	aprender	practicar	asistir

MODELO: You hear: Los fines de semana, el presidente...
          You write: *asiste a una clase de yoga.*

1. _____

2. _____

3. _____

4. _____

5. _____

1-47   ¿Estudiante o profesor? Students' and professors' activities are often similar. Listen to a student and a professor talk about themselves. To whom do the following statements refer?

     a. estudiante   b. profesor   c. los dos

1. Mira la televisión con su esposa. _____

2. Aprende inglés. _____

3. Lee libros de ciencia-ficción. _____

4. Come en la cafetería de la universidad. _____

5. Monta en bicicleta los fines de semana. _____

6. Llega a la universidad por la tarde. _____

7. Asiste a conferencias sobre biología. _____

8. Escribe composiciones. _____

MOSAICOS

 1-48 **¿Es típico?** Daniel (the American studying abroad in Spain) has found that many aspects of his lifestyle and routines common for college students in the United States are not so common among his new friends in Spain. Think for a moment of typical behaviors of American college students that might not be typical for students in other countries. Then listen to Daniel's statements: check the first column (**Yo**) if this statement is also true for you; check the second column (**Estudiantes en EE.UU.**) if you think this statement would be true for most American college students.

	Yo	Estudiantes en EE.UU.
1.	_____	_____
2.	_____	_____
3.	_____	_____
4.	_____	_____
5.	_____	_____
6.	_____	_____

Are you surprised that any of these behaviors are uncommon in other countries such as Spain?

PRONUNCIACIÓN

Enlace *(Linking)*

Carefully read the explanation of Spanish linking. Then listen to and repeat each of the phrases and sentences as indicated. Avoid pausing between words.

Spanish words are typically linked together in normal speech. If a Spanish word ends in a consonant and the next word begins with a vowel, the consonant forms a syllable with the following vowel.

Listen to and repeat the following sentences, avoiding pauses between the words.

1. Nosotros hablamos español.

2. Practicamos en la clase.

3. Ellos estudian español.

4. Ellas enseñan a las ocho.

If a word ends in **a, e,** or **o** and the next word begins with one of these vowels, but not the same one, the resulting combination is linked. Repeat the following sentences, avoiding pauses between the words. **Repitan las siguientes oraciones.**

1. Ana es optimista.

2. Paco está en la clase.

3. No habla español.

If a word ends in a vowel and the next word begins with the same vowel sound, the two vowels are linked in careful speech. In rapid speech, the two vowels are pronounced as one.

Now you will hear the words linked in careful speech. Repeat the phrases, avoiding any pauses between the words. **Repitan las siguientes frases.**

    una amiga americana   ocho horas   estudia alemán

Now you will hear the same words in rapid speech. Note that the two vowels are pronounced as one. **Escuchen.**

    una amiga americana   ocho horas   estudia alemán

When two words are linked by any combination of **a, e,** or **o** with **i** or **u,** the vowels form a diphthong, which is pronounced as one syllable.

Repeat the following, words pronouncing the vowel combinations as one syllable. **Repitan las siguientes frases.**

    mi amigo   la universidad   la historia   habla inglés

Stress and the written accent

Word stress is meaningful in both English and Spanish. In both languages all words generally have one stressed syllable. In some instances, a change in stress signals a change in meaning. For example, the English words *permit* and *present* may be stressed on either syllable. When the first syllable is stressed, these words are nouns. When the second syllable is stressed, they are verbs.

Noun	Verb
permit	permit
present	present

Now listen to the following sentence that uses both pronunciations of the word *permit*.

Without a parking permit, the police will not permit you to park here.

The differences in meaning due to stress are more common in Spanish than in English. One effect is to change the tense of a verb. Sometimes stress is indicated with a written accent.

Present: **hablo**   *Past:* **habló**

Now listen to the following sentence that uses both pronunciations.

Yo **hablo** hoy; él **habló** ayer.   *I speak today; he spoke yesterday.*

If you know how to pronounce a word, you can determine whether it needs a written accent by applying a few simple rules. Similarly, if you read an unfamiliar word and know these rules, the presence or absence of a written accent will tell you where to place the stress. Beginning with this lesson, you will learn the rules for accentuation. Here is the first rule:

Rule 1. Interrogative and exclamatory words have a written accent on the vowel of the stressed syllable. For example, in the interrogative word **cómo,** a written accent is needed over the stressed **o** of the first syllable.

1-49   Dictado. Listen and then write the interrogative and exclamatory words you hear.

1. _____   2. _____   3. _____

4. _____   5. _____   6. _____

Lección 2

Nombre: _____

Fecha: _____

Los hispanos en los Estados Unidos

A PRIMERA VISTA

2-1 **¿Es cierto?** Read the following sentences about several famous people and indicate whether they are **Cierto** (**C**) or **Falso** (**F**).

1. C F   Danny De Vito es bajo.

2. C F   Bill Gates es rico.

3. C F   Gloria Estefan es soltera.

4. C F   Shakira es delgada.

5. C F   George W. Bush es trabajador.

6. C F   Oprah Winfrey tiene los ojos azules.

7. C F   Penélope Cruz es pelirroja.

8. C F   Antonio Banderas es muy callado.

9. C F   Chayanne es alegre.

10. C F   Jennifer López tiene lentes.

2-2 **Completamente diferentes.** Last spring break you went on vacation to Mexico City and met Susana and Marta, two friends who live and study there. Susana and Marta do not look anything like each other. In fact, Marta is the exact opposite of Susana. Describe Marta to your best friend.

Susana	*Marta*
1. alta	_____
2. gorda	_____
3. rubia	_____
4. pelo corto	_____
5. divertida	_____
6. trabajadora	_____
7. simpática	_____

2-3   Nacionalidades. Here are the names of some very famous Hispanic people. Can you identify their country of origin? Match the country with the corresponding person, and write the nationality next to their name.

MODELO: Isabel Allende es <u>*Chile*</u>
           Isabel Allende es chilena.

   Venezuela   Puerto Rico   España   Guatemala

   México   Colombia   Estados Unidos   Cuba

1. Ricky Martin es _____.

2. Carolina Herrera es _____.

3. Fidel Castro es _____.

4. Enrique Iglesias es _____.

5. Jennifer López es _____.

6. Rigoberta Menchú es _____.

7. Emiliano Zapata es _____.

8. Gabriel García Márquez es _____.

2-4   El accidente. Ann has had a car accident and is suffering from amnesia. She cannot remember the colors! Help Ann remember the color of the following things.

1. una banana
   a. amarilla   b. verde   c. azul   d. marrón   e. gris

2. una esmeralda
   a. morada   b. blanca   c. gris   d. verde   e. azul

3. una pizarra
   a. roja   b. negra   c. carmelita   d. anaranjada   e. rosada

4. la nieve (snow)
   a. azul   b. rosa   c. blanca   d. gris   e. negra

5. la Coca-Cola
   a. verde   b. marrón   c. amarilla   d. morada   e. gris

EXPLICACIÓN Y EXPANSIÓN

Síntesis gramatical

1. Adjectives

		MASCULINE	FEMININE
SINGULAR		chico alto	chica alta
PLURAL		chicos altos	chicas altas
SINGULAR		amigo interesante	amiga interesante
		chico popular	chica popular
PLURAL		amigos interesantes	amigas interesantes
		chicos populares	chicas populares
SINGULAR		alumno español	alumna española
		alumno trabajador	alumna trabajadora
PLURAL		alumnos españoles	alumnas españolas
		alumnos trabajadores	alumnas trabajadoras

2. Present tense of the verb ser

yo	**soy**		nosotros/as	**somos**
tú	**eres**		vosotros/as	**sois**
Ud., él, ella	**es**		Uds., ellos/as	**son**

3. Ser and estar with adjectives

ser + *adjective* ⟶ norm; what someone or something is like

estar + *adjective* ⟶ comments on something; change from the norm; condition

4. Possessive adjectives

	mi(s)	*my*
	tu(s)	*your*
	su(s)	*your* (formal), *his, her, its, their*
nuestro(s), nuestra(s)		*our*
vuestro(s), vuestra(s)		*your* (familiar plural)

1. Adjectives

2-5   La universidad. The following statements describe objects and people you can find on a university campus. Indicate the object or person being described, in your opinion.

1. aburridas
   a. las profesoras   b. la historia   c. los libros   d. la estudiante

2. sincero
   a. mis amigas   b. el rector   c. la actriz   d. mis profesores

3. necesarios
   a. el diccionario   b. las clases   c. la biblioteca   d. los cuadernos

4. optimista
   a. el estudiante   b. las chicas   c. los amigos   d. las profesoras

5. moderno
   a. el laboratorio   b. los libros   c. las clases   d. la biblioteca

2-6   Cualidades esenciales. You and your friend are discussing the qualities a good president must have. Write a list of these qualities.

1. _____

2. _____

3. _____

4. _____

5. _____

6. _____

7. _____

2-7 **¿De qué color son las banderas?** Decide which national flags use the following color groups. Then complete the sentences, using adjectives of nationalities and the appropriate colors.

Colores de las banderas

rojo, azul, amarillo, blanco

rojo y amarillo

rojo, verde y amarillo

azul y blanco

rojo, azul y blanco

MODELO: Perú   rojo, blanco
           La bandera *peruana es roja y blanca.*

1. Argentina   La bandera _____

2. Bolivia   La bandera _____

3. Inglaterra   La bandera _____

4. España   La bandera _____

5. Venezuela   La bandera _____

2-8 **¿Cómo es usted?** You are very excited because you are going to Spain on a study abroad program. Write an e-mail message to your host family to introduce yourself. Write a description of yourself, including a physical description and a description of your personality.

De: _____

A: _____

Tema: Presentación

_____

_____

_____

_____

_____

_____

_____

2. Present tense and some uses of the verb *ser*

2-9   ¿De quién es? You have found a box that contains a number of objects whose owners you and your friend are trying to identify. Indicate the most logical owner for each of the following objects.

Stephen King   Christina Aguilera   Bill Gates   Alex Trebek   Shaggy

MODELO: ¿De quién es la televisión? *Es de Oprah.*

1. ¿De quién es el CD? Es de _____.

2. ¿De quién es la computadora? Es de _____.

3. ¿De quién es el libro? Es de _____.

4. ¿De quién es la enciclopedia? Es de _____.

5. ¿De quién es el perro? Es de _____.

2-10   ¿A quién se refiere? Mario is describing some people in his university. Indicate who is being referred to in each statement.

1. Es una profesora fantástica.
    a. ella   b. tú   c. yo

2. Son simpáticos y alegres.
    a. nosotros   b. ellos   c. él

3. Soy un estudiante inteligente.
    a. ella   b. él   c. yo

4. Es muy trabajador.
    a. él   b. nosotros   c. tú

5. Somos jóvenes y alegres.
    a. ustedes   b. nosotros   c. ellas

6. Eres soltero.
    a. yo   b. ella   c. tú

2-11   ¿Cómo son? Think about your life at the university and the things you have there. Describe these objects that you have or use.

MODELO: Mi cama: grande; nuevo; pequeño
           Mi cama *es nueva.*

1. tu carro: feo; bonito; nuevo

   Mi carro _____

2. tu cuarto: grande; pequeño; bonito

   Mi cuarto _____

3. tu compañero/a de cuarto: antipático; soltero; listo

   Mi compañero/a de cuarto _____

4. tu mejor amigo en la universidad: simpático; perezoso; alegre

   Mi mejor amigo en la universidad _____

5. tus clases: bueno; aburrido; interesante

   Mis clases _____

6. la cafetería: bueno; malo; grande

   La cafetería _____

7. tus profesores: joven; listo; interesante

   Mis profesores _____

8. tú: optimista; pesimista; listo

   Yo _____

3. *Ser* and *estar* with adjectives

2-12 **Conversación telefónica.** Carlos's mother is away from home on a business trip, and she has just called to find out how things are going at home. You are listening to the conversation, but there is a lot of static, and you are missing some words. Complete the conversation by writing in the words you cannot hear.

CARLOS: ¡Hola mamá! ¿Cómo (1) _____?

MAMÁ: Estoy bien, ¿y tú?

CARLOS: Bien. ¿Dónde estás?

MAMÁ: (2) _____ en mi habitación del hotel.

CARLOS: ¿Cómo se llama el hotel?

MAMÁ: Hotel Victoria.

CARLOS: ¿Cómo es?

MAMÁ: (3) _____ grande y lujoso.

CARLOS: ¿(4) _____ enfrente de la playa?

MAMÁ: No, no hay playa cerca. ¿Dónde (5) _____ tu padre?

CARLOS: Papá (6) _____ en el supermercado.

MAMÁ: (7) _____ tarde. Tengo una reunión. Regreso pronto.

2-13 **¿Qué pasa?** Read the following statements about Ana, a student at the Universidad de Granada, and decide how she is and/or feels in these situations. Make sure you write appropriate form of the verbs **ser** or **estar**.

MODELO: No tiene esposo. soltero
Está soltera.

cansado	trabajador	aburrido
gordo	inteligente	triste

1. Ana practica aeróbicos en el gimnasio por (*for*) dos horas. _____

2. Ana come muchos chocolates y dulces últimamente (*lately*). _____

3. Ana está en casa y no hace nada (*nothing*). _____

4. Ana trabaja todos los días. _____

5. Ana no estudia mucho, y saca muy buenas notas. _____

6. Ana asiste a un funeral. _____

2-14   Mi vida en la universidad. Your best friend is talking to you on the phone, describing his life at the University of Salamanca where he is participating in a study abroad program for a year. You are having trouble hearing him. Fill in the missing words to complete your friend's description.

La vida (*Life*) en Salamanca (1) _____ muy interesante. La universidad (2) _____ grande y antigua, y mis clases (3) _____ buenas. Hoy yo (4) _____ un poco (*a little; somewhat*) preocupado porque tengo un examen difícil en mi clase de español. La clase (5) _____ fácil, pero el profesor (6) _____ muy duro. Tengo muchos amigos, y estudio con un grupo de compañeros. (7) _____ seis estudiantes en la clase, y estudiamos juntos (*together*) los martes por la noche. Mis amigos (8) _____ nerviosos por (*on account of*) el examen, pero yo (9) _____ listo. También (10) _____ muy cansado por estudiar mucho, pero (11) _____ contento porque Salamanca y la universidad son espectaculares.

2-15 Una entrevista. You work for the school newspaper, and you have to write an article about the students and their reactions during final exams. You have decided to interview your roommate. Prepare the questions you are going to ask him/her.

MODELO: ¿En qué año *estás*?

1. ¿_____ contento/a en la universidad?

2. ¿_____ inteligentes tus profesores?

3. ¿_____ nervioso/a por tus exámenes?

4. ¿_____ difíciles tus exámenes?

5. ¿_____ listo/a para los exámenes?

6. ¿_____ responsable y trabajador?

4. Possessive adjectives

2-16 **¡A la playa!** A group of your friends at school is going to spend their Saturday morning (**sábado por la mañana**) at the beach. You want your friend John to join you all. While your friend Sally is trying to convince him to go, you all eavesdrop on the conversation from the other room. Fill in the following conversation with the words you are having trouble hearing.

SALLY: Mañana vienes (*you are coming*) a la playa con nosotros, ¿verdad?

JOHN: No, (1) _____ examen de matemáticas es el lunes, y quiero estudiar.

SALLY: Pero si (2) _____ examen es el lunes, estudias el domingo.

JOHN: Quiero estudiar todo el fin de semana. El profesor Carter es muy duro (*hard*), y (3) _____ exámenes son siempre muy difíciles.

SALLY: Es más (*more*) divertido estar en la playa... Además (*Also*) viene (4) _____ amiga favorita...

JOHN: ¿Jean?

SALLY: Sí, todos (5) _____ amigos vienen. ¡Anímate!

JOHN: Muy bien, y estudio el domingo. Pero si (*if*) saco una mala nota en (6) _____ examen, ¡será tu culpa (*it'll be your fault*)!

2-17 **Cosas favoritas.** Do you know your best friend well? Think of the things she/he likes or does not like, and complete each sentence about your best friend's favorite things.

MODELO: *Su* libro favorito es <u>*Don Quijote de la Mancha*</u>.

1. _____ programa de televisión favorito es _____

2. _____ actor/actriz favorito/a es _____

3. _____ restaurante favorito es _____

4. _____ grupos musicales favoritos son _____

5. _____ clases favoritas son _____

6. _____ pasatiempos (*hobbies*) favoritos son _____

2-18   ¿Qué opinas? Look at the following objects and people and indicate your opinion about them. Complete the sentences with the possessive adjective and the word that best describes how you feel about the object or person.

MODELO: las películas de James Dean
(a) *Sus* películas son (b) *aburridas*.

a. mis; tus; su; sus   b. interesantes; aburridas

1. la música de Madonna

    (a) _____ música es (b) _____.

    a. su; sus; mis; tu   b. buena; mala

2. los padres (*parents*) de tu amigo

    (a) _____ padres son (b) _____.

    a. su; sus; nuestros; tu   b. simpáticos; antipáticos

3. tus exámenes

    (a) _____ exámenes son (b) _____.

    a. mi; sus; mis; tu   b. fáciles; difíciles

4. tus vacaciones y las de (*those of*) tus amigos

    (a) _____ vacaciones son (b) _____.

    a. sus; nuestras; mis; tu   b. divertidas; aburridas

5. tu madre

    (a) _____ madre es (b) _____.

    a. nuestra; tu; mi; su   b. alegre; trabajadora

6. la novia de tu amigo

    (a) _____ novia es (b) _____.

    a. su; sus; mi; tu   b. optimista; realista

2-19   Los planes del verano. You are reading an article in the school newspaper about the summer plans of students in your school. It has been raining and your paper is wet, so some of the words are blurred. Complete the sentences with the appropriate possessive adjective to complete the article.

¡Llegan las vacaciones de verano! Y los estudiantes visitan a (1) _____ familias, o viajan (*travel*) con (2) _____ amigos o trabajan. Por ejemplo, Diego y Alfredo son dos hermanos (*brothers*) que viven en Miami con (3) _____ padres (*parents*) argentinos. (4) _____ padres viven en Miami, pero (5) _____ abuelos (*grandparents*) viven en Argentina. Este verano Diego y Alfredo visitan a (6) _____ abuelos en Argentina. (7) _____ amigo Julio y yo viajamos a California para visitar a (8) _____ amiga Ana, que estudia en Los Ángeles. (9) _____ amigos Carlos y Diana no viajan porque trabajan este verano. Carlos trabaja en una oficina; (10) _____ trabajo es muy fácil. Diana trabaja en un laboratorio; (11) _____ experimentos son muy interesantes.

ALGO MÁS: EXPRESSIONS WITH *GUSTAR*

2-20   ¿Qué les gusta? Indicate what the following people like or dislike.

1. A mí no me gusta...
   - a. las clases por la tarde.
   - b. la clase de alemán.
   - c. los conciertos de jazz.
   - d. las ciencias sociales.

2. A los norteamericanos les gusta...
   - a. las clases interesantes.
   - b. los fines de semana.
   - c. mirar televisión.
   - d. las vacaciones.

3. A los estudiantes no les gusta...
   - a. las ciencias.
   - b. estudiar mucho.
   - c. los exámenes.
   - d. las matemáticas.

4. A mi amigo le gustan...
   - a. las fiestas.
   - b. bailar tango.
   - c. usar la computadora.
   - d. la música clásica.

5. A mi hermana (*sister*) le gusta...
   - a. los videojuegos.
   - b. estudiar en la biblioteca.
   - c. las películas cómicas.
   - d. los libros de ciencia-ficción.

6. A mi amiga le gustan...
   - a. la universidad.
   - b. tomar café.
   - c. el chocolate.
   - d. los coches nuevos.

2-21   Primera fase. ¿Te gusta? Write sentences to express your likes and dislikes about the following subjects.

1. A mí _____ las discotecas.

2. A mí _____ la arquitectura colonial.

3. A mí _____ las películas (*films*) de Brad Pitt.

4. A mí _____ estudiar.

5. A mí _____ cantar.

Segunda fase. ¿Los conoces bien? Now think about your family and friends. Complete the sentences to indicate how the following people feel about each of these items.

1. A mi madre _____ los libros de John Grisham.

2. A mi hermano/a _____ la música de Eminem.

3. A mi mejor amigo/a _____ las comedias.

4. A mis amigos _____ bailar en las fiestas.

5. A mi padre _____ viajar.

MOSAICOS

2-22   Antes de leer. Hacer amigos en la red. Indicate whether in your opinion the following statements describe online dating.

1. Sí   No   Es una buena forma de hacer (*make*) amigos.

2. Sí   No   Es peligroso (*dangerous*).

3. Sí   No   Es imposible hacer buenos amigos.

4. Sí   No   Es posible encontrar (*find*) a la pareja (*partner*) ideal.

5. Sí   No   Es muy caro.

6. Sí   No   No es una alternativa buena para conocer (*to meet*) personas.

7. Sí   No   No es posible encontrar amor (*love*) en la red (*Web*).

A leer

2-23   **A leer. Online dating.** Read the following ad about online dating, and answer the questions that follow.

Amor Verdadero: Servicio de citas por Internet

¡Enamórate por las razones correctas!

Hay más de 100 millones de solteros (*single men and women*) en el mundo. ¡Buenas noticias!, ¿verdad? Pero a veces encontrar una pareja es muy difícil, especialmente a la persona correcta.

Este servicio de Internet es para solteros REALES que buscan relaciones REALES. Los anuncios (*ads*) personales describen con mucho detalle (*detail*) las características (*traits*) físicas y de la personalidad de los miembros (*members*).

Hay más de 3 millones de solteros-miembros de Amor Verdadero, y más de 50.000 nuevos miembros cada semana. Hay muchos vídeos y miles (*thousands*) de grabaciones disponibles (*available*) en nuestra página web. También hay servicios de mensajes instantáneos con vídeo, audio y texto, y líneas de chat.

Ponga su anuncio GRATIS para encontrar a la persona de sus sueños (*dreams*).

Indicate whether the following sentences are **Cierto** (**C**) or **Falso** (**F**) according to the ad of *Amor Verdadero*.

1. C   F   Amor Verdadero tiene muchos miembros activos.

2. C   F   En Amor Verdadero usted usa el teléfono para comunicarse con otros miembros.

3. C   F   Amor Verdadero es un servicio para buscar pareja.

4. C   F   El servicio es un poco caro (*a bit expensive*).

5. C   F   Amor Verdadero usa mucha tecnología.

2-24 **Después de leer. Tu perfil.** After reading the ad for *Amor Verdadero*, you have decided that you want to submit your profile. Fill in the following profile with the appropriate information.

Amor Verdadero

¡Enamórate por las razones correctas!

Nombre: _____   Sexo: Hombre   Mujer

Dirección: _____   Edad: _____

Número de teléfono: _____   Nacionalidad: _____

Dirección de correo electrónico: _____

Características físicas:

_____   _____

_____   _____

_____   _____

_____   _____

Características de la personalidad:

_____   _____

_____   _____

_____   _____

_____   _____

Gustos (música, aficiones [*hobbies*], intereses, actividades favoritas):

_____   _____

_____   _____

_____   _____

_____   _____

¿Qué tipo de persona busca? (edad [*age*], características físicas y de la personalidad, etc.)

_____   _____

_____   _____

_____   _____

¿Por qué deseas usar Amor Verdadero?

_____

_____

_____

_____

A escribir

2-25   Antes de escribir. ¡Por fin! You have received a response from *Amor Verdadero* with the profile of two people you might be interested in. Look at the following descriptions, and then in the numbered items indicate who is being described.

If you are looking for a male companion:

Anthony (A):	*Carlos* (C):
21 años	22 años
estadounidense	argentino
estudiante	estudiante
guapo	guapo
delgado	bajo
simpático	optimista
alegre	callado
pobre	rico
trabajador	listo

If you are looking for a female companion:

Allyson (A):	*Cristina* (C):
21 años	22 años
estadounidense	argentina
estudiante	estudiante
guapa	guapa
delgada	baja
simpática	optimista
alegre	callada
pobre	rica
trabajadora	lista

1. A   C   Su actitud es siempre positiva.
2. A   C   A veces necesita algo de dinero.
3. A   C   Habla poco (*not much*).
4. A   C   No es muy alto/a.
5. A   C   Es inteligente.
6. A   C   No es antipático/a.
7. A   C   No es gordo/a.

2-26   A escribir. La carta. Now select a person from the previous activity and write a letter to him/her. Introduce and describe yourself (your physical appearance, your personality, etc.). Suggest a meeting, and tell him/her your plans for that meeting (what you are going to do, where you are planning to go, etc.).

Querido/a _____,

_____

_____

_____

_____

_____

_____

_____

_____

_____

_____

_____

_____

_____

_____

_____

_____

_____

_____

2-27   Después de escribir. La llamada de teléfono. You are on a date with the person you met through *Amor Verdadero,* and your best friend calls you on your cell phone, wanting to know everything. Since your date stepped out for a second, you can talk to your friend and answer his/her questions.

1. ¿Dónde están?

   _____

2. ¿Están felices? ¿Alegres? ¿Aburridos? ¿Cansados? ¿Tranquilos? ¿Nerviosos?

   _____

3. ¿Cómo es la persona?

   _____

4. ¿Cómo son sus amigos? ¿Cómo es su familia?

   _____

5. ¿Qué le gusta hacer (*do*)? ¿Qué no le gusta?

   _____

6. ¿Son compatibles? ¿Por qué o por qué no?

   _____

7. ¿Tienen planes o no? (HINTS: **Sí, tenemos planes de** + *infinitive. Or* **No, no tenemos planes de** + *infinitive* **nada** [*nothing*].)

   _____

ENFOQUE CULTURAL

2-28　　Los hispanos en los Estados Unidos. Read again the **Enfoque cultural** section on pages 85–90 in your textbook and indicate whether the following statements about Hispanic people in the United States are **Cierto (C)** or **Falso (F)**.

1. C　F　Los chicanos son los inmigrantes ilegales mexicanos.

2. C　F　Los hispanos viven en muchos estados diferentes de los EE.UU.

3. C　F　Todos los inmigrantes hispanos vienen a EE.UU. por razones económicas.

4. C　F　Los países hispanos son muy diferentes con respecto a la comida.

5. C　F　El grupo hispano más grande en Miami es el de los cubanos.

6. C　F　La capital de Puerto Rico es San Juan.

7. C　F　Cuando un chicano dice que "anda brujo", quiere decir que tiene mala suerte.

8. C　F　"Babada" es una expresión puertorriqueña típica.

9. C　F　En Texas es posible admirar arquitectura mexicana.

10. C　F　San Juan de Puerto Rico está en el centro del país.

A PRIMERA VISTA

2-29 **¿Quién es?** Look at the illustrations of the four people below and think about some of the words and expressions you might use to describe each person. This will improve your listening comprehension.

Now listen to the descriptions and match them with the illustrations. Do not worry if you do not understand some words; listen for words you do know.

a	b	c	d

1. _____   2. _____   3. _____   4. _____

2-30 **La nueva amiga de Rafael.** Rafael is very outgoing, and he likes to meet everybody. He has already made friends with a new student. Some of what you have heard about her (read the statements below) is inaccurate. Listen to the conversation between these friends of Rafael and check whether what you heard is **Cierto (C)** or **Falso (F)**.

	CIERTO	FALSO
1. La amiga de Rafael se llama Antonia.	_____	_____
2. Antonia es norteamericana.	_____	_____
3. Estudia en la universidad este semestre.	_____	_____
4. Tiene dieciocho años.	_____	_____
5. Desea ser profesora de economía.	_____	_____

2-31   Más amigos hispanos. You want to meet more Hispanic friends, so you go to the Hispanic Cultural Center at your university. There you meet some native Spanish-speaking students: Ernesto, Ana, Claudia, and David. Listen to them describe themselves, and write the name next to the correct information.

1. ¿Quién tiene veintidós años, es morena y divertida? _____

2. ¿Quién tiene pelo negro, es alto y activo? _____

3. ¿Quién es chilena y pelirroja y tiene veintidós años? _____

4. ¿Quién es argentino, moreno y alto? _____

2-32   ¿Qué les gusta? You are now getting to know your new friends Claudia and David, and you are talking about the things you like and do not like to do. Listen to Claudia and David and write **Sí** or **No** to indicate their preferences in the following activities. Note that both may like some of the activities. HINT: **ir a (voy a)** = *to go to (I go to)*

	Claudia	*David*
1. montar en bicicleta	_____	_____
2. practicar béisbol	_____	_____
3. conversar con amigos en la computadora	_____	_____
4. tomar algo en un café	_____	_____
5. estudiar en la biblioteca	_____	_____
6. estudiar en casa	_____	_____

Which of the previous activities do you like or dislike to do?

Nombre: _____   Fecha: _____

EXPLICACIÓN Y EXPANSIÓN

1. Adjectives

 2-33   **¿Quién es?** Listen to the following adjectives and decide whether each describes Ana, Ernesto, Ernesto and David, or Ana or Ernesto. Keep in mind that Spanish adjectives agree in gender and number with the nouns they describe.

     a. Ana   b. Ernesto   c. Ernesto y David   d. Ana o Ernesto

1. _____   5. _____

2. _____   6. _____

3. _____   7. _____

4. _____   8. _____

 2-34   **¿Cómo son?** Your friend Alicia knows other Hispanic students, and she wants you to meet them. First read what Alicia says, noting the nouns in bold so that you can anticipate the gender and number of the adjectives describing them. Then listen to Alicia and fill in the missing adjectives.

Sí, **Nico y Elsa** son (1) _____. Son muy (2) _____, y me gusta

mucho conversar con ellos. **Nico** es muy (3) _____ y (4) _____.

Elsa es más (5) _____, pero es (6) _____ también. **Elsa** estudia

economía y es muy (7) _____ y (8) _____. Todos los días estudia

mucho en la biblioteca. **Nico** también es (9) _____, aunque es un poco

(10) _____. Pero **Nico** es muy (11) _____; es (12) _____ y

tiene los ojos (13) _____. También es (14) _____,

(15) _____.

Nombre: _____   Fecha: _____

---

2. Present tense and some uses of the verb *ser*

2-35   Hora y lugar. Tomorrow is Saturday, and there are many activities going on. You want to attend as many activities as possible, but you do not know when or where they will take place, so you call your friend Marcos, who is always well informed. Listen to him and write down when and where the activities will take place.

MODELO: You hear: La fiesta es a las ocho de la
                                                                         tarde en el parque.
                 Look for the event in the list: la fiesta
                 Write when it will take place under **¿Cuándo?**: *a las ocho*
                 Write where it will take place under **¿Dónde?**: *en el parque*

		¿CUÁNDO?	¿DÓNDE?
1.	el concierto de Marc Anthony	_____	_____
2.	la conferencia (lecture) sobre el Amazonas	_____	_____
3.	el baile de la Asociación de Estudiantes de Puerto Rico	_____	_____
4.	la película Amores perros	_____	_____
5.	la tertulia (conversation hour) en español	_____	_____

Will you be able to go to all these events?

2-36   La entrevista. The radio announcers are talking about Marc Anthony, who is in town for a concert. They are taking questions from callers who want to find out more about him. For some reason you cannot hear the questions, only the answers. Read the announcers' answers (below) and try to guess what the questions were. Then listen to the questions the callers made and match them with the corresponding answer.

1. _____ Marc Anthony es norteamericano.

2. _____ Marc Anthony es de Nueva York.

3. _____ Sus padres (*parents*) son de Puerto Rico.

4. _____ Es bilingüe: habla inglés y español.

5. _____ Marc Anthony es muy divertido y conversador.

6. _____ Su concierto es esta noche, en la plaza.

3. *Ser* and *estar* with adjectives

2-37   **¿Ser o estar?** Complete the sentences you hear by choosing a verb: (a) *ser,* (b) *estar,* or if both possibilities are correct, (c) *ser/estar*. If you choose (c), consider how using one instead of the other would change the meaning.

a. es   b. está   c. es/está

1. _____   4. _____

2. _____   5. _____

3. _____   6. _____

2-38   **Diferentes.** Everybody seems to be changing these days! You are talking about these people with your friend. Listen to his statements and respond both orally and in writing, expressing how they have changed. Use *estar* and an appropriate adjective, as in the **Modelo.**

MODELO: You hear: Marta es gorda.
          You say and write: *Sí, pero ahora está delgada.*

1. Sí, pero ahora _____

2. Sí, pero ahora _____

3. Sí, pero ahora _____

4. Sí, pero ahora _____

4. Possessive adjectives

2-39   **¿De quién?** Teresa and Miguel are siblings going off to college. As they pack, they have to figure out who owns what. Listen to their conversation and decide whether the following items belong to Teresa, Miguel, or both.

a. de Teresa   b. de Miguel   c. de Teresa y Miguel

1. la mochila _____

2. el diccionario _____

3. la computadora _____

4. el televisor _____

5. el auto _____

2-40   De Teresa y Miguel. Now that Teresa and Miguel are at college, they are telling their friends about their life back home, but they almost never agree! Listen to their statements and transform them using possessive adjectives, as in the **Modelo.**

MODELO: You hear: Nosotros tenemos una casa grande.
          You say and write: *Nuestra casa es grande.*

1. _____

2. _____

3. _____

4. _____

5. _____

ALGO MÁS: EXPRESSIONS WITH *GUSTAR*

2-41   La novelista. A famous Hispanic writer is visiting campus, and your professor has brought her to your class for an informal interview. Listen to her as she talks about the activities and the types of novels she likes or dislikes, and mark (**X**) in the appropriate columns below.

ACTIVIDADES	LE GUSTA	NO LE GUSTA
leer		
escribir por las mañanas		
escuchar música clásica		
NOVELAS	LE GUSTAN	NO LE GUSTAN
históricas		
románticas		
de misterio		

2-42 **¿Qué le gusta?** Your roommate and you are still getting to know each other, and today you are talking about things you like or do not like. First listen to your roommate's questions and answer truthfully (either **Sí** o **No**) in complete sentences. Then ask your roommate about the same activity, as in the **Modelo.**

MODELO: You hear: ¿Te gusta tomar café?
          You say and write: *Sí, me gusta tomar café.*
                                      OR *No, no me gusta tomar café.*

1. _____

2. _____

3. _____

4. _____

5. _____

MOSAICOS

2-43 **Un estudiante de intercambio.** You will hear two friends talking about Miguel Hernández, an exchange student. As you listen, try to focus on specific information about him to answer the following questions.

1. ¿De qué nacionalidad es Miguel Hernández? _____

2. ¿Cómo es su pelo? _____

3. ¿Qué clase tiene Miguel? _____

4. ¿Cuántos años tiene? _____

5. ¿Es simpático o antipático? _____

6. ¿Es inteligente o tonto? _____

PRONUNCIACIÓN

In this section you will learn about the pronunciation of letters **b, v,** and **d,** in Spanish.

b and v

In Spanish the letters **b** and **v** are pronounced the same. At the beginning of an utterance or after an **m** or **n**, the Spanish **b** and **v** are pronounced like the English *b*. Listen to and repeat the following words.

| bien | buenos | bonito | enviar | combate | vaca |

In all other positions the Spanish **b** and **v** are pronounced by allowing air to pass between the lips, which are almost closed. This sound does not exist in English. **Repitan las siguientes palabras.**

| sabe | Cuba | cabeza | uva | pavo | aviso |

The following words contain both pronunciations of **b** and **v** within the same words. **Repitan las siguientes palabras.**

| bebe | bebida | vive | bobo | barbero | víbora |

d

The Spanish **d** has two pronunciations, depending on its position in a word or sentence. At the beginning of a sentence or after **l** or **n**, the Spanish **d** is pronounced by placing the tip of the tongue against the back of the upper teeth. The airflow is interrupted until the tongue is retracted. **Repitan las siguientes palabras.**

| don | donde | doña | doctor | día | dinero |

In all other positions the **d** is similar to the pronunciation of the English *th* in the word *father*. **Repitan las siguientes palabras.**

| adiós | comida | saludos | usted | médico | lado |
| verdad |

Stress and the written accent

In Lección preliminar you learned Rule 1 for writing accents. Here is Rule 2:

Rule 2. All words that are stressed on the third syllable from the end of the word must have a written accent.

Repitan las siguientes palabras.

| física | sábado | simpático | gramática | matemáticas |

Say each of the following words aloud, stressing the third-from-the-last syllable. Note that each word has a written accent. You will hear a confirmation after you say each word.

1. artículo
2. bolígrafo
3. número
4. informática
5. párrafo

6. antipático
7. cómodo
8. película
9. teléfono
10. cronómetro

Lección 3

Nombre: _____

Fecha: _____

Las actividades y los planes

A PRIMERA VISTA

3-1   ¿Dónde? Read the list of activities Teresa does in her spare time, and indicate the most logical location for them to take place.

1. _____ Alquilo películas.   a. la biblioteca

2. _____ Descanso.   b. el apartamento

3. _____ Saco un libro.   c. la discoteca

4. _____ Lavo la ropa.   d. el videoclub

5. _____ Salgo con los amigos y bailo.   e. el cuarto

3-2   Las rutinas. Mario's weekly activities are grouped below. Indicate the word in each group that does not belong.

1. a. bailar   b. ir al cine   c. estudiar   d. alquilar películas

2. a. cenar   b. desayunar   c. hablar   d. almorzar

3. a. montar en   b. correr   c. practicar el fútbol d. descansar
      bicicleta

4. a. trabajar   b. cantar canciones   c. tocar la guitarra   d. ir a una fiesta

3-3   La comida. Marvin has just arrived in Spain from the United States and is staying at a friend's house. He is about to cook a meal when he realizes he does not know the names of the food items. Listen to Marvin's descriptions and indicate what item is being described. More than one answer may apply.

1. Es carne de animal marino, que vive en el océano.
   a. el pescado   b. el pollo   c. la hamburguesa

2. Es una fruta amarilla.
   a. el arroz   b. la banana   c. la naranja

3. Es frío, dulce y sólido.
   a. la leche   b. el helado   c. la lechuga

4. Se le pone (*it is added*) al pan.
   a. la mantequilla   b. la lechuga   c. la zanahoria

5. Verdura verde que le gusta a Popeye.

   a. las tostadas   b. las espinacas   c. las papas fritas

6. Comida típica del desayuno.

   a. los espaguetis   b. los huevos   c. el atún

3-4   Crucigrama. Complete the crossword puzzle based on the following questions.

Horizontales

2. Tú _____ un libro en la clase.

6. Ana y Laura no son pobres; son _____.

7. Yo _____ una hamburguesa con papas fritas.

8. Virginia _____ un diccionario en la librería.

10. La familia va a _____ la televisión a las ocho.

11. Los jóvenes nadan en la _____.

15. Rosa y Carlos estudian en la _____.

17. La chica _____ canciones peruanas.

18. Escuchamos música en _____ de María.

19. Los chicos ven películas en los _____.

20. Yo _____ música de U2 en la radio.

21. Vamos a ver *Todo sobre mi madre* en el _____.

22. Pedro vive en una _____ muy bonita.

Verticales

1. Mi familia va a _____ en California.

2. Van a ver _____ nueva película de Penélope Cruz.

3. Tú _____ los ejercicios en el cuaderno.

4. Víctor nada en el _____.

5. Tú _____ mucho café.

9. Marta y yo _____ mucho en la fiesta.

11. Tú _____ español en el laboratorio de lenguas.

12. Pedro practica el tenis en el _____.

13. Bernardo _____ la película con Luisa.

14. Yo aprendo a hablar _____ en mi clase.

15. Maruja _____ un refresco de limón.

16. Nicolás _____ el sol en la playa.

3-5 **¿Qué va a comer?** You are taking a class on nutrition, and your professor assigns you some homework. Based on what you think are the nutritional needs of the following people, indicate the best menu choice for them.

MENÚ			
PRIMER PLATO (FIRST COURSE)	*PLATO PRINCIPAL* (MAIN COURSE)	*POSTRE* (DESSERT)	*BEBIDA*
Sopa de tomate	Pollo con verduras	Helado	Agua con gas (*sparkling*)
Ensalada	Bistec con papas	Tarta	Cerveza
Camarones (*shrimp*) fritos	Hamburguesa con papas fritas		Vino
Sopa de pollo	Atún con verduras		Refrescos

1. Un niño de 18 meses: _____

2. Una joven de 21 años que está a dieta: _____

3. Un señor de 50 años que es diabético: _____

4. Una chica de 16 años que desea aumentar de peso (*weight*): _____

5. Un chico de 23 años que es vegetariano: _____

EXPLICACIÓN Y EXPANSIÓN

Síntesis gramatical

1. Present tense of regular -er and -ir verbs

comer (*to eat*)

yo	como	nosotros/as	comemos
tú	comes	vosotros/as	coméis
Ud., él, ella	come	Uds., ellos/as	comen

vivir (*to live*)

yo	vivo	nosotros/as	vivimos
tú	vives	vosotros/as	vivís
Ud., él, ella	vive	Uds., ellos/as	viven

2. Present tense of ir

ir (to go)

yo	voy	nosotros/as	vamos
tú	vas	vosotros/as	vais
Ud., él, ella	va	Uds., ellos/as	van

3. Ir + *a* + infinitive to express future action

Ana va a ser la presidenta.   *Ana is going to be the president.*

4. The present tense to express future action

¿Estudiamos esta noche?   *Are we going to study tonight?*

1. Present tense of regular -*er* and -*ir* verbs

3-6   La comida en la universidad. Sometimes healthful (**saludable**) eating at a university is a challenge. Complete the following sentences about you and your friends' eating habits.

1. Mis amigos y yo _____ (comer/no comer) en la cafetería de la universidad.

2. Mi amiga _____ (beber/no beber) café en la cafetería.

3. Mi amigo _____ (tomar/no tomar) ensaladas.

4. Tú _____ (comer/no comer) frecuentemente en la cafetería de la universidad.

5. Yo _____ (cenar/no cenar) en los restaurantes.

3-7   El periódico. Many people read a daily newspaper that is published in the city where they live. Indicate which paper these people read by completing the sentences with the verbs *leer* and *vivir*.

MODELO: Mark *vive* en Nueva York. Él *lee The New York Times*.

1. Pedro _____ en Lima. Él _____ *El Comercio*.

2. Los estudiantes _____ en México. Ellos _____ *Excélsior*.

3. Ustedes _____ en Buenos Aires. Ustedes _____ *La Nación*.

4. Tú _____ en Bogotá. Tú _____ *El Tiempo*.

5. Alicia y yo _____ en Madrid. Nosotros _____ el *ABC*.

3-8   Su instructor/a de español. Select the word that most logically completes the following sentences about your instructor's possible daily activities.

1. _____ mucho por teléfono.
   a. habla   b. asistes   c. vienen

2. _____ correos electrónicos.
   a. come   b. haces   c. escribe

3. _____ solamente en español en clase.
   a. cenan   b. alquila   c. escribe

4. _____ en el parque los fines de semana.
   a. vive   b. corre   c. cantan

3-9   La rutina en la universidad. Michael is a student in introductory Spanish, and he has written this paragraph about his and his roommate's life at the university. Read the paragraph and complete the sentences appropriately.

asistir	comer	hacer	hacer
beber	beber	descansar	alquilar
cenar	lavar	ir	comer

Christopher y yo somos estudiantes en la universidad. De lunes a viernes nosotros
(1) _____ a clases de español, matemáticas, inglés y ciencias políticas. A las 12:00
(2) _____ en el centro de estudiantes; nos gustan las hamburguesas, y siempre (3) _____
Coca-Cola. Por la tarde después de nuestras clases, (4) _____ ejercicio. A nosotros nos
gusta jugar al fútbol. Después (5) _____ en casa y, más o menos a las 6:30 de la tarde,
(6) _____ algo ligero (*something light*). Los sábados (7) _____ la ropa, y luego (8) _____
algunas películas. A veces (9) _____ con unos amigos en un restaurante, y vamos a los
bares y (10) _____ cervezas. Otras veces (*Other times*) (11) _____ a alguna fiesta. Los
domingos son muy aburridos: (12) _____ la tarea para el lunes.

2. Present tense of *ir*

3-10   **¿Adónde va?** Read the sentences about Juana and her friends' needs. Complete the
sentences by indicating where they are going to go to get what they need.

a la discoteca	al cine	a la librería	a la residencia estudiantil
al supermercado	a la cafetería	a la playa	a la universidad

1. Ana necesita comprar un libro para su clase de literatura inglesa. Ana _____.

2. Carmen y José necesitan pollo y verduras para la cena. Ellos _____.

3. Tú asistes a una clase que es a las once de la mañana. Tú _____.

4. Gonzalo y yo deseamos beber café. Nosotros _____.

5. Tú deseas ver una película de Brad Pitt. Tú _____.

6. Ustedes están muy cansados y desean descansar. Ustedes _____.

7. Lucía desea bailar y celebrar el fin de una semana larga (*long*). Ella _____.

8. Sonia y su novio desean tomar el sol. Ellos _____.

3-11   **Los planes.** Alain and his friends are planning to go to the beach on Saturday.
Complete the sentences below to explain their plans.

1. Yo _____ (ir/no ir) a las diez de la mañana con mi hermano.

2. Ana y Pedro _____ (ir/no ir) a las once de la mañana.

3. Mi hermano y yo _____ (ir/no ir) caminando.

4. Carlos y Rosa _____ (ir/no ir).

5. Luisa _____ (ir/no ir) con Ana y Pedro en el auto.

3. *Ir* + *a* + infinitive to express future action

3-12   **¿Qué van a hacer?** Considering where the following people are located, indicate what they are going to do.

_____ 1. En el café la señora Menéndez...   a. van a leer libros.

_____ 2. En el cine tú...   b. va a tomar un refresco.

_____ 3. En mi casa yo...   c. vas a ver una película.

_____ 4. En la biblioteca ellos...   d. voy a hacer la tarea.

_____ 5. En el concierto Ana y yo...   e. vamos a escuchar música clásica.

3-13   **¿Qué van a hacer ahora?** Complete the following sentences by indicating what you think these people are going to do in their respective locations.

MODELO: Carmina está en una boutique. Ella *va a comprar unos jeans*.

| ver una película | comprar un libro | tomar una cerveza |
| descansar | tomar el sol | escuchar música |

1. Alicia está en la librería. Alicia _____.

2. Tú estás en una fiesta en casa de tu amigo. Tú _____.

3. Los muchachos están en el cine. Ellos _____.

4. Yo estoy en mi habitación en casa. Yo _____.

5. Marta y José están en la playa. Ellos _____.

6. Carmen y yo estamos en un concierto. Nosotros _____.

4. The present tense to express future action

3-14   **¿Qué hacemos?** You call your friend to find out his/her plans for later in the day. Indicate the best response for each question.

_____ 1. ¿A qué hora cenamos?   a. Vamos a la discoteca.

_____ 2. ¿Qué hacemos esta noche después de cenar? b. Cenamos a las ocho de la tarde.

_____ 3. ¿Adónde vamos a bailar esta noche? c. Vamos al cine.

_____ 4. ¿A qué hora estamos en casa?   d. Vamos a casa a las tres de la mañana.

_____ 5. ¿Qué hacemos mañana?   e. Vamos a la playa y tomamos el sol.

3-15   **El fin de semana.** Think about your plans for the weekend. Write out your plans, using the verbs provided, as necessary.

| trabajar | leer | comer | escuchar | ver | escribir |
| bailar | ir | estudiar | estudiar | mirar | hablar |

Sábado

A las 9:00 de la mañana _____

A las 12:30 de la tarde _____

A las 5:30 de la tarde _____

A las 10:00 de la noche _____

Domingo

A las 11:30 de la mañana _____

A las 2:00 de la tarde _____

A las 6:00 de la tarde _____

A las 9:00 de la noche _____

5. Numbers 100 to 2,000,000

3-16 **Bingo.** Mario, Rosa, and Carlos are playing Bingo, and one of them has already won. Cross out the numbers on their cards that have been called, and then circle the name of the winner.

Números cantados:

doscientos treinta

setecientos doce

dos mil quinientos dieciocho

cuatrocientos veintitrés

cuatrocientos sesenta y cinco

novecientos sesenta y cuatro

quince mil setecientos doce

quinientos once

ochocientos cuarenta y nueve

seiscientos cincuenta y cinco

seis mil seis

seiscientos sesenta y seis

ROSA

320	413	676
15.712	712	512
230	6.060	964
665	2.518	575

MARIO

230	511	2.518
666	712	964
849	655	423
15.712	465	6.006

CARLOS

774	656	2.185
220	475	323
612	6.066	501
849	51.612	655

3-17 **¡A pensar!** Mario and Jorge are working on math homework. Help them complete the calculations by following the pattern. Write out your answer; do not use numerals.

MODELO: 2, 4, 6, *ocho*

1. 1.000.000, 1.050.000, 1.100.000, _____

2. 8.184, 7.784, 7.384, 6.984, _____

3. 1.100, 990, 880, 770, _____

4. 2.213, 2.313, 2.413, _____

5. 6.176, 3.088, 1.544, 772, _____

ALGO MÁS: SOME USES OF *POR* AND *PARA*

3-18   Conversación de teléfono. John and his girlfriend, Jennie, are talking on the phone. She is telling him her plans for tonight, a girls' night out. The connection is breaking up, so John is having difficulty understanding her. Help John understand Jennie by completing each sentence with *por* or *para*.

JENNIE: Esta noche vamos a un restaurante. Mis amigas caminan (1) _____ el restaurante ahora.

JOHN: ¿Y tú? ¿Cuándo vas?

JENNIE: Yo voy a trabajar (2) _____ media hora más, y después voy.

JOHN: ¿Vas a escribir ahora el artículo (3) _____ la clase de historia?

JENNIE: No, esta noche no, pero (4) _____ mañana está listo.

JOHN: ¡Qué bien! (*Great!*)

JENNIE: Después del restaurante vamos (5) _____ la discoteca.

JOHN: ¿Qué discoteca?

JENNIE: Columbus. Vamos a bailar (6) _____ cuatro horas.

JOHN: ¿Y después?

JENNIE: Después vamos (7) _____ la casa de Amanda.

JOHN: Bien, nos vemos mañana.

JENNIE: Bueno, hasta entonces.

3-19   La carta. Carmen is reading a letter that her daughter Ana sent her from Argentina, where Ana is completing a study abroad program. The dog got the letter earlier and tore some parts of it. Complete the letter with the missing words to help Carmen understand it.

Hola mamá:

¡(1) _____ fin tengo tiempo (2) _____ escribir! Te escribo esta carta (3) _____ ti y (4) _____ papá. Estoy muy contenta en Buenos Aires. Me gusta mucho caminar (5) _____ las calles de la ciudad (6) _____ la tarde. Voy a clase todos los días. Las clases son muy difíciles, pero estudio (7)_____ tres horas todas las noches. Bueno, no tengo tiempo ahora, la próxima semana escribo más. Muchos besos y abrazos, Carmen.

MOSAICOS

A leer

3-20   Antes de leer. De vacaciones. Briefly look at the article about México City, México, in exercise 3-21 and answer the following questions.

1. ¿Dónde es más probable que aparezca este artículo?
   a. una revista de negocios
   b. una revista de viajes
   c. una revista de cocina
   d. una revista de modas

2. ¿Cuál es la función principal del artículo?
   a. informar a los turistas de las actividades posibles en esta cuidad
   b. avisar de los peligros que hay en esta ciudad
   c. describir las comidas más populares en esta ciudad

3-21   A leer. ¿Qué hacemos en Ciudad de México? Read the article about Mexico City and indicate whether the sentences that follow are **Cierto (C)** or **Falso (F)**.

La Ciudad de México: Una ciudad fascinante

La Ciudad de México es una ciudad fascinante, con muchas actividades para grandes y pequeños. Esta ciudad tiene una extensa oferta cultural, de turismo ecológico y de turismo de aventura. En la Ciudad de México, aburrirse ¡es imposible!

Oferta cultural:

- Caminar por el Paseo de la Reforma.

- Admirar el Palacio Nacional: los murales de Diego Rivera.

- Ver el Templo Mayor.

- Ir a la "Casa Azul", residencia de Frida Kahlo.

- Ir a la Zona Rosa: el Museo de Cera (*wax*) y al Museo Ripley.

- Ir a la Colonia Roma: el Museo Ruth Lechuga, con su colección de arte popular mexicano.

- Entrar en el Museo Dolores Olmedo, donde está la colección de pinturas de caballete (*easel*) de Diego Rivera y Frida Kahlo más grande (*largest*) de todo el país.

- Visitar la Ciudad Universitaria; el Estadio Olímpico, donde se celebraron (*past tense of* **celebrar**) los Juegos Olímpicos de 1968; la Rectoría y la Biblioteca de la famosa Universidad Nacional Autónoma (la UNAM).

- Visitar las Pirámides de Teotihuacán, en el Estado de México: las Pirámides del Sol y de la Luna, la Calzada de los Muertos y el Templo del Quetzal-Papalótl.

- Visitar la zona de Chapultepec.
- Visitar el Centro Histórico.
- Ver la Catedral Metropolitana.

Para los niños:

- Visitar el Zoológico, donde la familia puede (*can*) ver los osos panda y otros animales exóticos.
- Caminar por el bosque Chapultepec o remar (*row*) en el lago de Chapultepec.
- Ir al Museo Universum, el primer museo interactivo para la difusión de la ciencia en América Latina y el más grande (*biggest*) del continente.

Turismo ecológico: Ir al Parque Ecológico de Xochimilco, donde se pueden observar muchas aves.

Turismo de aventura: Para los jóvenes y los amantes (*lovers*) de experiencias intensas, hay muchas posibilidades: Aventura Vertical (Oriente), el Escalódromo Carlos Carsoli al Norte, el Parque Ecológico San Nicolás Totolapan, Atoltecayotl Milpa Alta, y Guías Azteca Turismo Alternativo.

Artesanías: Visitar el Mercado de San Juan o el de la Ciudadela, en el centro de la ciudad.

Comer:

La hacienda de los Morales: comida internacional	El lago: bar, discoteca
El mesón del Cid: comida española	Taquerías y restaurantes para probar la comida local

Quedarse (**to stay**):

Tulip Inn Ritz, en el centro histórico	Hotel Royal Zona Rosa, 5☆ tradición cosmopolita
Hotel Best Western Estoril, 4☆ experiencia y tradición	

1. C F No es buena idea ir con niños a la Ciudad de México porque no hay actividades para los niños.

2. C F En esta ciudad se puede (*can*) visitar la residencia de Diego Rivera.

3. C F En el Museo Universum los niños pueden aprender sobre la ciencia y divertirse.

4. C F En la Ciudad de México se puede comer comidas de otros países.

5. C F La UNAM es una universidad muy pequeña en el centro de la ciudad.

6. C F Para comprar artesanías es buena idea visitar el Museo Ruth Lechuga.

3-22   **Después de leer. De viaje.** You are planning to go to Mexico City on a vacation with your friend. She calls you on the phone to find out what types of activities you like to do so that she can start planning the trip. Answer your friend's questions.

1. ¿Te gustan los museos? ¿Qué tipo de arte te gusta más?

   _____

2. ¿Te gusta caminar mucho, o debemos alquilar un coche?

   _____

3. ¿Eres una persona que te gustan las aventuras, o eres más (*more*) un tipo de persona de actividades tranquilas? ¿Qué tipo de actividades te gustan más?

   _____

4. ¿Te gustan los animales? ¿Cuáles son tus animales favoritos?

   _____

5. ¿Eres una persona que te gusta probar (*try*) comidas nuevas?

   _____

A escribir

3-23   Antes de escribir. Planning. Here again you have a list of activities you can do in Mexico City and the places where you can stay and eat. Select those that interest you most.

Destinos

_____ el Paseo de la Reforma

_____ el Palacio Nacional

_____ el Templo Mayor

_____ el Centro Histórico

_____ la Ciudad Universitaria

_____ el Bosque y el Lago de Chapultepec

_____ el Escalódromo Carlos Carsoli

_____ la Zona de Chapultepec

_____ la Catedral Metropolitana

_____ la "Casa Azul"

_____ las Pirámides de Teotihuacan

_____ el Zoológico

_____ el Parque Ecológico Xochimilco

_____ la Aventura Vertical

Museos

_____ Museo de Cera

_____ Museo Ripley

_____ Museo Ruth Lechuga

_____ Museo Dolores Olmedo

_____ Museo Universum

Mercados

_____ Mercado de San Juan

_____ Mercado de la Ciudadela

Restaurantes

_____ Comida mexicana

_____ Comida española

_____ Comida internacional

_____ Taquerías

Hoteles

_____ Tulip Inn Ritz

_____ Hotel Royal Zona Rosa

_____ Hotel Best Western Estoril

_____ Pensión

3-24   A escribir. Vacaciones fantásticas. You are spending two weeks in Mexico City with your friend. Write a postcard to a classmate in your Spanish class. Tell him/her where you are staying and your plans for the next few days, based on the selections you made in activity 3-23. Use **Querido/a** + [name, followed by colon] (e.g., **Querida Ana:**) to address your friend, and use **Un saludo cariñoso de** + [your name] as a closing.

_____

_____

_____

_____

_____

_____

3-25   Después de escribir. De vuelta. You and your friend just returned from Mexico City. Indicate the places you saw, refering back as necessary to the reading about Mexico City in exercise 3-21.

1. _____ Universum   a. mercado

2. _____ Teotihuacan   b. bosque

3. _____ Xochimilco   c. museo

4. _____ Ciudadela   d. universidad

5. _____ Chapultepec   e. parque ecológico

6. _____ UNAM   f. pirámides

ENFOQUE CULTURAL

3-26   Perú. Read again the **Enfoque cultural** section on pages 121–126 in your textbook, and answer the following questions about Perú.

1. Los jóvenes peruanos van a las peñas cuando quieren...
   a. ver una obra de teatro.
   b. ver una película.
   c. escuchar música, cantar y bailar.
   d. tomar un café al aire libre.

2. La antigua capital del imperio inca es...
   a. Lima.
   b. Nazca.
   c. Cuzco.
   d. Machu Picchu.

3. Una zona desértica en Perú es...
   a. Cuzco.
   b. Lima.
   c. Nazca.
   d. Sacsayhuaman.

4. En Perú, una palabra equivalente a "trabajo" es...
   a. bacán.
   b. chancón.
   c. chamba.
   d. selva.

5. Machu Picchu es...
   a. una ciudad inca.
   b. una ciudad maya.
   c. una fortaleza en ruinas.
   d. una playa famosa.

6. Para expresar que algo está muy bien, en Perú usan la palabra...
   a. mochaica.
   b. chancón.
   c. chimú.
   d. maldito.

7. En el verano muchas familias peruanas...
   a. actúan en obras de teatro.
   b. van a la playa.
   c. van al cine juntos.
   d. aprenden bailes folclóricos.

8. El huayno es...
   a. un museo de joyería.
   b. un tipo de baile folclórico.
   c. una ruina inca famosa.
   d. una zona de la selva amazónica.

A PRIMERA VISTA

3-27 **Diversiones.** Roberto and Elena are good friends and have done many things together. But now one of them is studying abroad, so their activities are different. Listen to them once, focusing on getting the general idea. Then listen again and indicate whether the following statements are **Cierto** or **Falso.**

	CIERTO	FALSO
1. Roberto va al cine con sus amigos.		
2. Roberto escucha música en casa.		
3. Roberto conversa con sus amigos en un café.		
4. A Roberto le gusta hablar de política.		
5. A Roberto no le gusta leer novelas.		
6. Roberto nunca lee el periódico o revistas.		
7. Elena estudia sólo (*only*) arte.		
8. Elena es norteamericana.		
9. Elena va a Perú durante las vacaciones.		
10. A Elena no le gusta tocar la guitarra.		
11. Elena canta canciones peruanas.		
12. A Elena le gusta bailar en casa de sus amigos.		

3-28 **El fin de semana.** You will listen to three college students talk about their weekend activities. Below are listed the weekend activities they will mention; are they similar to or different than yours?

escuchar música	ir al cine	leer el periódico
ver televisión	bailar en la discoteca	leer revistas
tomar algo en un café	tocar la guitarra	conversar en la computadora

Now listen to the brief descriptions of Mario, Emilio, and Patricia. Based on what you hear, imagine who might do each of the activities mentioned above.

Now listen to a conversation among the students and complete the sentences below with the correct activities from the list above. Write the activities in the order in which they are mentioned.

1. Las actividades de Mario: *leer el periódico*, _____ y _____.

2. Las actividades de Emilio: _____, _____ y _____.

3. Las actividades de Patricia: _____, _____ y _____.

3-29   En el supermercado. It is your turn to go grocery shopping for you and your roommate. Your shopping list is long, and you realize you would not have enough money to buy everything. You call your roommate to find out what she really needs. Listen to her and select the items she wants you to buy.

jugo de naranja _____	*agua mineral* _____
leche _____	*pollo* _____
cereal _____	*papas* _____
pan _____	*lechuga* _____
huevos _____	*tomate* _____
arroz _____	*fruta* _____
refrescos _____	*helado* _____
cerveza _____	*chocolate* _____

3-30   En el restaurante. Marisa and Javier are going to have dinner at a restaurant in Lima, Perú. Look at the waitress's questions, on the left, and choose the appropriate response from the right. Then listen to their conversation at the restaurant and check your answers, making any necessary changes. HINT: You will hear the expression **para mí** = *for me,* and the word **camarones,** the plural of **camarón** = *shrimp.*

1. Buenas tardes. _____

2. ¿Qué desea comer, señora? _____

3. Muy bien, ¿y para beber? _____

4. Y el señor, ¿qué quiere comer? _____

5. La especialidad es el ceviche. _____

6. ¿Y desea un plato principal (*main course*)? _____

7. ¿Y desea beber cerveza también? _____

8. ¿Desean ustedes algo más? _____

a. Una cerveza, por favor.

b. Pues un ceviche de camarones para mí.

c. No, cerveza no. Para mí, vino.

d. Para mí, pescado con papas fritas.

e. Buenas tardes.

f. Sí, para plato principal quiero un bistec.

g. Sí, una ensalada de lechuga, por favor.

h. Uhm... ¿cuál es la especialidad de la casa?

EXPLICACIÓN Y EXPANSIÓN

1. Present tense of regular *-er* and *-ir* verbs

 **3-31   ¿Quién come pan?** You and your friends are having dinner at a restaurant. The waitress has lost the order, so you try to recall who is having what. Write the appropriate person (**yo, tú, nosotros, Jorge,** or **Pedro y Julia**) next to the food items mentioned.

MODELO: You hear: Comemos pan.

 You see and write: _____ *nosotros*

1. _____

2. _____

 3. _____

4. _____

5. _____

8. _____

6. _____

9. _____

7. _____

3-32   Su rutina en la universidad. Now that everyone has their food, you are eating and talking about your activities at college. Listen to your friends' questions, and answer, both orally and in writing, with statements that are true for you. You can say **Sí** or **No**, followed by a complete sentence:

MODELO: You hear: ¿Vives con amigos?
                You say and write: Sí, vivo con amigos. *OR* No, no vivo con amigos.

1. _____

2. _____

3. _____

4. _____

5. _____

3-33   Estudiantes de primer año. At the other side of the table, Pedro and Julia are talking and comparing their experiences as freshmen. Listen to their conversation once to get the general gist: Who is having more difficulties, Pedro or Julia? Are they doing similar things? Then listen to their conversation again and complete the following text with the verb forms you hear.

JULIA: Pedro, ¿cómo te va?

PEDRO: Regular. No me gusta la vida de estudiante. Es muy difícil. (1) _____ a muchas clases, estudio mucho y estoy muy cansado.

JULIA: Sí, es difícil... (2) _____ libros, (3) _____ tarea y (4) _____ mucho, pero yo no estoy cansada. ¿Qué (5) _____ normalmente?

PEDRO: Pues en el desayuno no (6) _____, pero (7) _____ café. Y en el almuerzo como hamburguesas y papas fritas, y bebo un refresco.

JULIA: Sí, muchos estudiantes (8) _____ hamburguesas y papas fritas, y (9) _____ refrescos. Pero yo también (10) _____ ensalada, verduras y pescado. Y (11) _____ en el parque todos los días para estar fuerte. Y tú, ¿(12) _____ o (13) _____ ejercicio en el gimnasio por la noche?

PEDRO: No, por la noche (14) _____ la televisión en casa; ¿tú no (15) _____ la televisión?

JULIA: Sí, el sábado mis amigas y yo (16) _____ la televisión y descansamos.

Give Pedro some advice for his first year at college.

MODELO: *Debes comer verdura y ensalada.*

1. _____

2. _____

3. _____

2. Present tense of *ir*

 3-34   ¿Adónde va de vacaciones? Dani and Cristina are planning their vacation with some friends. They will be traveling separately at first, and then they will meet.

Look at the map to get acquainted with the names of the cities the students will visit. Then listen to Dani and Cristina and write next to the friends' names the city where each is going.

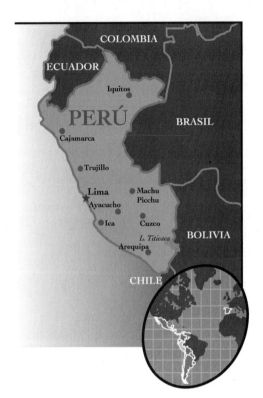

1. Dani _____

2. Cristina _____

3. Elisa _____

4. Diego y Enrique _____

5. Todos los amigos _____

 3-35   Actividades y lugares. Listen to the questions and respond orally and in writing. Use the appropriate form of the verb **ir** and a place from the list below.

la discoteca	la biblioteca	el cine	el restaurante
la cafetería	la playa	la librería	

MODELO: You hear: ¿Adónde va el profesor para cenar?
           You write and say: *Va al restaurante.*

1. _____   4. _____

2 _____   5. _____

3. _____   6. _____

3. *Ir* + *a* + infinitive to express future action

 3-36 Laura y sus amigos. It is Laura's first semester at college. She has a lot of new friends, and she wants you to join them. First look at the illustrations of her weekend activities. Then listen to Laura's description of her weekend and write when she and her friends are going to do each activity.

MODELO:    You hear: Vamos a tomar el sol en la playa esta tarde.
You write next to the appropriate illustration: *esta tarde*

1.   2.   3.   4.   5.   6.

1. _____   4. _____

2. _____   5. _____

3. _____   6. _____

3-37 ¿Qué va a hacer para aprender español? What can you do to improve your Spanish other than to attend class and study? Listen to the assessment questions to find out how much you are doing to improve your Spanish. Respond truthfully by writing and saying affirmative or negative statements.

MODELO: You hear: ¿Vas a hablar en español con un amigo hispano?
You say and write: *Sí, voy a hablar en español con un amigo hispano.*
OR No, *no voy a hablar en español con un amigo hispano.*

1. _____

2. _____

3. _____

4. _____

5. _____

Can you think of other things you are going to do to improve your Spanish?

4. The present tense to express future action

 3-38 **¿Con quién?** You would like to do something fun, but you do not want to do it by yourself. You call your friend Mario, but he has other plans. But he saw your common friends earlier, and he knows what everyone is doing. Listen to him and match each person with the activities they will be doing tonight.

1. Federico   _____   a. ver la televisión

2. Lidia   _____   b. tocar la guitarra y cantar

3. Sonia   _____   c. estudiar psicología

4. Irene   _____   d. hacer la tarea de economía

5. Manuel y María   _____   e. tener una fiesta

6. Mario   _____   f. ir al cine

Now write a sentence about what you will be doing tonight and with whom.

_____

 3-39 **Los planes de Mónica.** Mónica is a very busy person. Listen to her plans for next week and imagine what is written in her agenda. Follow the format you find in the entry Mónica has already written.

lunes, 11 de octubre

martes, 12 de octubre

miércoles, 13 de octubre

jueves, 14 de octubre

viernes, 15 de octubre

sábado, 16 de octubre

domingo, 17 de octubre
Voy al cine.

Nombre: _____   Fecha: _____

5. Numbers 100 to 2,000,000
_____

3-40 Identificación. Your instructor often asks you to open the book to a specific page number. You will hear one number from each of the following groups. Circle the number you hear. To maximize your listening comprehension, and for further numbers practice, read out loud all the numbers in each series before listening.

MODELO: You see and read out loud: 273 238 136 163 613
         You hear and circle: 163

1.	277	287	368	167
2.	104	205	405	504
3.	213	312	203	103
4.	406	624	704	640
5.	100	101	110	1.000

3-41 ¿Adónde voy? You have taken a part-time job delivering for a local restaurant. You leave with your first orders but realize that you do not have the complete addresses: the house numbers are missing! You call the restaurant and get the missing information for your deliveries. Listen and complete the addresses using numerals.

MODELO: You hear: Avenida de Buenos Aires trescientos treinta y seis
         You complete: Avenida de Buenos Aires 336

1. Calle María de Molina _____   4. Calle Princesa _____

2. Plaza Mayor _____   5. Calle de Lima _____

3. Paseo de la Castellana _____   6. Avenida de la Ilustración _____

ALGO MÁS: SOME USES OF *POR* AND *PARA*

3-42 ¿Por o para? Lola and Paco made reservations for a trip, and now their friends are asking them questions about it. Listen to the questions and complete the answers with **por** or **para**.

1. Vamos _____ Lima.

2. _____ supuesto.

3. Vamos a nadar y a caminar _____ la playa.

4. Vamos a estar _____ cinco días.

3-43   Para viajar a Perú. For a great vacation, you need to do a little planning. Read the following text, where advice is given to tourists coming to Perú. Complete the spaces with **por** or **para.**

Para viajar a otro país, usted debe prepararse. (1) _____ ejemplo, usted debe hacer reservas de avión y de hotel. Es posible hacer las reservas (2) _____ teléfono o (3) _____ Internet. (4) _____ supuesto usted también debe tener un pasaporte (5) _____ viajar a Perú.

En los aeropuertos la seguridad es muy importante ahora, y muchas veces usted debe esperar (6) _____ una o dos horas. (7) _____ eso es importante ir temprano (8) _____ el aeropuerto.

Now listen to the audio and check your answers. Make any necessary changes.

MOSAICOS

3-44   Las vacaciones de Lola y Paco. Lola and Paco are planning their vacation, and they discuss a travel package they have found. First listen to their conversation for the gist: Where is the trip? What is their reaction to the information they have so far? Then listen to the questions and review the choices below. Listen to the conversation again to check on your answers and make any changes necessary. HINT: You will hear the word **sólo** = *only.*

1. a. Lima   b. Perú (tres ciudades)   c. Miami

2. a. siete días   b. diez días   c. dos semanas

3. a. 250 dólares   b. 25.000 dólares   c. 2.500 dólares

4. a. Cuzco   b. Lima   c. Machu Picchu

5. a. Para hacer las   b. Para confirmar sus   c. Para hacer unas
      reservas.   reservas.   preguntas.

6. a. 667-2245   b. 267-3245   c. 667-3245

PRONUNCIACIÓN

Carefully read the explanation of how the Spanish consonants **g, j, r,** and **rr** are pronounced. Repeat the words after the speaker when prompted.

g and j

At the beginning of an utterance or after **n**, the Spanish **g**, when followed by **l, r, a, o,** or **u,** is pronounced like the English *g* in *garden*. **Repitan las siguientes palabras.**

    gata   gusta   gorila   gracias   globo   domingo

In all other positions, the Spanish **g**, when followed by **l, r, a, o,** or **u,** is pronounced with no interruption to the airflow. The sound is similar to the rapid and relaxed pronunciation of English *g* in *sugar*. **Repitan las siguientes palabras.**

    la gata   amigo   lugar   regular   lechuga   negro

In the syllables **gue** and **gui**, the letter **g** is pronounced as above, but the **u** is not pronounced. **Repitan las siguientes palabras.**

    gueto   guitarra   guía   Miguel   seguir   espaguetis

When the **u** must be pronounced in the combination **gue** and **gui**, Spanish shows it in writing with two dots over the **u: ü.** This symbol is called **diéresis** in Spanish. Note that the pronunciation of the **g** is the same as you practiced before. **Repitan las siguientes palabras.**

    nicaragüense   lingüista   antigüedad   vergüenza   güiro

In Spanish the pronunciation of the letter **g**, in the syllables **ge** and **gi**, and the letter **j** is very similar to the pronunciation of English *h* in the word *heel*. **Repitan las siguientes palabras.**

    general   vegetal   gigante   gimnasio   joven   jueves

r and rr

In Spanish whenever the letter **r** occurs between vowels or after a consonant, its pronunciation is similar to the English *d, dd, t,* or *tt* in words such as *matter, water,* or *ladder* when pronounced rapidly by an American. **Repitan las siguientes palabras.**

    pero   señora   moreno   camarero   tres   otro

The Spanish **rr** and **r**, at the beginning of a word or after **n** or **l**, are pronounced by placing the tip of the tongue on the upper ridge of the gum and tapping it several times. This sound does not exist in English. **Repitan las siguientes palabras.**

corro   arroz   rico   Roberto   rápido   refresco

Stress and the written accent

In previous chapters you learned Rules 1 and 2 for writing accents. Here is Rule 3:

Rule 3. Words that are stressed on the next-to-last syllable have no written accent if they end in **n**, **s**, or a vowel. They do have a written accent if they end in any other letter. **Repitan las siguientes palabras.**

e<u>xa</u>me<u>n</u>   <u>ca</u>sa<u>s</u>   <u>ce</u>na   <u>so</u>pa   le<u>chu</u>ga   to<u>ma</u>te

Read and listen to the following words that stress the next-to-last syllable. Note that they do not have a written accent, because they end in **n**, **s**, or a vowel. You will hear a confirmation after you read each word.

1. comida
2. cerveza
3. ceviche
4. pescado
5. papas

6. bebidas
7. espaguetis
8. cines
9. comen
10. toman

Remember, words stressed on the next-to-last syllable have an accent mark if they do not end in **n**, **s**, or a vowel. The following words are outside these parameters and therefore must carry an accent. **Repitan las siguientes palabras.**

<u>lá</u>piz   <u>ú</u>til   <u>dé</u>bil   <u>már</u>ti<u>r</u>   <u>Fé</u>li<u>x</u>   ca<u>rác</u>te<u>r</u>

Read the following words, stressing the next-to-last syllable. Note that the words have a written accent because they do not end in **n**, **s**, or a vowel. You will hear a confirmation after you read each word.

1. fácil
2. suéter
3. álbum
4. Bolívar

5. sándwich
6. portátil
7. Velázquez
8. difícil

Lección 4

Nombre: _____

Fecha: _____

La familia

A PRIMERA VISTA

4-1   **¿Quién es?** Match the following descriptions with the family members.

1. _____ hija de mis padres

2. _____ hermano de mi padre

3. _____ hijos de mis hijos

4. _____ madre de mi madre

5. _____ hijos de mis tíos

a. tío

b. abuela

c. primos

d. hermana

e. nietos

4-2   **La familia de Julia.** Look at Julia's family tree to complete the sentences that follow.

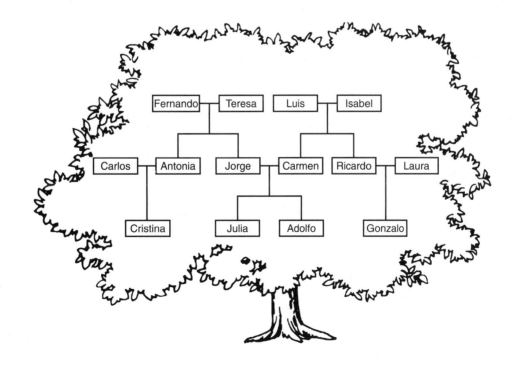

Lección 4   La familia   ▦ WB117

MODELO: Jorge es *el esposo* de Carmen.

1. Fernando es _____ de Julia.

2. Cristina y Adolfo son _____.

3. Ricardo es _____ de Julia.

4. Carmen es _____ de Adolfo.

5. Cristina es _____ de Jorge.

6. Adolfo es _____ de Luis.

7. Julia y Adolfo son _____.

8. Antonia es _____ de Adolfo.

4-3   Los famosos. Indicate the kind of relationship the following famous people share.

MODELO: Mary Kate Olsen y Ashley Olsen   *hermanas*

1. Julio Iglesias y Enrique Iglesias   _____

2. Charlie Sheen y Emilio Estévez   _____

3. Gloria Estefan y Emilio Estefan   _____

4. Michael Jackson y Janet Jackson   _____

5. La reina Isabel II de Inglaterra y el príncipe William   _____

4-4   ¿Y su familia? Now write a description of your own family. Be sure to mention the name of each family member, his/her age, and his/her relationship with other family members (whether the person you are describing is someone's father, mother, sister, nephew, grandson, etc.). Also, if you are describing brothers and sisters, be sure to mention whether the person you are describing is the oldest, the youngest, and so on.

_____

_____

_____

_____

_____

EXPLICACIÓN Y EXPANSIÓN

Síntesis gramatical

1. Present tense of stem-changing verbs (e → ie, o → ue, e → i)

pensar (*to think*)

yo	pienso		nosotros/as	pensamos
tú	piensas		vosotros/as	pensáis
Ud., él, ella	piensa		Uds., ellos/as	piensan

volver (*to return*)

yo	vuelvo		nosotros/as	volvemos
tú	vuelves		vosotros/as	volvéis
Ud., él, ella	vuelve		Uds., ellos/as	vuelven

pedir (*to ask*)

yo	pido		nosotros/as	pedimos
tu	pides		vosotros/as	pedís
Ud., él, ella	pide		Uds., ellos/as	piden

2. Adverbs

	ADJECTIVE		ADVERB
FEMININE FORM:	rápida	→	rápidamente
NO SPECIAL FEMININE FORM:	fácil	→	fácilmente

Nombre: _____   Fecha: _____

3. *Present tense of* hacer, poner, salir, traer, *and* oír

yo	hago	nosotros/as	hacemos
tú	haces	vosotros/as	hacéis
Ud., él, ella	hace	Uds., ellos/as	hacen
yo	pongo	nosotros/as	ponemos
tú	pones	vosotros/as	ponéis
Ud., él, ella	pone	Uds., ellos/as	ponen
yo	salgo	nosotros/as	salimos
tú	sales	vosotros/as	salís
Ud., él, ella	sale	Uds., ellos/as	salen
yo	traigo	nosotros/as	traemos
tú	traes	vosotros/as	traéis
Ud., él, ella	trae	Uds., ellos/as	traen
yo	oigo	nosotros/as	oímos
tú	oyes	vosotros/as	oís
Ud., él, ella	oye	Uds., ellos/as	oyen

4. Hace *with expressions of time*

Hace dos horas que juegan.   *They have been playing for two hours.*

1. Present tense of stem-changing verbs (*e → ie, o → ue, e → i*)

4-5 ¿Qué quieren para su cumpleaños? What do you think the following people want for their birthday? Complete the sentences, choosing the item you most logically associate with them.

soñar con (*dream about*) una computadora perfecta   pedir un piano nuevo

querer un micrófono especial   querer un Óscar

MODELO: Stephen King *quiere una novela de misterio.*

1. Elton John _____

2. Enrique Iglesias _____

3. Penélope Cruz y Antonio Banderas _____

4. Bill Gates _____

4-6   La carta a los Reyes Magos. Michel is a five-year-old boy who lives in Spain. He has written a letter to the three Wise Men (**los tres Reyes Magos**), telling them the gifts (**los regalos**) he and his parents want. He has stained the letter with chocolate ice-cream, so some parts are illegible. Help Michel complete the letter so that he can mail it and get what he wants.

Queridos Reyes Magos,

Mis amigos (1) _____ (decir) que los Reyes Magos no existen, pero yo (2) _____ (pensar) que no es así (*it isn't so*). Este año (3) _____ (querer) muchas cosas porque soy muy bueno. Mi mamá no (4) _____ (querer) muchas cosas, pero sí (5) _____ (soñar; *dream*) con una casa nueva. Mi papá (6) _____ (querer) un libro y un televisor nuevo. Este año yo (7) _____ (pedir) un auto de juguete (*toy car*), una bicicleta, libros, una consola de videojuegos (*videogames*) y tres juegos. (8) _____ (preferir) una bicicleta roja, por favor. También Lassie, mi perrita (*little dog*), necesita una casita. Ahora ella (9) _____ (dormir) en el jardín (*yard*). Mis papás y yo (10) _____ (querer) un auto nuevo también.

Bueno, pues es todo. Gracias por los regalos. En la mesa hay leche y galletas (*cookies*).

Un beso,
Michel

4-7   ¿Qué piden? You and your friends like eating out. Complete the following sentences with what each of your friends would order in these restaurants.

pedir arroz frito   pedir espaguetis   pedir una hamburguesa

pedir tacos   pedir salmón

1. En un restaurante italiano mi amiga Laura _____

2. En un restaurante chino mis amigos _____

3. En un restaurante mexicano nosotros _____

4. En un restaurante de comida rápida yo _____

5. En un restaurante francés mi amigo _____

4-8 **¿Pueden o no pueden?** Indicate whether the following people can or cannot do the following activities.

MODELO: Bill Gates *puede* comprar una mansión.

1. Una persona ciega (*blind*) _____ manejar (*drive*) un auto.

2. Un bebé de tres meses _____ caminar.

3. Una señora de 90 años _____ nadar cinco millas.

4. Los estudiantes _____ usar la computadora.

5. Una persona muy pobre _____ ir de vacaciones a Hawaii.

6. Los niños de diez años _____ beber alcohol.

2. Adverbs

4-9 **Mi mundo.** Everyone experiences the world differently. Complete the following sentences with the choice that best describes your personal experience.

1. Me gusta comer...
   a. lentamente   b. rápidamente   c. continuamente

2. Mi autor favorito escribe...
   a. románticamente   b. honestamente   c. fácilmente

3. Los profesores de mi universidad visten (*dress*)...
   a. formalmente   b. informalmente   c. elegantemente

4. Por lo general, analizo los problemas...
   a. inmediatamente   b. lentamente   c. lógicamente

5. Prefiero viajar...
   a. regularmente   b. frecuentemente   c. esporádicamente

6. Yo resuelvo los problemas...
   a. fácilmente   b. tranquilamente   c. rápidamente

7. En público hablo...
   a. rápidamente   b. perfectamente   c. claramente

8. Manejo (*I drive*) mi auto...
   a. diariamente   b. frecuentemente   c. lentamente

4-10   ¿Cómo lo hacen? Complete the sentences to indicate how the following people and things perform these actions.

MODELO: Las personas nerviosas en público hablan *nerviosamente*.

1. Los políticos sinceros hablan _____.

2. Los autos rápidos andan _____.

3. El ejecutivo elegante viste _____.

4. Las personas tranquilas resuelven los problemas _____.

5. Las personas románticas viven _____.

6. Las personas honestas se comportan _____.

4-11   En la universidad. A reporter for the school newspaper is writing an article about the routines of university students. Think of your daily life as a student and answer the reporter's questions.

Choose adjectives from the list and make them adverbs or think of your own adverbs to answer the questions.

relativo	rápido	fácil	simple	frecuente
básico	lento	tranquilo	regular	general

MODELO: ¿Cómo desayunas? *Desayuno tranquilamente.*

1. ¿Cómo estudias? _____

2. ¿Cómo manejas? _____

3. ¿Cómo paseas? _____

4. ¿Cómo hablas? _____

5. ¿Cómo trabajas? _____

6. ¿Cómo haces amigos? _____

3. Present tense of *hacer, poner, salir, traer,* and *oír*

4-12   Cristina y su familia. Cristina is an exchange student from Argentina. You and she are discussing the differences in the routines of Argentineans and people from the United States. Complete Cristina's description of her family's routine. Are her family's routine and your family's routine similar or different?

salir	poner	oír	traer	hacer

Por la mañana mi padre (1) _____ de casa a las siete de la mañana. Mi padre siempre (2) _____ la radio del auto y (3) _____ las noticias. Llegan a la universidad a las ocho. Mi padre va a la oficina, y mi hermano Carlos va a la biblioteca y allí (4) _____ su tarea. Yo (5) _____ el despertador para las ocho de la mañana. Yo (6) _____ de la casa a las nueve de la mañana y llego a la universidad a las nueve y media. Primero voy a la clase de biología y (7) _____ los experimentos en el laboratorio. Cuando termino, voy a mis otras clases.

Por la noche mi mamá (8) _____ música mientras prepara la cena. Mi padre llega a las seis más o menos y siempre (9) _____ pan fresco (*fresh*) para la cena. Mi hermano y yo (10) _____ la mesa, y todos cenamos juntos y hablamos sobre las actividades del día.

Now, select the statement that is most appropriate:

La rutina de la familia de Christina y la rutina de mi familia son similares.
La rutina de la familia de Christina y la rutina de mi familia son muy diferentes.

4-13   ¿Qué hacemos? Marta and Luisa were telling Carlos their usual weekend activities. Carlos was confused because Marta and Luisa were talking at the same time. Help Carlos make sense of what he was able to hear.

salir de casa	traer vino	hacer aerobic
oír música	poner la mesa	poner flores

MARTA: El sábado por la mañana voy al gimnasio y (1) _____.

LUISA: ¡Qué bien! ¡A mí también me gusta mucho ir al gimnasio! Yo los sábados por la noche voy a un concierto y (2) _____.

MARTA: Sí, me encantan los conciertos. Yo muchas veces los sábados por la noche me quedo en casa, preparo la cena, (3) _____ y ceno con mi novio.

LUISA: Eso es muy romántico, ¿no?

MARTA: Sí, también (4) _____ para beber durante la cena y a veces (5) _____ en la mesa para decorar.

LUISA: Yo los fines de semana no me quedo en casa; (6) _____ y paseo en el parque con mi perro o voy al cine o de compras (*shopping*).

MARTA: ¡Eres muy activa Luisa! Un día podemos ir de compras juntas.

LUISA: ¡Qué bien!

Based on the conversation between Marta and Luisa, indicate who likes the following activities:

	Marta	*Luisa*
1. Quedarse en casa los fines de semana	_____	_____
2. Cenar con su novio	_____	_____
3. Pasear con el perro	_____	_____
4. Ir al cine	_____	_____

4-14   ¿Qué hace Carlos? Carlos is very active and likes to do a lot of things. Look at the places where he goes and guess what he might do there.

traer helados	nadar en el agua	poner la mesa	oír música rock	hacer la tarea

MODELO: En una clase de cocina *hace un pastel.*

1. En la cocina (*kitchen*) _____

2. En un concierto _____

3. En la biblioteca _____

4. En la playa _____

5. En una fiesta de niños _____

4. *Hace* with expressions of time

4-15   ¿Cuánto tiempo hace que...? Your cousin, whom you have not seen for a long while, is visiting you. You are catching up on all you have or have not done since you saw each other. Complete the sentences, saying how long you have (or have not) been doing each activity.

MODELO: jugar tenis
Hace dos años que juego tenis./Juego tenis (desde) hace dos años.
OR Hace dos años que no juego tenis./No juego tenis (desde) hace dos años.

1. hacer ejercicio _____

2. ir de vacaciones _____

3. ver una película buena _____

4. ir a un concierto _____

5. visitar a tu abuela _____

6. comprar un auto nuevo _____

ALGO MÁS: SOME REFLEXIVE VERBS AND PRONOUNS

4-16   Una mañana en la vida de Ashley. Ashley is a student in introductory Spanish, and she has written a paragraph for her instructor about her morning routines. Ashley is having difficulties with her Spanish. Help her complete the paragraph so that she can get a good grade in her class.

peinarse   levantarse   vestirse   secarse   bañarse

A las siete de la mañana, suena el despertador y (1) _____. Apago (*turn off*) el despertador

y (2) _____. Después del baño, (3) _____ con la toalla (*towel*), (4) _____ el cabello (*hair*)

y (5) _____ con unos *jeans* y una blusa. Después voy a desayunar.

4-17   ¿Qué hacen por la mañana? Your instructor has asked you to write a composition about daily routines of university professors. Prepare a set of questions to interview different professors about what they do in the mornings.

1. ¿A qué hora (levantarse) _____?

2. ¿Cuándo (bañarse) _____?

3. ¿Cuándo (vestirse) _____?

4. ¿_____ (lavarse) el pelo todos los días?

MOSAICOS

A leer

4-18.   Antes de leer. ¿Cómo se titula? Read the first two lines of the article in exercise 4-19 and decide which would be the best title for it.

a. La Fundación Amor y Paz: Casa y dinero para las familias pobres jóvenes

b. La Fundación Amor y Paz: Guardería para niños pobres

c. La Fundación Amor y Paz: Gran ayuda para familias de recursos limitados

4-19   A leer. La Fundación Amor y Paz. Read the following article about a Colombian couple that started a nonprofit organization (**organización sin fines de lucro**) in Cali. Indicate whether the statements that follow are true (**C**) or false (**F**). (HINT: **Decidió** and **publicó** are past tense verbs.)

En la ciudad de Cali vive un joven matrimonio que se dedica a ayudar (*help*) a las familias pobres. Ayudan a los padres a buscar trabajo y mantienen una guardería (*day-care center*) para los niños.

Este joven matrimonio es muy respetado y admirado en la ciudad. Él, Camilo Gómez Buendía, licenciado (*graduated*) en ciencias económicas, decidió un día dejar (*quit*) su carrera para comenzar esta labor. Su esposa, Mónica Jaramillo de Gómez, es su compañera de trabajo. Su padre, el conocido periodista (*well-known journalist*) Fernando Jaramillo Torres, publicó un artículo sobre esta obra sin fines de lucro, y la reacción del público fue extraordinaria. Hoy en día la Fundación Amor y Paz ayuda a más de cien familias a rehacer su vida.

Mónica es la tercera (*third*) hija del matrimonio Jaramillo. Ella y su madre, Blanca Giraldo de Jaramillo, entrevistan a las familias, y con psicólogos y voluntarios ofrecen la ayuda necesaria a las familias que se acercan (*approach*) a la fundación. Los hijos de Camilo y Mónica, de tres y cinco años, se unen (*join*) a los juegos y actividades de la guardería, y de esta forma (*thus*) toda la familia participa en esta bella obra.

1. C F La Fundación Amor y Paz ofrece (*offers*) casas para las familias de recursos limitados.

2. C F La guardería de la fundación cuesta mucho.

3. C F La madre de Mónica coopera en la fundación.

4. C F La fundación busca trabajo a las familias que lo necesitan.

5. C F Camilo y Mónica no tienen hijos.

6. C F El padre de Mónica es psicólogo y ayuda a entrevistar a las familias.

4-20 **Después de leer. ¿Qué más?** Do you know of any organization similar to **La Fundación Amor y Paz?** What programs might they be able to offer in addition to the ones they already offer? Make a suggestion list to the foundation.

1. _____

2. _____

3. _____

4. _____

5. _____

6. _____

A escribir

4-21   Antes de escribir. Ayuda. Many people and services are needed to run a foundation like **La Fundación Amor y Paz.** Select from the following list the things you think the foundation might need. Then add at least two more items to the list.

_____ personas para cuidar (*take care of*) los niños

_____ psicólogos

_____ personas de la limpieza (*cleaning*)

_____ contable (*accountant*)

___✓___ _____

_____ local para cuidar a los niños

_____ comida

_____ director

_____ personas para entrevistar a las familias

___✓___ _____

4-22   A escribir. Voluntario. You have decided to volunteer to help *La Fundación Amor y Paz*. Write an introduction letter to the Colombian couple. Tell them about your background (what you study, your family, etc.), how you think you can help, when you could go, how long you could stay, and so on.

_____

_____

_____

_____

_____

_____

_____

_____

_____

_____

_____

4-23   Después de escribir. En Colombia. You were accepted as a volunteer in *La Fundación Amor y Paz* and have been living in Cali for two weeks. Your mother calls you and wants to know how things are going. Answer her questions in the space provided.

1. ¿Cómo es la fundación? _____

2. ¿Cuál es tu trabajo? ¿Cómo es tu trabajo? _____

3. ¿Conoces a mucha gente? _____

4. ¿Cómo son tus compañeros de trabajo? _____

5. ¿Qué planes tienes ahora? ¿Cuándo vuelves a casa? _____

ENFOQUE CULTURAL

4-24   La familia hispana y Colombia. Read again the **Enfoque cultural** section on pages 157–162 in your textbook, and indicate whether the following statements about family life in Hispanic countries and about Colombia are **cierto (C) or falso (F)**.

1. _____ Una de las cosas más importantes para un hispano es su familia.

2. _____ La mayoría de las personas hispanas viven lejos (*far*) de sus familias y no se ven frecuentemente.

3. _____ A los tíos favoritos se les llama padrinos.

4. _____ En Colombia no hay playas porque está en el interior.

5. _____ La Candelaria es un barrio antiguo en la ciudad de Bogotá.

6. _____ La cumbia es uno de los tipos de música más populares en Colombia.

7. _____ Si (*If*) los colombianos te quieren pedir un favor, dicen que tienen "mucho camello".

8. _____ Si algo es muy difícil, los colombianos dicen que "no es soplar y hacer botellas".

9. _____ Bogotá es una ciudad muy rica; las zonas pobres están lejos de la ciudad.

A PRIMERA VISTA

4-25   La familia de Julieta. Look at Julieta's family tree and think about her relatives. How many siblings does she have? How about other relatives? Is her family similar to yours?

Now you will hear a number followed by a word identifying a person's relation to Julieta. Write that number next to that person's name in the family tree.

MODELO: You hear: 0 [zero], abuelo
           You write: *0* (next to the name don Felipe)

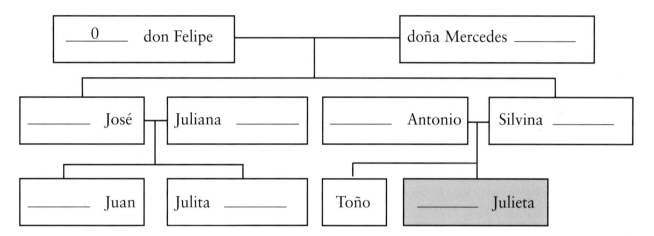

4-26   Más sobre la familia de Julieta. Look at Julieta's family tree again and answer the questions you hear.

MODELO: You hear: ¿Cómo se llama el abuelo de Julieta?
           You say and write: *Don Felipe.*

           You hear: ¿Quién es don Felipe?
           You say and write: *El abuelo.*

1. _____   4. _____

2. _____   5. _____

3. _____   6. _____

4-27   ¿Y cómo es tu familia? Is your family similar to or different from Julieta's? Listen to the following questions and answer with complete sentences, both orally and in writing. HINT: **vivo/a** = *alive, living*.

1. _____

2. _____

3. _____

4. _____

5. _____

6. _____

7. _____

8. _____

4-28   El bautizo. Baptism is a very important celebration in most Spanish and Latin American homes. Read the statements below before listening to the description of the baptism (**el bautizo**) of a new member of the Romero family. Then indicate whether each statement is **Cierto** or **Falso**. Do not worry if you do not understand every word.

	CIERTO	FALSO
1. Los Romero van a celebrar el bautizo de su primer (*first*) hijo.		
2. El niño se llama Fernando José por (*after*) su padrino.		
3. Los abuelos van a ser los padrinos.		
4. El bautizo va a ser en una iglesia (*church*).		
5. Sólo la familia va al bautizo.		

Nombre: _____ Fecha: _____

4-29   Las familias de Alicia y Florentino. You will hear Alicia Ramos Jaramillo and Florentino Rodríguez, two college students from Bogotá, describing their immediate and extended families. Before listening, try to anticipate which relatives might be mentioned. Then listen once just to get the gist.

Now look at the following charts about these families. Try to identify what is missing. Then listen again and complete the chart with the information you hear. Do not worry if you do not understand every word; listen as many times as necessary.

LA FAMILIA DE ALICIA			
NOMBRE	**RELACIÓN**	**TRABAJO/OCUPACIÓN**	**¿CÓMO ES?**
Arturo		profesor	
		trabaja en una librería	conversadora
Juan Carlos	hermano		listo
Mónica			
	primo	estudiante	
			muy inteligente

LA FAMILIA DE FLORENTINO			
NOMBRE	**RELACIÓN**	**TRABAJO/OCUPACIÓN**	**¿CÓMO ES?**
Ernesto		director de la biblioteca nacional	
		trabaja en un banco y en casa	muy ocupada
Pedro			
Esther			trabajadora
	hermano		
Antonia	hermana		
		no trabaja	
Leonor			

Are Alicia and Florentino's families similar? Are they similar to what you consider a "typical" American family?

1. Present tense of stem-changing verbs (e→ie, o→ue, e→i)

4-30   La rutina de Nico. Nico is from Colombia, but this year he is studying in the United States. Although many of his daily activities are still the same, his routine has changed in some ways. Listen to Nico and indicate whether the following statements refer to his life in Colombia, the United States, or both (*en los dos*).

	COLOMBIA	EE.UU.	LOS DOS
1. Nico no entiende todo en clase.			
2. Nico duerme ocho horas.			
3. Las clases empiezan muy temprano.			
4. Nico puede ir a biblioteca hasta (*until*) las doce de la noche.			
5. Nico juega al fútbol.			
6. Nico tiene amigos.			

4-31   ¿Quién es? Listen to Nico talk about things he and other people (including you) do at college. Indicate whether his statements refer to himself (**yo**), you (**tú**), his roommate Marcos, both Marcos and himself (**Marcos y yo**), or his friends (**mis amigos**).

a. yo   b. tú   c. Marcos   d. Marcos y yo   e. mis amigos

1. _____   5. _____

2. _____   6. _____

3. _____   7. _____

4. _____   8. _____

4-32 Las actividades de Nico. Look at the following sentences, which have been taken from Nico's description of his activities in exercise 4-30. Listen to him again and complete the sentences with the missing verbs.

1. Mis compañeros de clase _____ a decirme (*tell me again*) las cosas que son difíciles para mí.

2. En Colombia _____ ocho horas porque normalmente _____ ir a clases por la tarde.

3. En Colombia y en Estados Unidos _____ mucha tarea.

4. Casi todos los estudiantes _____ a la biblioteca y al laboratorio de computadoras, yo también _____ a la biblioteca frecuentemente.

5. Aquí los libros _____ mucho dinero.

6. En Colombia _____ al fútbol.

7. En los Estados Unidos _____ el béisbol o basquetbol.

8. En diciembre _____ a Colombia, y _____ ver a mi familia y a mis amigos.

9. Pero _____ volver a los Estados Unidos para visitar a mis amigos americanos. Y ellos también _____ visitarme en Colombia.

4-33 La programación en español. Nico sometimes watches Spanish television channels such as Univisión and Telemundo, and he suggested that you also watch some Spanish programs for practice. He mentioned some programs he likes, but you do not know what time they are on, so you call him to find out.

Below is the list of the programs you want to watch. Ask Alejandro what time each program is on. Then listen to his answer and write the time next to the program.

MODELO: You see: la telenovela
         You ask: ¿A qué hora empieza la telenovela? (telenovela = *soap opera*)
         You hear: La telenovela empieza a las cuatro de la tarde.
         You write: *4:00*

1. *El show de Cristina*   _____

2. los noticieros   _____ y _____

3. los deportes   _____

4. *Plaza Sésamo*   _____

5. *El musical*   _____

2. Adverbs

4-34   Pablito conversa con su tío. Pablito is very close to his uncle, and they often call and visit each other. Listen to a portion of a conversation between Pablito and his uncle. Then select the word that best completes each statement, according to what you heard.

1. Pablito tiene clase de guitarra...
   a. semanalmente   b. diariamente   c. raramente

2. Pablito practica la guitarra...
   a. semanalmente   b. diariamente   c. raramente

3. Pablito y sus compañeros practican más de dos horas...
   a. normalmente   b. siempre   c. raramente

4. Pablito y sus compañeros tocan...
   a. muy bien   b. regular   c. mal

5. Pablito vuelve a casa...
   a. lentamente   b. tranquilamente   c. rápidamente

6. Pablito hace la tarea y sale a jugar...
   a. temprano   b. mientras   c. después

4-35   Pablito y su tío siguen su conversación. Pablito and his uncle continue their conversation. You will hear Pablito's questions and you will see his uncle's answers below. Write the number of each question next to the appropriate answer.

_____ Mañana, Pablito, mañana.

_____ Porque generalmente no tengo tiempo.

_____ Realmente prefiero el violín.

_____ Sí, pero no frecuentemente.

_____ Mal, porque no practico mucho.

Now listen to the complete dialogue and check your answers.

3. Present tense of *hacer, poner, salir, traer,* and *oír*

4-36   Un día difícil. Pancho's mother is a very busy person and wants her family to share some of the housework, but Pancho does not like doing chores. Listen to the conversation between Pancho and his mother once to get the gist: What chores is Pancho asked to help with? Does he do them?

Now listen to their conversation again and complete the sentences below with an appropriate verb form. Choose from among the verbs below (you will need to use one of them twice).

hacer   poner   salir   traer   oír

1. Pancho no contesta, pero él sí _____ a su mamá.

2. Pancho está ocupado porque _____ tarea.

3. La madre de Pancho siempre _____ huevos y café.

4. Finalmente, Pancho _____ la mesa y _____ las tostadas.

5. Pancho _____ a las 8:30 de la mañana.

4-37   Pancho también. Pancho's mother wants him to help out more at home, as his siblings do, but Pancho says he already does his share. Listen to Pancho's mother and imagine Pancho's response, as in the Modelo. Respond both orally and in writing.

MODELO: You hear: Ellos ponen la mesa.
           You say and write: *Yo pongo la mesa también.*

1. _____

2. _____

3. _____

4. _____

5. _____

4. *Hace* with expressions of time

4-38   **¿Cuánto tiempo hace?** You will hear a brief description of a boy and his activities. Before listening to the description, look at the sentences below. Then as you listen to the description, complete the following sentences with the correct time.

MODELO: Agustín es mi sobrino *hace 10 años.*

1. Agustín vive en esa casa _____.

2. Estudia en la Escuela Moderna _____.

3. Agustín y Pablo son amigos _____.

4. Tiene una bicicleta _____.

5. Tiene un perro (*dog*) _____.

ALGO MÁS: SOME REFLEXIVE VERBS AND PRONOUNS

4-39   **Dos hermanos diferentes.** Miguel and Álvaro are twins, but they do not have the same habits. You will hear Miguel talk about himself and his brother. Indicate whether the following statements refer to Miguel, Álvaro, or both (*los dos*). Read the statements before listening to the passage.

	MIGUEL	ÁLVARO	LOS DOS
1. ¿Quién se levanta a las siete?			
2. ¿Quién duerme hasta las once los fines de semana?			
3. ¿Quién come cereal?			
4. ¿Quién no siempre desayuna?			
5. ¿Quién se baña rápidamente?			
6. ¿Quién se baña y se viste lentamente?			
7. ¿Quién duerme siete horas por lo menos (*at least*)?			

MOSAICOS

4-40   Visita al museo. You are visiting friends in Bogotá, Colombia. One of them wants to take you to a museum tomorrow. Apparently, there is a lot to see, so you want to spend *two hours* at the museum. Look at your agenda to check the activities you have already planned for tomorrow.

```
miércoles, 3 de octubre

  9:00    Desayuno con Marina.
 10:00    _____
 11:00    _____
 12:00    _____
  1:00    _____
  2:00    Como con Mirella y su familia.
  3:00    Hago compras con Mirella.
  4:00    _____
  5:00    _____
  6:00    _____
```

Your friend has left a message on your answering machine. Listen to it and write down what she is doing tomorrow at the times you are free. If she does not mention any activity for a particular time, write **nada** (*nothing*).

MODELO: You see: 10:00
           You hear: Yo tengo una clase de inglés a las diez.
           You write: *clase de inglés*

1. 11:00 _____

2. 12:00 _____

3. 1:00 _____

4. 4:00 _____

5. 5:00 _____

6. 6:00 _____

Based on both your schedules, and keeping in mind you want two hours at the museum, complete the following statement.

7. Podemos ir al museo a las _____.

Listen to your friend's message again and complete the information you need:

8. ¿Cómo se llama el museo? Museo _____

9. ¿Dónde está? En la calle _____

10. ¿Cuánto cuesta? _____ pesos.

PRONUNCIACIÓN

This section explains pronunciation of the Spanish letters **l, m, n,** and **ñ.**

l

At the beginning of a syllable, the pronunciation of the Spanish and English l is very similar. At the end of a syllable, the Spanish l has the same pronunciation, whereas the English *l* is quite different. Compare the pronunciation of the following words. **Lucas,** *Lucas*; **hotel,** *hotel*. **Repitan las siguientes palabras.**

     lápiz   libro   mal   papel   el   español   alto

m and n

The Spanish and English **m** are pronounced the same way. **Repitan las siguientes palabras.**

mamá   malo   amable   moreno   mesa   mexicano

At the beginning of a syllable, the Spanish and English **n** are pronounced the same way. At the end of a syllable, however, the Spanish **n** may vary according to consonant that follows it. Before **p**, **b**, and **v**, the Spanish **n** is pronounced like an **m**; before **g**, **k**, **j**, **q**, **ca**, **co**, and **cu**, the Spanish **n** is pronounced like **ng**. **Repitan las siguientes palabras.**

noche   un bolígrafo   un viejo   un periódico   un japonés

inglés   un casete   un cohete   encuesta

ñ

The Spanish **ñ** is similar to the pronunciation of *ni* in the English word *onion* or *ny* in *canyon*. **Repitan las siguientes palabras.**

español   señora   mañana   pequeño   tamaño

Stress and the written accent

In previous chapters you have learned some rules for writing accents. Here is Rule 4:

Rule 4. Words that are stressed on the last syllable have an accent mark if they end in **n**, **s**, or a vowel. They have no accent mark if they end in any other letter.

Repitan las siguientes palabras.

est**án**   est**ás**   est**á**   ingl**és**   alem**án**   auto**bús**

Read the following words. Note that these words do have a written accent because they end in **n**, **s**, or a vowel and are stressed on the last syllable. You will hear a confirmation after you have read each word.

1. francés   3. café   5. bebé   7. atún

2. portugués   4. jabón   6. esquí   8. perdón

Whenever you make a word plural, you often add another syllable to the word. This extra syllable makes the accent fall naturally on the penultimate syllable, removing the need for a written accent. These words have no written accent in the plural form because the stress naturally falls on the next-to-last syllable. **Repitan las siguientes palabras.**

japonés	japoneses	alemán	alemanes
autobús	autobuses	jabón	jabones

Remember that words that are stressed on the last syllable have no written accent if they end in any letter except **n**, **s**, or a vowel. **Repitan las siguientes palabras.**

habla<u>r</u>   verda<u>d</u>   españo<u>l</u>   feli<u>z</u>   borrado<u>r</u>

Read the following words that are stressed on the last syllable. Note that they have no written accent. You will hear a confirmation after you read each word.

1. vegetal
2. pared
3. alquilar
4. azul

5. borrador
6. terminar
7. papel
8. universidad

Lección 5

La casa y los muebles

A PRIMERA VISTA

5-1   ¿Dónde los pongo? You are helping a friend move into a new apartment. Decide where in the house the following furniture, fixtures, and appliances should go.

a. el dormitorio   c. el comedor   e. el baño

b. la sala   d. la cocina   f. la terraza

1. _____ la cama   6. _____ la mesa de noche

2. _____ el sofá   7. _____ la barbacoa

3. _____ la butaca   8. _____ el refrigerador

4. _____ el microondas   9. _____ la piscina

5. _____ el lavabo   10. _____ la ducha

5-2   Mi casa. Betty is telling you about the house she is going to rent. Complete her description to find out what the house looks like.

lavaplatos	sillas	piscina	sofá	lavabo
refrigerador	mueble	cama	chimenea	mesa

La casa que voy a alquilar es grande, pero no tiene nada; no tiene ningún (*any*)
(1) _____, así que (*so*) tengo que traer mi propia (*own*) (2) _____
para poder dormir. También traigo mi (3) _____ para poder sentarme (*sit*) a
mirar la televisión, y una (4) _____ con varias (5) _____ para poder
comer. La cocina sí está completamente equipada (*equipped*). En la cocina tengo un
(6) _____ para conservar la comida fría y un (7) _____ para lavar los
platos. En el baño hay un (8) _____ de mármol (*of marble*) para lavarme las
manos. ¡Es muy bonito! Además, en el salón hay una (9) _____ para poder hacer
fuego (*fire*) y estar caliente en invierno (*winter*). Y lo mejor de todo, en el jardín hay una
gran (10) _____ donde puedo bañarme con mis amigos en verano (*summer*).

5-3   **Crucigrama.** Complete the crossword puzzle by answering the following clues. All words refer to parts of the house, furniture, or appliances.

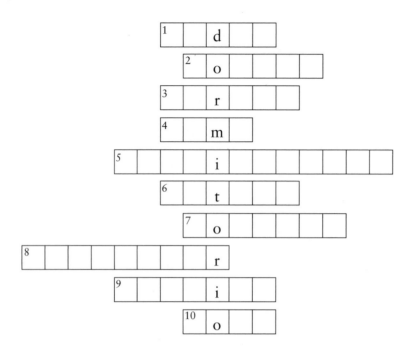

1. Podemos escuchar programas gracias a este aparato eléctrico.

2. Preparamos la comida en esta parte de la casa.

3. Aquí hay plantas, y los niños pueden jugar y correr. A veces también hay una piscina.

4. Es el mueble donde nos acostamos (*lie down*) para dormir.

5. Es el electrodoméstico que mantiene frías las comidas.

6. Es una silla grande y cómoda que tiene brazos (*arms*).

7. Las personas normalmente comen en esta parte de la casa.

8. Vemos y escuchamos programas gracias a este aparato eléctrico.

9. Es la decoración que ponemos en las ventanas.

10. Es el mueble donde pueden sentarse dos o tres personas.

5-4   ¿Qué deben hacer? Your friends always call you when they are in a situation in which they do not know what to do. Read your friends' dilemmas and give them advice.

1. Tu amiga tiene un viaje (*trip*) muy importante mañana. Cuando va al armario a buscar los jeans y las blusas que quiere llevar, ve que todo está sucio. ¿Qué debe hacer?
   a. sacar la basura
   b. lavar la ropa (*clothes*)
   c. pasar la aspiradora
   d. comprar un lavaplatos

2. Tu amigo quiere vender su apartamento. Hoy va a venir un agente, y su apartamento está muy sucio y desordenado. ¿Qué debe hacer?
   a. poner la mesa
   b. usar el microondas
   c. limpiar los muebles
   d. planchar la ropa

3. Tu amigo va a hacer una barbacoa en el jardín de su casa esta tarde. Quiere invitarte a ti y a otros amigos. ¿Qué debe hacer?
   a. tender la ropa fuera
   b. hacer la cama
   c. barrer la terraza
   d. pasar la aspiradora

5-5   Tareas domésticas. You are having a party in your fraternity or sorority, and you have to prepare the house. Each member receives a piece of paper on which is written a household item, and they need to guess which chore they must complete. Help your friends decide what they need to do.

MODELO: la mesa *poner la mesa*

1. la lavadora: _____

2. la secadora: _____

3. la plancha: _____

4. el lavaplatos: _____

5. la basura: _____

6. el piso: _____

7. el refrigerador: _____

8. el baño: _____

9. los muebles: _____

10. las camas: _____

5-6   **¿Cuándo hace estas tareas domésticas?** You just moved into your own apartment. Your mother calls to find out how things are going and how you are handling the household chores. Answer her questions.

1. ¿Con qué frecuencia pasas la aspiradora?

    _____

2. ¿Cuándo haces la cama?

    _____

3. ¿Lavas y secas los platos después de cada comida? ¿Tienes lavaplatos?

    _____

4. ¿Con qué frecuencia planchas la ropa?

    _____

5. ¿Sacas la basura? ¿Con qué frecuencia?

    _____

EXPLICACIÓN Y EXPANSIÓN

Síntesis gramatical

1. Present progressive

yo	estoy		
tú	estás		hablando
Ud., él, ella	está	+	comiendo
nosotros/as	estamos		escribiendo
vosotros/as	estáis		
Uds., ellos/as	están		

2. Expressions with tener

Tengo mucho calor (frío, miedo, sueño, cuidado).

Tienen mucha hambre (sed, suerte, prisa).

3. Direct object nouns and pronouns

me	*me*	
te	*you*	(familiar, singular)
lo	*you*	(formal, singular), *him, it* (masculine)
la	*you*	(formal, singular), *her, it* (feminine)
nos	*us*	
os	*you*	(familiar plural, Spain)
los	*you*	(formal & familiar, plural), *them* (masculine)
las	*you*	(formal & familiar, plural), *them* (feminine)

4. Demonstrative adjectives and pronouns

this	**esta** butaca	**este** cuadro	these		**estas** butacas	**estos** cuadros
that	**esa** casa	**ese** horno	those		**esas** casas	**esos** hornos
(*over there*)	**aquella** persona	**aquel** edificio	(*over there*)		**aquellas** personas	**aquellos** edificios

5. Saber and conocer (to know)

	SABER	CONOCER
yo	sé	conozco
tú	sabes	conoces
Ud., él, ella	sabe	conoce
nosotros/as	sabemos	conocemos
vosotros/as	sabéis	conocéis
Uds., ellos/as	saben	conocen

1. Present progressive

5-7   ¿Qué están haciendo y por qué? Look at what Marcos and his friends are doing and indicate why you think they are doing it.

MODELO: __a__ Lola está lavando la ropa.   a. Está sucia.

1. _____ Marcos está caminando hacia (*toward*) el gimnasio.

   a. Es el cumpleaños de su madre.

2. _____ Jaime está pidiendo (*ordering*) un pastel.

   b. Quiere ir al concierto mañana.

3. _____ Juan está comiendo una hamburguesa.

   c. Le gusta hacer ejercicio.

4. _____ Alicia está hablando con el profesor.

   d. Tiene hambre.

5. _____ Marta está comprando un boleto.

   e. Tiene una nota mala en el examen.

5-8   ¿Qué están haciendo? Based on where the following students are, indicate what they are doing now.

MODELO: Marta está en la cafetería. *Está tomando café.*

lavar los platos	poner la mesa	leer un libro
bailar	pasear y conversar	comprar un diccionario
ver una película		

1. Laura está en la librería; _____

2. Marcos está en el parque; _____

3. Enrique está al lado del fregadero; _____

4. Isabel está en la discoteca; _____

5. Rosana está en el comedor; _____

6. Carlos está en el cine; _____

7. Estela y Ricardo están en la biblioteca; _____

5-9   **Una conversación por teléfono.** Amanda is studying in Mexico for a year. Today she is feeling homesick, so she calls home to find out what everybody is doing.

hacer	dormir	estudiar	escuchar
ver	leer	reparar	

AMANDA: ¡Hola Mamá! ¿Qué tal estás? ¿Qué (1) _____ ahora?

MAMÁ: ¡Hola Amanda! (2) _____ la televisión. Dan mi telenovela favorita.

AMANDA: ¡Qué bueno! Y ¿dónde está papá?

MAMÁ: Está en el garaje. (3) _____ el auto, que tiene algún problema.

AMANDA: ¡Papá es tan buen mecánico! Y mi hermana Rosi, ¿qué hace?

MAMÁ: Tu hermana está en la biblioteca, (4) _____ un libro nuevo.

AMANDA: Claro, como siempre. ¿Y qué hace mi hermana Laura?

MAMÁ: Laura (5) _____ todavía (*still*) porque anoche (*last night*) fue a una fiesta y ahora está cansada.

AMANDA: ¿Y Roberto?

MAMÁ: Roberto y su amigo Enrique (6) _____ música en la habitación de Roberto. ¿Y tú qué haces?

AMANDA: (7) _____ para un examen de español. Bueno, mamá, te dejo (*I'll let you go*) porque tengo que estudiar.

MAMÁ: Bueno, hija. Cuídate y llama pronto.

2. Expressions with *tener*

5-10   **¿Qué tienen?** Read about the situations of Ángela and her friends and indicate how they feel.

1. Ángela trabaja mucho y duerme muy poco. Por eso siempre...
   a. tiene suerte.   b. tiene sueño.   c. tiene razón.

2. Jorge juega al tenis los sábados por la mañana. Después de jugar toma refrescos porque...
   a. tiene frío.   b. tiene miedo.   c. tiene sed.

3. Elena y Claudia están a dieta. Sólo toman jugo para el desayuno y vegetales y frutas para el almuerzo. A la hora de la cena ellas...
   a. tienen hambre.   b. tienen prisa.   c. tienen calor.

4. Ángela y su novio Carlos siempre juegan a la lotería, y nunca ganan (*win*). No....
   a. tienen cuidado.   b. tienen suerte.   c. tienen razón.

5. La clase de español empieza a las ocho de la mañana. Son las ocho menos diez, y María está todavía (*still*) en la cafetería. Roberto quiere hablar con ella pero no puede porque ella...

   a. tiene frío.   b. tiene sed.   c. tiene prisa.

5-11 ¿Qué tienen que hacer? You work at a magazine for teenagers. You write a column in which you give people advice when they are in a perplexing situation. Read the following questions from your readers and tell them what they have to do.

MODELO: Estoy muy preocupado porque saco muy malas notas en la universidad. Quiero sacar muy buenas notas, pero me gusta mirar televisión y jugar al golf. Los fines de semana voy a fiestas los sábados. ¿Qué puedo hacer?

Juan *tiene que estudiar más.*

     comer comida sana (*healthy*) y hacer ejercicio   tomar el autobús   sacar su pasaporte

     comprar discos compactos nuevos   hablar con él   practicar

1. Estoy un poco gordo y quiero bajar de peso (*lose weight*). Como una hamburguesa y papas fritas en el almuerzo, y por la tarde como helado con mis amigos. Nunca corro, y no me gusta hacer ejercicio. Prefiero conversar con mis amigos. ¿Qué puedo hacer?

   Ernesto _____

2. Soy una muchacha norteamericana, pero tengo parientes en Managua, Nicaragua. Voy a ir a Nicaragua durante mis vacaciones, y voy a pasar dos semanas con mis parientes. Mis padres y hermanos no pueden venir conmigo (*with me*), y es mi primer viaje al extranjero (*abroad*).

   Elena _____

3. Juego en una competencia muy importante de fútbol americano la semana próxima. Mis amigos y yo estamos muy nerviosos porque queremos ganar (*win*). ¿Qué hacemos?

   Michael y sus amigos _____

4. Tengo un estéreo nuevo para los discos compactos. La música que tengo está pasada de moda (*out of fashion*), y mis amigos van a venir esta tarde a mi casa para escuchar música. ¿Qué hago?

   Amparo _____

5. Estoy enfadado (*angry*) con mi compañero de apartamento. Siempre tengo que hacer todas las tareas domésticas: limpiar los muebles, limpiar el baño, pasar la aspiradora. Mi compañero no hace nada. Ya no aguanto más (*I can't bear it any longer*). ¿Qué puedo hacer?

   Mario _____

6. Tengo un trabajo muy bueno, pero está muy lejos de mi casa. Normalmente voy al trabajo en mi auto, pero en estos días no está funcionando (*working*). No quiero perder mi trabajo. ¿Qué puedo hacer?

   Rebeca _____

5-12   ¿Qué hacemos? Indicate where Joanna and her friends have to go or what they need to do to get what they want.

limpiar los muebles   regar las plantas   ir a la cafetería

estudiar   ir a la librería   pedir comida al restaurante

MODELO: Jean necesita ropa (*clothing*) nueva. *Jean tiene que ir de compras.*

1. Ana quiere comprar un libro. Ana _____

2. Joanna quiere sacar buena nota en el examen de español. Joanna _____

3. Henry quiere cenar lasaña de carne. Henry _____

4. Yo quiero tomar un café con leche. Yo _____

5. Mary y Julia quieren tener el apartamento limpio. Ellas _____

6. Sergio quiere tener muchas flores (*flowers*) bonitas. Sergio _____

---

3. Direct object nouns and pronouns

5-13   Las opiniones de Maricela. Read the following statements, in which Maricela explains how she feels about several people. Write down her attitude toward each person or persons.

MODELO: Su padre: *A su padre lo quiere mucho.*

Hola, me llamo Maricela. Hay muchas personas importantes en mi vida. Quiero mucho a mis padres, son personas muy especiales. También aprecio mucho a mis abuelos. Ellos siempre vienen de visita durante las vacaciones. Tengo una buena relación con mis hermanos. Mis hermanas y yo tenemos edades similares así que comprendo muy bien a mis hermanas. También tengo una buena relación con mis amigas. Siempre escucho con paciencia a mi amiga Karen cuando me cuenta sus problemas. Nosotras estudiamos juntas (*together*) en la universidad. Me gustan mucho mis clases y respeto mucho a mis profesores. Admiro a mis familiares, y también admiro mucho al presidente de los Estados Unidos. Soy una persona tranquila pero odio a los terroristas.

1. Su madre: _____

2. El presidente de EE.UU.: _____

3. Sus abuelos: _____

4. Sus profesores: _____

5. Sus hermanas: _____

6. Los terroristas: _____

7. Su amiga Karen: _____

5-14   ¿Qué pasa? You are watching a news program about the rich and the famous, but the television volume is low because your roommate is studying in the next room. Read the following news script and fill in the words you could not hear.

Buenas tardes, en el programa de hoy tenemos muchas noticias interesantes. Primero, nuestros reporteros están en la recepción después de la ceremonia de los premios Óscar. Hoy van a entrevistar (1) _____ varios artistas españoles. Los reporteros de este programa van a buscar (2) _____ Antonio Banderas porque quiere hablar (3) _____ público americano sobre su nueva película. Ahora en sus pantallas (*screens*) pueden ver (4) _____ Penélope Cruz, la actriz española que espera ganar (*win*) un Óscar algún día.

En otras noticias, las hermanas Williams, las famosas jugadoras de tenis, compran un perro nuevo. Dicen que quieren (5) _____ perro porque puede cuidar la casa y cuidar (6) _____ la familia. Todas las tardes una de las hermanas saca (7) _____ perro a pasear. Los fotógrafos tienen fotos de las hermanas Williams paseando (8) _____ perro, que se llama Toby.

5-15   La telenovela. Your mother is watching a popular Venezuelan soap opera. You are in your room and can hear parts of the characters' conversations. Complete the following conversation with the words you could not hear.

PABLO: Virginia, ¿tú (1) _____ quieres de verdad?

VIRGINIA: Sí Pablo, (2) _____ quiero mucho.

PABLO: Virginia, (3) _____ extraño (*miss*) mucho.

VIRGINIA: Yo también.

PABLO: Voy a ir a tu casa ahora mismo porque necesito (4) ver _____.

VIRGINIA: No puedes venir ahora porque mi mamá está en casa. Tú (5) _____ comprendes, ¿verdad?

PABLO: Sí, Virginia, (6) _____ comprendo.

VIRGINIA: Bueno.

PABLO: Pero a tu mamá no (7) _____comprendo. ¿Por qué no comprende que nos amamos?

VIRGINIA: ¡Ay Pablo! No sé. Ten paciencia (*be patient*); nuestro amor seguro gana (*surely will win*).

5-16   Mi familia. Read the following paragraph about Raquel's family. Then find the five third-person direct pronouns and indicate to whom they refer.

Mi familia es muy interesante. Mi madre trabaja en un banco y después va a casa y limpia la casa. La respeto y admiro mucho porque trabaja muy duro (*hard*). Además, es muy cariñosa. Mi padre también es muy cariñoso. Mi hermano y yo siempre reñimos (*fight*), pero lo quiero mucho. Tengo dos hemanas gemelas; tenemos una buena relación. Las quiero mucho. Mis abuelos viven lejos, en Lima, pero los visito una vez al año, durante las vacaciones. Mi tía Margarita está soltera, y aunque tiene 40 años vive con mis abuelos. Mi tía quiere mucho a mi abuela y siempre la ayuda con las tareas domésticas.

1. *La* se refiere (*refers*) a _____.

2. *Lo* se refiere a _____.

3. *Las* se refiere a _____.

4. *Los* se refiere a _____.

5. *La* se refiere a _____.

4. Demonstrative adjectives and pronouns

5-17   De compras. You and your friend are looking at various items in a store. Complete the questions you are going to ask the store attendant.

1. Ves un reloj en la pared (*wall*). El dependiente está un poco lejos, pero te acercas (*get near*) dónde está él y le preguntas: ¿Cuánto cuesta _____ reloj?

2. El dependiente tiene una guitarra en la mano. Tú le preguntas: ¿Cuánto cuesta _____ guitarra?

3. Tu amiga te da unos casetes que te gustan mucho, y le preguntas al dependiente: ¿Cuánto cuestan _____ casetes?

4. También ves al otro lado de la tienda unas películas. Se las señalas (*You point them out*) al dependiente, que está a tu lado, y preguntas: ¿Cuánto cuestan _____ películas de allí?

5. Tu amiga tiene un mapa en su mano, y tú lo necesitas para la clase de geografía. Le preguntas al dependiente: ¿Cuánto cuesta _____ mapa?

5-18 **¿Qué es esto?** Roseanne is looking at various things at a Nicaraguan store, and she wants to find out what they are. Complete the following conversation with the salesman, who is behind the counter, using *esto, eso,* or *aquello*.

ROSEANNE: ¿Qué es (1) _____ que está ahí al lado suyo (*your side*)?

VENDEDOR: ¿(2) _____? Es un molinillo (*little grinder*). Lo usamos para batir (*grind*) el chocolate o el "tiste", una bebida de maíz y cacao.

ROSEANNE: ¿Y (3) _____ que está allá? ¿Qué es?

VENDEDOR: Es un "guacal". Es una calabaza seca (*dry gourd*), y la usamos para servir la comida. Y también servimos unos pequeños que se usan para servir bebidas.

ROSEANNE: ¿Y (4) _____ que está aquí?

VENDEDOR: (5) _____ es una "maraca", un instrumento musical. Usamos dos, una en cada mano, y con ellas seguimos el ritmo de la música.

5-19 **¿Dónde quiere los muebles?** You are spending two weeks at the home of a friend in Managua. She has bought a few things for her home. You are in your room and can partially hear the conversation your friend is having with the delivery man. Complete the conversation with the words you failed to hear.

EMPLEADO: ¿Dónde quiere (1) _____ espejo que tengo aquí?

SRA. RUIZ: En (2) _____ dormitorio de ahí.

EMPLEADO: Y ¿dónde pongo (3) _____ lámparas que están ahí?

SRA. RUIZ: La lámpara blanca va aquí, y las otras dos en (4) _____ habitación pequeña.

EMPLEADO: ¿Y (5) _____ cuadros que están aquí?

SRA. RUIZ: (6) _____ cuadro de ahí va detrás del sofá.

EMPLEADO: ¿Y (7) _____ otro?

SRA. RUIZ: (8) _____ otro va en el comedor.

5. *Saber* and *conocer* (to know)

5-20   La familia de su novio. Patricia is a Mexican girl who is going out with a boy from Austin, Texas. Patricia's mother is worried that he is not Mexican, and she wants to know how well Patricia knows the family of her boyfriend. Help the mother complete the questions with the correct form of *saber* or *conocer*.

1. ¿ _____ a toda la familia?

2. ¿ _____ cocinar bien la mamá de tu novio?

3. ¿ _____ si tu novio pasa la Navidad con sus padres?

4. ¿ _____ a sus hermanos?

5. ¿ _____ conducir (*drive*) bien tu novio?

6. ¿ _____ el padre de tu novio hablar español?

5-21   El chico nuevo. Christine and Amanda are in your Spanish class and are talking about a new student in the class. They are whispering behind you, and you can hear parts of the conversation. Complete the conversation with the words that you could not hear. Use a correct form of **saber** or **conocer.**

CHRISTINE: Amanda, ¿(1) _____ a ese chico?

AMANDA: Sí, se llama Michael Stewart, y es muy amigo de mi hermano. ¿Por qué?

CHRISTINE: Es muy guapo y...

AMANDA: Lo quieres (2) _____, ¿verdad?

CHRISTINE: Sí, ¿(3) _____ qué estudia?

AMANDA: (4) _____ que estudia ciencias económicas.

CHRISTINE: ¿(5) _____ dónde vive?

AMANDA: Creo que vive en la residencia estudiantil, pero no estoy segura. Mi hermano es el que (*the one who*) lo (6) _____ muy bien.

CHRISTINE: Mira, viene a sentarse (*sit*) donde estamos nosotras.

AMANDA: Magnífico, así lo puedes (7) _____.

5-22   **¿Cuál es el problema?** Read the following situations and write an explanation of each problem.

MODELO: María y Juan tienen unos invitados (*guests*) a comer en su casa, y están muy preocupados. El arroz no está bien cocinado (*cooked*), y el pollo no tiene sal (*salt*).

María y Juan no saben cocinar.

1. Pedro y Héctor están lavando la ropa blanca con unas cortinas rojas. Su ropa blanca ¡ahora está rosada! _____

2. En la fiesta todos los estudiantes están bailando, excepto Humberto, que prefiere mirar.

   _____

3. Son las once de la noche, y un hombre toca a la puerta de Mariví. Ella mira por la ventana, pero no abre (*open*) la puerta. _____

4. John Foster entra en un restaurante de Santa Ana, una ciudad de El Salvador. Él pide agua y algo de comer, pero el camarero no entiende lo que (*that which*) dice.

   _____

5. Tus tíos están en Nueva York. Ellos tienen un mapa, pero están perdidos (*lost*).

   _____

ALGO MÁS: MORE ON ADJECTIVES

5-23   **¿En qué orden?** You are in a doctor's waiting room, where everyone has taken a number. Look at the numbers and indicate the order in which the patients will see the doctor.

1. Ana: uno _____	a. quinto
2. Carlos: dos _____	b. noveno
3. Regina: tres _____	c. segundo
4. Mario: cuatro _____	d. décimo
5. Isabel: cinco _____	e. primero
6. Irene: seis _____	f. octavo
7. Miguel: siete _____	g. sexto
8. Lucía: ocho _____	h. cuarto
9. Ignacio: nueve _____	i. séptimo
10. Mariví: diez _____	j. tercero

5-24 **¿Qué opina?** Indicate what you think of the following things and places.

buen   bueno/a   gran   grande   mal   malo/a   primer   primero/a

1. la Torre Eiffel: _____

   _____

2. el Pentágono: _____

   _____

3. el Museo Guggenheim en Bilbao, España: _____

   _____

4. las cataratas (*falls*) del Niágara: _____

   _____

5. el director de cine Pedro Almodóvar: _____

   _____

MOSAICOS

A leer

5-25 **Antes de leer. El título.** Read the title of the article in exercise 5-26 and decide to which job it probably refers. _____

5-26 **A leer. El trabajo peor pagado.** Read the following article and indicate whether the statements that follow are **cierto** (C) or **falso** (F).

"El trabajo peor pagado (*worst paid*)"

Las amas de casa realizan cada día una labor de trabajo inmensa, pero no reciben ningún salario por su trabajo. En muchos casos el trabajo de estas mujeres pasa desapercibido (*unnoticed*), y no reciben ni el agradecimiento (*gratitude*) de sus familias.

Aunque (*Although*) es cierto que en los últimos (*last*) años se ve un aumento de mujeres en las diferentes áreas del mundo laboral —en la industria, el comercio, e incluso (*even*) en la política— y como es natural reciben un salario por su trabajo, la mayoría de las mujeres latinas se dedican a trabajos del hogar como limpiar la casa, lavar, planchar la ropa, coser (*sew*), cuidar los hijos, atender (*tend*) al marido etcétera.

El gran problema para las mujeres que trabajan en casa persiste; no reciben salario ni recompensa (*compensation*) por las interminables horas de dedicación al hogar. Esta práctica es totalmente injusta; las mujeres tienen que recibir un salario por su trabajo en la casa. Lo mejor es que los esposos, antes (*before*) del matrimonio, se pongan de acuerdo en (*agree on*) la cantidad (*amount*) de dinero que la mujer va a recibir.

Es muy común en los hombres latinos una actitud bastante machista; los hombres piensan que las mujeres deben quedarse en casa y cumplir su papel (*role*) de esposa y de madre, y realizar todas las tareas domésticas. Estos hombres creen que es su obligación trabajar fuera de la casa para sustentar (*support*) económicamente a la familia. Según estos hombres las tareas domésticas son la responsabilidad absoluta de la mujer; el hombre cumple con sus horas de.trabajo fuera de la casa, y en el hogar espera atenciones de la esposa y los hijos, y no quiere responsabilidades domésticas.

Una situación más justa es en la que todos en el hogar son responsables de las tareas domésticas. Así la vida es más fácil para todos. Seguramente va a pasar algún tiempo antes de que la mujer reciba el reconocimiento de la sociedad por el trabajo que hace en casa.

1. C F Las mujeres latinas reciben un salario por su trabajo en casa.

2. C F Los hombres trabajan para ganar dinero para sustentar a la familia.

3. C F En estos países todas las mujeres trabajan en la casa.

4. C F Los hombres quieren que las mujeres trabajen fuera de la casa.

5. C F Todos los hombres latinos son machistas.

5-27   Después de leer. ¿Qué opinas? This article was published in a magazine together with a survey to find out the opinions of the readers with respect to this topic. Answer the following questions.

	SÍ	NO
1. ¿Crees que las mujeres que trabajan en casa deben recibir un salario?	_____	_____
2. ¿Crees que es justo que los hombres no colaboren en las tareas domésticas?	_____	_____
3. ¿Crees que las mujeres deben trabajar fuera de casa para ayudar económicamente a la familia?	_____	_____
4. ¿Crees que parte de las tareas domésticas son responsabilidad de los hijos?	_____	_____
5. ¿Crees que en los países hispanos la situación de la mujer cambia rápidamente?	_____	_____

5-28 **Antes de escribir ¿Y en tu casa?** Think about your own household. Who takes care of the following chores? How often are they done?

	TÚ	MAMÁ	PAPÁ	HERMANO/A	NADIE	OTRA PERSONA	FRECUENCIA
Cocina							
Compra la comida							
Limpia la casa							
Lava la ropa							
Cose (*sews*)							
Plancha la ropa							
Cuida el jardín							
Cuida a los niños							

5-29 **A escribir. La carta.** Write a letter to the author of the article and tell her about your own family experience and how it compares to the families she describes. Remember to mention:

- how the work is divided in your home;
- which chores are done in your house, and how often;
- how your home compares to that of the families described in the article.

_____

_____

_____

_____

_____

_____

_____

_____

_____

5-30   Después de escribir. ¿Es típica? The author of the article has received your letter and is very interested in families in the United States. She has written you some questions about the distribution of chores in American homes. Answer the writer's questions.

1. ¿Es tu familia típica con respecto a la distribución de las tareas domésticas?

    _____

2. En las familias estadounidenses, ¿son las mujeres las que realizan las tareas domésticas?

    _____

3. ¿En los Estados Unidos hay muchas mujeres que trabajan fuera de casa?

    _____

4. ¿Crees que las mujeres que trabajan en casa deben recibir un salario? ¿Por qué?

    _____

ENFOQUE CULTURAL

5-31   Read again the **Enfoque cultural** section on pages 197–202 in your textbook, and indicate whether each statements below is **cierto (C)** or **falso (F)**.

1. _____ Las viviendas en los países hispanos son todas muy similares.

2. _____ En muchos países hispanos es más común tener servicio doméstico que en los Estados Unidos.

3. _____ En las casas de Latinoamérica se puede ver influencia precolombina.

4. _____ La capital de Nicaragua es Granada.

5. _____ El parque El Imposible es una playa tropical de El Salvador.

6. _____ La capital de Honduras es Tegucigalpa.

7. _____ En Copán se pueden visitar ruinas mayas muy interesantes.

8. _____ El Lago Managua está al sur de Nicaragua.

9. _____ En Nicaragua usan la palabra *chavalo* para decir que una persona es fuerte.

10. _____ En Honduras un sinónimo de *niño* es *güirro*.

A PRIMERA VISTA

5-32   ¿Qué apartamento es? You work at the University Housing Center, helping new students and faculty find a place to live. The Center receives information on available housing as well as requests from members of the university community. Three messages on the answering machine describe new available properties. One of these properties has been diagrammed and faxed to your office.

First look at the apartment's layout. Next, listen to the three messages and identify the description that matches the apartment. Complete the sentence that follows by writing **1, 2** or **3.**

Finally, listen to the description of the correct apartment again. Identify the rooms that were not labeled in the diagram.

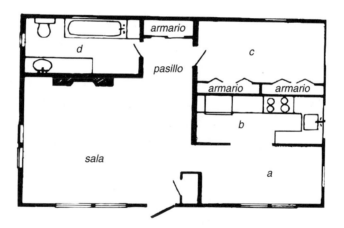

Éste es el apartamento número _____.

MODELO: a. _sala_

a. _____

b. _____

c. _____

d. _____

5-33 **El apartamento de Sonia.** You realize that the apartment you just reviewed (in exercise 5-32) would be perfect for your friend Sonia. It turns out she really likes it and ends up renting it. A common friend who helped Sonia fix up her place tells you about it. Before listening, anticipate where you could find the items listed below. Then listen to your friend and indicate where each piece of furniture or appliance is.

| | a. la sala | b. el cuarto | c. la cocina | d. el comedor | e. el pasillo |

1. el refrigerador   _____

2. la estufa   _____

3. el cuadro   _____

4. la alfombra   _____

5. el escritorio   _____

6. la mesa y las sillas   _____

7. la lavadora   _____

8. la mesa de noche   _____

9. la butaca   _____

10. las cortinas   _____

5-34 **Una casa para la familia Hurtado.** Professor Hurtado and his family are also looking for house. It has been difficult to find a place for a family, but one of your colleagues has good news. Listen to him and indicate whether each of the following statements are **Cierto** or **Falso**.

	CIERTO	FALSO
1. Los señores Hurtado quieren una casa en un barrio tranquilo.		
2. Los señores Hurtado tienen siete hijas.		
3. La abuelita visita a la familia a veces.		
4. La casa tiene dos pisos.		
5. Hay cuatro dormitorios en la casa.		
6. No hay terraza, pero hay piscina.		

5-35   ¿En qué parte de la casa? You are helping the Hurtado family move to their new house. The moving company is bringing all of their belongings, and the movers ask where to put each item. Listen to their questions and answer, telling them to put each item in the room where it is usually found.

MODELO: You hear: ¿Dónde quiere la cómoda?
           You say and write: *[En] el dormitorio.*

1. En _____   5. En _____

2. En _____   6. En _____

3. En _____   7. En _____

4. En _____   8. En _____

5-36   Las tareas domésticas. A big family in a big house requires a lot of housework! The chart below lists the members of the Hurtado family and some of the household chores that need to be done.

Look at the chart and anticipate any chores you do or do not expect a particular family member to do. Then listen to Mr. and Mrs. Hurtado talk about the distribution of house chores in the family. Indicate on the chart who does each chore.

	SR. HURTADO	SRA. HURTADO	LA ABUELITA	LAS HIJAS
1. cocinar				
2. pasar la aspiradora				
3. lavar los platos				
4. sacar la basura				
5. tender la ropa				
6. secar los platos				
7. cortar el césped				
8. planchar				
9. lavar el auto				

Who does these chores in your family? What chores do you do where you currently live?

1. Present progressive

5-37   ¿Qué está haciendo la familia de Ana? You are studying with your friend Ana when her aunt Esther calls. Everyone is busy doing other things, so they cannot come to the phone. Listen to Ana and indicate what each person is doing by writing the letter of the activity next to the name of the appropriate person. HINT: You will hear the word **ya** = *already*.

1. la madre _____   a. está sacando la basura.

2. el abuelo _____   b. está lavando los platos.

3. Ana _____   c. está estudiando para un examen.

4. la abuela _____   d. está conversando con un amigo.

5. el padre _____   e. está durmiendo en su cuarto.

5-38   ¿Qué está haciendo tu familia? You call home, and your father answers the phone. He tells you everything is as usual. You bet you could guess what everybody is doing right now. Look at the list of the family members who live at home and ask your father whether they are doing the activity indicated.

MODELO: You see: mamá/lavar los platos
You say: ¿Mamá está lavando los platos?

→ If you hear: Sí, es verdad.
You write: Mamá está lavando los platos.

→ If you hear: No, Mamá está pasando la aspiradora.
You write: Mamá está pasando la aspiradora.

1. tú/mirar la televisión <u>Papá...</u>_____

2. Clara/estudiar _____

3. Luis/comer un sándwich _____

4. Pablo/leer un libro _____

5. el abuelito/oír el radio _____

6. el perro/dormir en la cocina _____

Can you guess what your own family members are doing at this moment?

2. Expressions with *tener*

5-39 **¿Qué tienen?** In this lesson you have learned various expressions using the verb **tener.** Do you remember what they mean? Listen to the descriptions of your friends' situations and choose the best expression with **tener** to describe them.

MODELO: You hear: Marta está corriendo en el parque y quiere beber agua.
You say and write: Marta tiene sed.

1. Roberto _____

2. Andrés _____

3. Los niños _____

4. María _____

5. Miguel _____

5-40 **Los compañeros de piso.** This is the first time you have lived with roommates, and it is not easy! You call your friend to complain, and she has some advice for you. First look at your complaints on the left and her suggestions on the right. Then match each problem with your friend's advice. Finally, listen to your friend and check your answers.

1. ¡Los platos están sucios! _____   a. Tienes que limpiar la sala.

2. ¡Hay mucha basura en la cocina! _____   b. Tienes que hablar con ellos.

3. ¡No tengo leche para mi cereal! _____   c. Tienes que comprar leche.

4. ¡La sala está muy sucia! _____   d. Tienes que lavar los platos.

5. ¡Mis compañeros de piso no hacen nada! _____   e. Tienes que sacar la basura.

5-41 **Responsabilidades.** You finally talk to Felipe and Tina, your roommates, and agree to share the housework. Tina is out, so Felipe and you come up with the chart below for this week. When Tina returns, she asks you about it. Listen to her and answer her questions both orally and in writing.

	LUNES	MARTES	MIÉRCOLES	JUEVES	VIERNES	SÁBADO
Yo	Lavar los platos	Barrer el piso	Pasar la aspiradora	Lavar los platos	Limpiar el baño	Comprar comida
Tina	Limpiar la sala	Lavar los platos	Limpiar la cocina	Sacar la basura	Lavar los platos	Pasar la aspiradora
Felipe	Sacar la basura	Limpiar el baño	Lavar los platos	Barrer el piso	Limpiar la sala	Lavar los platos

MODELO: You hear: ¿Qué tengo que hacer el lunes?
         You say and write: *Tienes que limpiar la sala.*

1. _____

2. _____

3. _____

4. _____

5. _____

6. _____

3. Direct object nouns and pronouns

5-42   La primera fiesta. You and your roommates are planning a house-warming party in your new apartment. Felipe and you talk about what needs to be done. Listen to him and respond with the appropriate option below. Do this orally and by writing the corresponding letter in each space.

_____ 1. ¡Claro! Los llamo yo.

_____ 2. Sí, buena idea. Tina las puede traer también.

_____ 3. Bueno, tú la puedes ordenar, ¿no?

_____ 4. Sí, es verdad. Lo tenemos que limpiar.

_____ 5. Tina va al supermercado; ella los puede comprar.

5-43   Preparando la fiesta. The party is tonight, and some things have been left undone. Tina is talking about what needs to be done, but in her haste she fails to complete her sentences. Listen to her and identify what she is talking about.

1. a. el pan   b. la ensalada   c. los refrescos   d. las flores

2. a. el baño   b. la cocina   c. los cuartos   d. las mesas

3. a. el coche   b. la fruta   c. los platos   d. las sábanas

4. a. a Luis   b. a Linda   c. a Lisa y Oscar   d. a Mirta y Ana

5. a. el teléfono   b. la mesa   c. los discos   d. las sillas

5-44   El perfecto anfitrión (*host*). Your guests are finally here, and you are happy to help them however you can. Listen to their questions and select the appropriate responses. Remember to respond orally as well.

1. a. Claro que puedes tomarlo.   c. Claro que puedes tomarlos.

    b. Claro que puedes tomarla.   d. Claro que puedes tomarlas.

2. a. Sí, pueden usarlo.   c. Sí, pueden usarlos.

    b. Sí, pueden usarla.   d. Sí, pueden usarlas.

3. a. Lo tenemos en la cocina.   c. Los tenemos en la cocina.

    b. La tenemos en la cocina.   d. Las tenemos en la cocina.

4. a. Sí, están junto a la puerta; ¿lo ves?   c. Sí, están junto a la puerta; ¿los ves?

    b. Sí, están junto a la puerta; ¿la ves?   d. Sí, están junto a la puerta; ¿las ves?

5. a. Lo está tocando Tomás.   c. Los está tocando Tomás.

    b. La está tocando Tomás.   d. Las está tocando Tomás.

5-45   Al día siguiente. The party was great, and everybody had fun. Now it is time to clean up and get ready for classes on Monday. Affirmatively answer Felipe and Tina's questions about what you have to do today. NOTE: If you have the option to place the pronoun before a conjugated form of the verb or to attach the pronoun to an infinitive or gerund, do the first (as in the **Modelo**).

MODELO: You hear: ¿Vamos a limpiar el apartamento?
          You say and write: *Sí, lo vamos a limpiar.*

1. _____

2. _____

3. _____

4. _____

5. _____

6. _____

7. _____

4. Demonstrative adjectives and pronouns

5-46   **¿Cerca o lejos?** You go to the department store with your parents to buy furniture and other things for your apartment. Indicate in the chart whether the objects and persons your parents mention are next to you (**al lado**), a short distance from you (**cerca**), or relatively far from you (**lejos**).

MODELO: You hear: Ese espejo es muy pequeño para el baño.
          You mark the chart (see below).

	AL LADO	CERCA	LEJOS
Modelo		X	
1.			
2.			
3.			
4.			
5.			
6.			

5-47   **Los muebles.** You have decided what you want to buy. Listen to the salesman's questions and answer using the cues.

MODELO: You hear: ¿Qué mesa quiere?
          You see: (cerca)
          You say and write: [Quiero] *esa mesa*.

1. (al lado) Quiero _____

2. (lejos)   Quiero _____

3. (al lado) Quiero _____

4. (cerca) Quiero _____

5. (lejos) Quiero _____

6. (cerca) Quiero _____

5-48   Más cosas para el apartamento. Now that you have the furniture, you look for other items for your new home. Your parents offer some suggestions, but you do not have the same taste. Listen to their suggestions and choose an appropriate response.

1. Sí, pero yo prefiero _____.
   a. éste   b. ésta   c. éstos   d. éstas

2. Sí, pero a mí me gusta _____.
   a. ése   b. ésa   c. ésos   d. ésas

3. Sí, pero _____ son mejores (*better*).
   a. aquél   b. aquélla   c. aquéllos   d. aquéllas

4. Sí, pero quiero _____.
   a. éste   b. ésta   c. éstos   d. éstas

5. Sí, pero _____ es más bonita.
   a. éste   b. ésta   c. éstos   d. éstas

5-49   ¡Qué confusión! After you chose your furniture, the salesman tagged it so that nobody would take it while you finished shopping. Now you are ready to take your furniture, but the tags are on the wrong pieces! Listen to the salesman's questions and answer, both orally and in writing, according to the location cues: next to you (**al lado**), a short distance from you (**cerca**), or relatively far from you (**lejos**). NOTE: Even though stress marks are optional in demonstrative pronouns, please write them in this activity.

MODELO: You hear: ¿No quiere esta mesa?
           You see: (lejos)
           You say and write: [No, no quiero] *ésta; quiero aquélla.*

1. (lejos)   No, no quiero _____

2. (cerca)   No, no quiero _____

3. (al lado)   No, no quiero _____

4. (lejos)   No, no quiero _____

5. (al lado)   No, no quiero _____

5. *Saber* and *conocer* (to know)

5-50   Buscando trabajo. Ernesto is applying for a summer job at one of the university's offices. Listen to his interview with Mr. Martínez at the human resources department, and complete the statements below with an appropriate form of **saber** or **conocer.**

1. Ernesto _____ usar computadoras.

2. Ernesto _____ al profesor González.

3. Ernesto _____ inglés y francés.

4. Ernesto _____ que el trabajo son 30 horas por semana.

5. Ernesto _____ a otras personas que trabajan allí.

5-51   ¿Y usted? Imagine your Spanish professor says he needs an assistant and you would like to apply for the job. Answer his questions truthfully, with complete sentences.

1. _____

2. _____

3. _____

4. _____

5. _____

6. _____

ALGO MÁS: MORE ON ADJECTIVES

5-52   ¿En qué piso? You are training for a job at the information center of an important department store. Listen to your partner answer some clients' questions, and use the following word list to take notes in your chart.

sábanas y toallas	baños	muebles	perfumes y jabones	calculadoras
ropa de niños	electrodomésticos	libros	mantas	oficinas

ALMACENES QUINTA AVENIDA: DIRECTORIO

Piso 6 _____

Piso 5 _____ _____

Piso 4 _____

Piso 3 _____

Piso 2 _____

Piso 1 _____

MOSAICOS

5-53   Una reunión familiar. Your neighbors, the Arizas, seem to be busy cleaning the house. First listen once for the general idea: why are they cleaning? Then listen again, paying more attention to the details: what is each person doing?

Now listen to the following statements and indicate whether each is **Cierto** or **Falso**. After you finish, you may listen again to confirm your answers.

	CIERTO	FALSO
1.		
2.		
3.		
4.		
5.		

PRONUNCIACIÓN

This section explains the pronunciation of the Spanish letters **ll, y,** and **x.** Read the descriptions carefully, and then listen to and repeat the words indicated.

ll and y

In most parts of the Spanish-speaking world, **y** and **ll** are pronounced like the English *y* in the word *yoke,* but with more friction. At the end of a word, **y** sounds very similar to the Spanish **i,** but if the next word begins with a vowel, **y** is pronounced like English *y* in *yoke.* **Repitan las siguientes palabras.**

    yo   llamo   ella   calle   estoy   muy bien   muy alto

x

Before a consonant, the Spanish **x** is pronounced like the English *ks* or *s.* **Repitan las siguientes palabras.**

    experiencia   explicación   experimento   texto   extensión

Between vowels, **x** is pronounced like *ks.*

    examen   sexo   existir   exacto   éxito

Nombre: _____ Fecha: _____

Stress and the written accent

Here is the last rule for writing accents:

Rule 5. A written accent is placed on some one-syllable words to distinguish them from words with the same spelling but a different meaning. For example, the word **el**, meaning *the*, has no written accent, but the word **él**, meaning *he*, does.

el	*the*		él	*he*
se	*himself, herself*		sé	*I know*
si	*if*		sí	*yes*
te	*(to) you, yourself* (familiar)		té	*tea*
tu	*your*		tú	*you*

5-54 Dictado. Listen to the following sentences and fill in the blanks with the correct words. Remember to use stress marks appropriately to differentiate between words that are otherwise spelled in the same way.

1. _____ trabajas con _____ padre.

2. Alicia dice que _____ tiene _____ cuadro.

3. ¿Cómo _____ llamas?

4. _____ siempre tomas _____.

5. _____, yo vivo en esa calle.

6. _____ tienes dinero, podemos ir al cine.

7. Yo _____ que ellos viven cerca.

8. Ella _____ baña y _____ viste rápidamente.

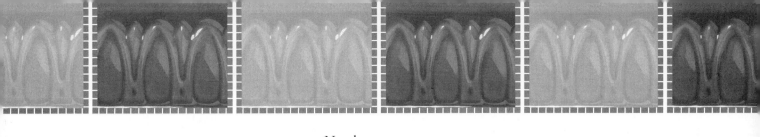

Lección 6

La ropa y las tiendas

A PRIMERA VISTA

6-1   ¿Qué te pones? Are you one of those people who really care about their appearance? Indicate what would match best if you were wearing the following items.

_____ 1. abrigo   a. zapatos tenis

_____ 2. camisa   b. medias

_____ 3. falda   c. paraguas

_____ 4. sudadera   d. corbata

_____ 5. impermeable   e. bufanda

6-2   La moda. Read the following statements about clothing and fashion and indicate whether each is **cierto (C)** or **falso (F)**.

_____ 1. Si vas a la playa necesitas una corbata.

_____ 2. El arete es un accesorio que se pone en el dedo.

_____ 3. Es una buena idea llevar zapatos de tacón (*with heels*) para correr.

_____ 4. Algunos hombres guardan (*keep*) su dinero en la billetera.

_____ 5. Cuando llueve (*rains*) es buena idea llevar un impermeable.

_____ 6. El camisón es una prenda que se usa principalmente para ir a dormir.

_____ 7. Normalmente las chicas llevan calzoncillos debajo de los vestidos.

_____ 8. El algodón es un tipo de tela sintética.

6-3 **¿Quién es?** Read the following descriptions and indicate who is most likely being described.

1. Esta chica lleva un traje azul, de falda y chaqueta. Lleva una blusa de seda de color blanco con rayas azules. También lleva pantimedias y zapatos de tacón (*heels*).
   a. una chica que va a la playa
   b. una estudiante que va a clase
   c. la presidenta de una compañía en una reunión de negocios

2. Esta chica lleva unos pantalones cortos y una sudadera. También lleva una camiseta blanca y unos zapatos de tenis.
   a. una chica que va a hacer ejercicio
   b. una secretaria en la oficina
   c. una estudiante en una fiesta

3. Este chico lleva una bata y un piyama. También lleva unas zapatillas de casa.
   a. un chico que va a la universidad
   b. el presidente de una compañía en su oficina
   c. un chico que está mirando la televisión en casa

4. Esta chica lleva un vestido de color entero, y un traje de baño de rayas. También lleva unas sandalias y unas gafas de sol.
   a. una chica que va a una fiesta el sábado por la noche
   b. una ejecutiva que está trabajando en su oficina
   c. una chica que está en una isla venezolana

5. Esta persona lleva un traje pantalón de rayas, con una camisa de color entero. Lleva corbata y zapatos.
   a. un abogado (*lawyer*) que está en la corte
   b. un médico (*physician*) en la sala de operaciones
   c. una persona que se está levantando (*getting up*)

6. Esta persona lleva pantalones vaqueros y un suéter. Lleva un abrigo y unas botas de cuero. También lleva una gorra de invierno (*winter*).
   a. una persona que va a esquiar (*ski*)
   b. una estudiante que va a su graduación
   c. una modelo en viaje (*trip*) de negocios (*business*)

6-4   De compras. You are on vacation in Mexico City, and you are going shopping with your friends. Indicate what you would tell the salesperson in each situation.

1. You are trying on a pair of jeans, but they are too big.
   a. Me quedan bien.
   b. Quisiera una talla más pequeña.
   c. Me quedan estrechos.

2. You bought a blouse in one of the stores in the mall a couple of hours ago. You have decided you do not like the fabric, so you go back to the store to exchange the blouse.
   a. Me queda grande.
   b. Quisiera cambiarla.
   c. Me gusta mucho el color.

3. You are in a very classy shop, and you would like to try on a suit.
   a. Quisiera cambiar este traje.
   b. Quisiera probarme este traje.
   c. Quisiera comprar este traje.

4. You want to know if the pants you like are on sale.
   a. ¿Los pantalones están vendidos?
   b. ¿Los pantalones están rebajados?
   c. ¿De qué talla son los pantalones?

5. You will pay in cash.
   a. Voy a pagar con un cheque.
   b. Voy a usar una tarjeta de crédito.
   c. Voy a pagar en efectivo.

EXPLICACIÓN Y EXPANSIÓN

Síntesis gramatical

1. Preterit tense of regular verbs

	HABLAR	COMER	VIVIR
yo	hablé	comí	viví
tú	hablaste	comiste	viviste
Ud., él, ella	habló	comió	vivió
nosotros/as	hablamos	comimos	vivimos
vosotros/as	hablasteis	comisteis	vivisteis
Uds., ellos/as	hablaron	comieron	vivieron

2. Preterit of ir and ser

yo	fui	**nosotros/as**	fuimos
tú	fuiste	**vosotros/as**	fuisteis
Ud., él, ella	fue	**Uds., ellos/as**	fueron

3. Indirect object nouns and pronouns

me	*to or for me*	**nos**	*(to), (for) us*
te	*to or for you* (familiar)	**os**	*(to), (for) you* (familiar)
le	*to or for you* (formal), *him, her, it*	**les**	*(to), (for) you* (formal) *them*

4. The verb dar

	PRESENT	PRETERIT
yo	doy	di
tú	das	diste
Ud., él, ella	da	dio
nosotros/as	damos	dimos
vosotros/as	dais	disteis
Uds., ellos, ellas	dan	dieron

5. Gustar and similar verbs

Indirect object pronoun + gusta/gustó + *singular noun/pronoun*

Indirect object pronoun + gustan/gustaron + *plural noun/pronoun*

Nombre: _____   Fecha: _____

1. Preterit tense of regular verbs

6-5 **¿Quién habla?** Marisol and her friends went to Mexico last spring break. Read what Marisol and her friends did, and indicate whether each sentence refers to herself, **yo,** her friend, **Javier,** her friends and her, **Elena, Javier y yo,** or only her friends, **Javier y Elena.**

    a. yo   b. Javier   c. Elena, Javier y yo   d. Javier y Elena

1. Bailaron en una fiesta. _____

2. Habló mucho por teléfono con su madre. _____

3. Miré la televisión por la tarde. _____

4. Almorzaron a las dos y media de la tarde. _____

5. Bailamos en una discoteca hasta las cinco de la mañana. _____

6. Comí en un restaurante mexicano. _____

7. Bebimos margaritas en la playa. _____

6-6 **¿Cuándo?** Carmen and her family do some of the following activities. Read what Carmen tells you about her family's activities, and indicate whether each activity takes place in the present (**hoy**) or in the past (**la semana pasada**).

    a. hoy   b. la semana pasada

1. Miraron las noticias en la televisión. _____

2. Viajo a Paris de vacaciones con los amigos. _____

3. Llamé a mis amigos por teléfono. _____

4. Nada en el mar. _____

5. Tomó un café con una amiga. _____

6. Comieron pasta en el restaurante. _____

7. Asistí a clase de español. _____

6-7   **¿Qué hizo Anabel? ¿Qué hicieron sus amigos?** Complete the chart by indicating what Anabel and her friends did last weekend. Write the activities in the past tense, using the following preterit forms of the activities.

1. Las actividades de Anabel: viernes → ir a una discoteca; almorzar en la cafetería; tener un examen

2. Las actividades de Anabel: sábado → ver una película; dormir mucho

3. Las actividades de los amigos de Anabel: viernes → practicar un deporte; salir con amigos; comer en un restaurante

4. Las actividades de los amigos de Anabel: sábado → asistir a una conferencia; tomar café

	el viernes	**el sábado**
ANABEL		
LOS AMIGOS DE ANABEL (ELLOS)		

2. Preterit of *ir* and *ser*

6-8   Unas vacaciones en Venezuela. Primera fase. William and his friends went on a vacation to Venezuela. William thinks he learned a lot of Spanish while there, and he is trying to tell you all about the vacation in Spanish. Help William complete his story by filling in the blanks with a form of **ser** or **ir.**

¡Hola, amigos! El año pasado mis vacaciones (1) _____ perfectas. Mis amigos y yo (2) _____ a Venezuela para visitar Caracas, el Parque Nacional Canaima y la Isla Margarita. Primero nosotros (3) _____ a Caracas y visitamos la casa donde nació Simón Bolívar. La visita (4) _____ muy interesante. Mario Infante, uno de los miembros del grupo, es venezolano y (5) _____ nuestro guía (*guide*). Nosotros (6) _____ al Parque Nacional Canaima y nos gustó mucho, pero el momento espectacular de la excursión (7) _____ cuando vimos el Salto Ángel, las cataratas (*waterfalls*) más altas (*highest*) del mundo. Finalmente, (8) _____ a la Isla Margarita. Por el día nadamos y tomamos el sol en la playa y por la noche, (9) _____ a las discotecas y bailamos. (10) _____ muy divertido. Conocimos a muchos venezolanos. (11) _____ las mejores vacaciones de nuestra vida.

Segunda fase. Now look at all the verb forms you used in **Primera fase** and indicate whether they correspond to the verb **ser** or the verb **ir.**

	a. ser		b. ir
1.	_____	7.	_____
2.	_____	8.	_____
3.	_____	9.	_____
4.	_____	10.	_____
5.	_____	11.	_____
6.	_____		

6-9   Tus vacaciones. A reporter from the school newspaper is researching common vacation spots for college students and what students do while there. He is interviewing you; answer his questions about your own experiences.

1. ¿Dónde fuiste el año pasado de vacaciones?

    _____

2. ¿Cómo fueron tus vacaciones?

    _____

3. ¿Con quién fuiste a esas vacaciones?

_____

4. ¿Qué fue lo mejor del viaje?

_____

5. ¿Qué fue lo peor del viaje?

_____

3. Indirect object nouns and pronouns

6-10 ¿Quién hace las tareas domésticas? You are listening to Carlota and her friend Arantza as they talk about the household chores and who does them in their house. Complete their conversation with the words you could not hear well. Use indirect object pronouns.

CARLOTA: Yo tengo mucha suerte. Mi madre (1) _____ lava la ropa.

ARANTZA: ¡Qué bien! En mi casa yo lavo y plancho la ropa.

CARLOTA: Además, mi mamá (2) _____ lava y plancha la ropa a mis hermanos.

ARANTZA: Yo hago mi cama todos los días. ¿Y tú?

CARLOTA: Mi mamá (3) _____ hace la cama a mí y a mis hermanos todos los días.

ARANTZA: ¿Tu madre también (4) _____ prepara la comida?

CARLOTA: ¡Claro! Ella (5) _____ prepara la comida a mí, a mis hermanos y a mi papá.

ARANTZA: Y tú, ¿no ayudas?

CARLOTA: De vez en cuando (6) _____ limpio los muebles a mi madre.

ARANTZA: En mi casa, yo hago muchas tareas. Siempre paso la aspiradora, limpio los muebles y ayudo en muchas otras cosas.

CARLOTA: Yo también ayudo. ¡(7) _____ preparo un pastel a todos en el cumpleaños de mi mamá!

8. Based on the conversation, which of the following statements is most accurate.
   a. Carlota hace más (more) tareas domésticas que (than) Arantza.
   b. Arantza es la persona a cargo de las tareas domésticas en su casa.

6-11 Un programa de televisión. You and some friends are in charge of the costumes for a television program. What clothing would you and your friends give these actors for their roles?

vestidos elegantes con zapatos de tacón (*heels*)

un traje azul con una corbata roja

un traje de baño y unas sandalias

unos pantalones de cuero y una camiseta de colores

unos pantalones cortos y zapatos de tenis

MODELO: A la presidenta de una compañía *le damos una falda y una blusa con un saco.*

1. A una cantante de rock para un concierto _____.

2. A unos niños para jugar en el parque _____.

3. A unas estudiantes para una fiesta formal _____.

4. A un ejecutivo para una reunión _____.

5. A una estudiante para ir a la playa _____.

---

4. The verb *dar*

6-12 Su cumpleaños. Think back to your last birthday. Your friend wants to know what presents you received. Answer your friend's questions, indicating what the following people gave you for your birthday. Use a form of the verb **dar.**

MODELO: ¿Qué te regaló tu tío?

Mi tío *me dio un libro.*

1. ¿Qué te regalaron tus padres?

Mis padres _____

2. ¿Y tu hermano?

Mi hermano _____

3. ¿Y tus abuelos?

Mis abuelos _____

4. ¿Y tu novio/a?

Mi novio/a _____

6-13   Una fiesta de cumpleaños especial. Sandra has organized a special birthday party for her friend Andrea. She had an announcement in their school newspaper, making the party open to anyone who wanted to attend. Some interesting people have come and brought presents for Andrea. Look at the presents and write sentences indicating who gave them to Andrea.

1. un profesor de física

2. los payasos

3. su amiga

4. unos ciclistas

5. unos escritores

a. una bicicleta

b. unas novelas románticas

c. un libro sobre Einstein

d. unos discos compactos

e. unas narices grandes y rojas

1. _____.

2. _____.

3. _____.

4. _____.

5. _____.

5. *Gustar* and similar verbs

6-14   Alicia y sus amigos. Alicia is explaining what she and her friends like to wear. Indicate the most appropriate response in each situation.

Hola. Me llamo Alicia, y quiero hablar de mis gustos y los gustos de mis amigos con respecto a la ropa:

1. Yo siempre llevo vaqueros porque los vaqueros...
   a. me gusta mucho.
   b. te gustan mucho.
   c. me gustan mucho.

2. Marta y José siempre llevan zapatillas de deporte porque las zapatillas de deporte...
   a. les encantan.
   b. les encanta.
   c. le encantan.

3. Juan y yo llevamos colores fuertes frecuentemente porque... los colores fuertes.
   a. nos queda bien.
   b. les queda bien.
   c. nos quedan bien.

4. Roberto no quiere corbata porque la corbata...
   a. no les gusta para nada (*at all*).
   b. no le gustan para nada.
   c. no le gusta para nada.

5. Anabel nunca lleva faldas porque las faldas...
   a. no le quedan bien.
   b. no les queda bien.
   c. no les quedan bien.

6-15   ¿Y a usted, qué le gusta? You have read Alicia and her friends' likes and dislikes with respect to clothing. Now write what you do or do not like for clothes. Use the following expressions.

interesar   encantar   caer bien   caer mal   gustar   importar   parecer

1. A mí _____

2. A mí _____

3. A mí _____

4. A mí _____

6-16   De compras. Your friends went shopping on Friday and are telling you all about it. Complete the conversation.

BERTA: Me (1) _____ mucho el centro comercial.
              a. gustó   b. gustaron

ANA: A mí también. Sobre todo nos (2) _____ los trajes que vimos en el almacén La Moda.
              a. gustó   b. gustaron

HILDA: Y a Rita le (3) _____ muy bonitos también.
              a. pareció   b. parecieron

BERTA: Sí, pero también le (4) _____ mal la dependienta.
              a. cayó   b. cayeron

ANA: ¡Ay Berta! Tú sabes cómo es Rita. A ella sólo le (5) _____ las boutiques elegantes con dependientas muy finas.
              a. interesa   b. interesan

HILDA: Bueno, pero le (6) _____ ir de compras con nosotras. Dice que quiere ir otra vez.
              a. encantó   b. encantaron

ALGO MÁS: SOME MORE USES OF *POR* AND *PARA*

6-17 **¿Por qué?** Read the following sentences and decide why these people did what they did. Write sentences using **por** or **porque**.

las rebajas en su tienda favorita   es muy pequeña

le quedan grandes   lo va a necesitar este invierno (*winter*)

el color

1. Ana fue de compras _____

2. Rosario cambió los pantalones _____

3. Rosana no compró la blusa _____

4. Sara va a cambiar la falda _____

5. Carlos va a comprar el abrigo _____

6-18 **Los regalos.** You are in charge of assigning presents for a party that several celebrities will attend. Indicate who should receive each of the following presents.

a. Cindy Crawford   c. Camilo José Cela   e. Melanie Griffith

b. Elton John   d. David Copperfield   f. Gabriela Sabatini

1. El bolígrafo de oro (*gold*) es para _____.

2. La fotografía de Antonio Banderas es para _____.

3. La raqueta de oro es para _____.

4. El piano es para _____.

5. El traje de baño es para _____.

6. La capa de mago (*magician's cape*) es para _____.

MOSAICOS

A leer

6-19 **Antes de leer. Ropa y accesorios. Primera fase.** Are you concerned about your appearance (**la apariencia**)? Are accessories important to you? Fill in the following chart with the clothes and accessories you would wear in these situations.

LUGAR O ACTIVIDAD	ROPA	ACCESORIOS
una fiesta en la universidad		
una entrevista de trabajo		
celebración en familia del 4 de julio		
un día en la playa		
su clase de español		

Segunda fase. Based on your responses in **Primera fase,** mark the scale according to how important your appearance and accessories are to you. (Extremely important-1, and not important at all-5.)

Importancia de la apariencia	1	2	3	4	5
Importancia de los accesorios	1	2	3	4	5

6-20   A leer. Ocasiones especiales. Read the following ad about accessories and then answer the questions about it. **NOTE:** Write "C" (**cierto**) or "F" (**falso**) for the first five questions.

En general, tienen diversas formas y colores y son de una gran variedad de materiales. Pero indudablemente son imprescindibles. Pueden ser exóticos, simples, elegantes. Son definitivamente nuestros amigos inseparables: los accesorios. ¡Un complemento obligatorio para la mujer que desea verse elegante e interesante!

Son ideales para todo tipo de vestuario y pueden transformar a una mujer sencilla en el centro de atención de un evento social. Un vestido sencillo, pero elegante, un par de aretes grandes o pequeños, un collar

MODA

de hermosas perlas cultivadas o de fantasía fina y una pulsera del mismo estilo pueden causar una impresión inolvidable entre los invitados.

Pero, ¡cuidado! Cada pequeña o gran transformación femenina debe ir acompañada del accesorio adecuado para la ocasión.

No se olvide que el grado de formalidad del evento determina la ropa y los accesorios que debemos usar. Probablemente para una fiesta en la oficina es recomendable hacer cambios menos notorios: llevar un lápiz labial más fuerte, unos aretes diferentes a los que usamos diariamente o unos zapatos de tacones más altos. Una invitación a un picnic, por otro lado, va a exigir ropa informal y menos accesorios.

Pero para una fiesta de Navidad o de Año Nuevo, debemos abrir las puertas de nuestro armario: es la hora de lucir bolsas elegantes y de ponerse vestidos de lentejuelas brillantes, pantalones y trajes finos, zapatos de moda y, por supuesto, accesorios extravagantes e irresistibles, acompañados de un toque de maquillaje exótico.

1. _____ Los accesorios son poco variados.

2. _____ Si una mujer desea ser elegante, debe usar accesorios.

3. _____ Un collar de perlas puede causar una buena impresión en las personas que lo ven.

4. _____ En una fiesta de la oficina, conviene llevar muchos accesorios.

5. _____ Un vestido de lentejuelas es un accesorio.

6. Según el anuncio, en una fiesta en la oficina es bueno...
   a. llevar la misma ropa que llevamos todos los días.
   b. usar algo exótico para impresionar a los compañeros de trabajo.
   c. cambiar un poco la ropa y los accesorios que nos ponemos normalmente.

7. Para ir a un picnic, una mujer puede ponerse...
   a. zapatos de tacón alto.
   b. vaqueros.
   c. un vestido con lentejuelas.

8. Para las fiestas de fin de año las mujeres deben...
   a. usar ropa menos extravagante.
   b. revisar sus closets y sacar su ropa vieja.
   c. ponerse ropa elegante y formal con los accesorios apropiados.

9. Los accesorios más adecuados para una ocasión formal son...
   a. un collar de perlas cultivadas y unos aretes muy pequeños.
   b. un collar de fantasía y una pulsera del mismo estilo.
   c. un vestido sencillo pero elegante.

6-21   Después de leer. El vestuario apropiado. You have read about accessories and appropriate clothing for different situations. Read about how the following people are dressed and indicate where they might be going: an office party, a picnic, or a Christmas party.

     a. fiesta de la oficina   b. un picnic   c. una fiesta de Navidad

1. _____ María José lleva un vestido negro, zapatos de tacón alto, aretes de oro con pequeñas perlas y un collar de perlas cultivadas. Está maquillada (*She has on makeup*), y tiene los labios (*lips*) pintados de un color suave pero seductor.

2. _____ Iñaki lleva un traje gris oscuro y una corbata verde y rojo. Tiene un arete y reloj pulsera (*wrist*) de oro. En el bolsillo (*pocket*) de su chaqueta se ve un pañuelo que combina (*matches*) con la corbata.

3. _____ Estíbaliz lleva un suéter color café claro, unos jeans y unas botas de cuero. En una oreja (*ear*) tiene un arete en forma de pequeño sol, y en la otra un arete en forma de pequeña luna. Está ligeramente (*slightly*) maquillada con un poco de tinte (*mascara*) en las pestañas (*eyelashes*).

6-22   A escribir. La fiesta de graduación. As you read in the article, it is very important to wear the appropriate clothes and accessories for a situation. Think about your high school prom and list what you wore that day.

ROPA Y ZAPATOS	ACCESORIOS	MAQUILLAJE

6-23 **Una experiencia inolvidable.** Attending the prom was probably a memorable experience. People in Spain do not celebrate the prom. Write a letter to Jordi, a high school student from Spain, telling him about your prom. Remember to mention the following:

- when it happened (what year, month, etc.)
- where it happened
- who was with you
- what were you and your date wearing
- what happened, step by step

Querido Jordi,

_____

_____

_____

_____

_____

_____

_____

_____

_____

_____

_____

_____

_____

_____

6-24 **¡Fantástico!** Jordi is really impressed by your letter and wants to know more about your experience. Answer his questions.

1. ¿Qué fue lo que más te gustó de la fiesta de graduación? [**Lo que más me gustó...** = *What I liked best* (or *the most*)...]

_____

2. ¿Todos los estudiantes tienen una fiesta de graduación?

_____

3. ¿Hay otras celebraciones especiales en las que (*in which*) tienes que ponerte elegante?

_____

4. ¿Cuál es tu celebración favorita? ¿Por qué?

_____

5. ¿Hay otras celebraciones especiales en las que no necesitas ropa elegante?

_____

ENFOQUE CULTURAL

6-25 **De compras en Latinoamérica y conociendo Venezuela.** Read the **Enfoque cultural** on pages 235–240 of your textbook and decide whether each of the following sentences is **cierto (C)** or **falso (F)**.

1. _____ En las grandes ciudades hispanas hay centros comerciales que ofrecen muchos productos y servicios.

2. _____ Es común regatear en los centros comerciales hispanos.

3. _____ En los centros comerciales hispanos se puede pagar en efectivo o con tarjeta de crédito.

4. _____ En los mercados al aire libre se ofrecen muchos productos diferentes.

5. _____ En los mercados al aire libre los precios son fijos.

6. _____ Los precios en los centros comerciales son más altos que en los mercados.

7. _____ Entre los recursos naturales de Venezuela, el petróleo ocupa un lugar muy importante.

8. _____ La ciudad de los caballeros es una gran ciudad muy cosmopolita e importante en Venezuela.

9. _____ El Salto del Ángel es la catarata más alta del mundo.

10. _____ Para decir que una persona está de mal humor, los venezolanos dicen que tiene "la cara amarrada".

A PRIMERA VISTA

6-26   De compras. You are at the shopping mall with your new Venezuelan friend, Diana. She spots some other Venezuelan friends of hers and tells you what they are wearing so that you can identify them. Listen to her and mark what each person is wearing. (Three items are not being worn by anyone.)

	ALEJANDRA	**JAIME**	**RICARDO**
1. camisa			
2. suéter			
3. camiseta			
4. blusa			
5. vaqueros			
6. falda			
7. pantalones			
8. zapatos			
9. zapatos de tenis			
10. botas			
11. sandalias			
12. corbata			
13. bolsa			

6-27   ¿Qué compraron? Diana and you say hello to her friends. They still have not bought anything, but they tell you what they are going to buy. Listen to them and indicate each person's purchases, which are illustrated below.

1. Alejandra

____
____

(a)   (b)   (c)   (d)   (e)

2. Jaime

_____
_____

    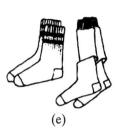

(a)   (b)   (c)   (d)   (e)

3. Ricardo

_____
_____

    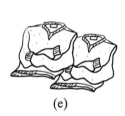

(a)   (b)   (c)   (d)   (e)

6-28   Vamos a comprar. Now Diana and you are going to do your own shopping. It is Diana's first winter in the United States, and she is going to the Northeast. You advise her to buy warm clothing. Think of some items she might need. Then listen to her questions and respond, both orally and in writing, following the model below.

MODELO: You hear: ¿Qué es mejor? ¿las sandalias o las botas?
           You say and write: [Tienes que comprar] *las botas.*

1. Tienes que comprar _____

2. Tienes que comprar _____

3. Tienes que comprar _____

4. Tienes que comprar _____

5. Tienes que comprar _____

6-29   Un cambio. While Diana is paying for her purchase, you hear a conversation between a lady and the sales assistant. First listen to their conversation to get the gist. Then look at the statements below and indicate whether they are true (**Cierto**) or false (**Falso**). Lastly, correct the false statements to make them true. HINT: **casi igual** = *almost the same*.

	Cierto	*Falso*
1. La señora quiere comprar una blusa.	_____	_____
2. El problema es que la blusa le queda larga.	_____	_____
3. La señora necesita la talla 40.	_____	_____
4. La ropa que le muestra la vendedora cuesta más o menos como la otra.	_____	_____
5. La señora va a probarse un vestido.	_____	_____

EXPLICACIÓN Y EXPANSIÓN

1. Preterit tense of regular verbs

6-30   El fin de semana. It is Monday again, and Miguel and Beatriz are talking about their weekends. Listen to them and mark whether it was **Miguel, Beatriz** or **los dos** (both) who did the following:

	MIGUEL	**BEATRIZ**	**LOS DOS**
1. levantarse temprano			
2. desayunar en un café			
3. mirar la televisión			
4. comer con sus padres			
5. hablar con una amiga			
6. dormir una siesta (*nap*)			
7. estudiar español			
8. salir con los amigos			

6-31 **¿Quién?** Now Miguel is talking about what other people did. He is not going to mention who did these things, but you can figure it out by paying attention to verb forms. Listen to him and indicate to whom he is referring.

	MIGUEL (YO)	TÚ	RAÚL	RAÚL Y MIGUEL	RAÚL Y LEO
1.					
2.					
3.					
4.					
5.					
6.					
7.					
8.					

6-32 **Entrevista con el detective.** While you were at the mall yesterday a valuable necklace was stolen from a jewelry store. You think you saw the thief, and a detective asks about what happened. Answer using the cues below.

MODELO: You hear: ¿A qué hora llegó usted al centro comercial?
          You see: (una y media)
          You answer: *Llegué a la una y media.*

1. (a las dos) _____

2. (los dependientes) _____

3. (los collares) _____

4. (rápidamente) _____

5. (a la policía) _____

2. Preterit of *ir* and *ser*

6-33   **¿Ir o ser?** As you have learned, the verbs **ir** and **ser** have similar forms in the preterit, so you have to rely on context to assign the right meaning. Because these are very frequently used verbs, it is important to practice this skill. Listen to each sentence and decide whether the verb it contains is a form of **ser** or **ir**.

	SER	IR
1.		
2.		
3.		
4.		
5.		
6.		

6-34   **El viaje del abuelo.** Grandparents always have interesting stories! Listen to this grandfather reminisce about a trip he took to Venezuela when he was a young man. Then complete the following paragraph about his trip. The missing words are preterit forms of the verbs **ir** and **ser**. HINT: You will hear the word **verano** = *summer.*

El abuelo visitó Venezuela en 1950. (1) _____ a Caracas, la capital de Venezuela, para

visitar a un amigo y su familia. En Caracas (2) _____ a algunos lugares históricos y otros

modernos. Su amigo Jorge y el abuelo (3) _____ a una fiesta en un club y después

(4) _____ a caminar. El abuelo dice que (5) _____ un viaje extraordinario.

What stories will you tell your grandchildren? Briefly write about in the space below about one of your memorable trips (e.g., Where did you go? What did you do?). If you cannot recall any memorable trip, invent one!

_____

_____

_____

_____

3. Indirect object nouns and pronouns

6-35   **Los regalos de Navidad.** Most people go shopping at least once a year to buy Christmas gifts for their relatives and friends. Think about some popular gifts.

Ernesto is doing part of his Christmas shopping too. Listen to him and complete the chart with the information you hear about the gifts he is going to buy. HINT: **esquiar** = to ski.

¿PARA QUIÉN? (NOMBRE, RELACIÓN)	¿QUÉ?	¿DÓNDE?
Gabriel y Felipe, hermanos	unas entradas (*tickets*)	
Ester, amiga		
		una tienda

6-36   **¿A quién?** Your friend Adriana has been shopping, and she brings many bags with gifts. Listen to her and mark whether she bought these things for **herself**, for **her parents**, for **her sister**, or for **you** (*para ti*).

    a. para Adriana   b. para sus padres   c. para su hermana   d. para ti

1. una billetera _____

2. un suéter de algodón _____

3. unas gafas de sol _____

4. un disco compacto de Julio Iglesias _____

5. una bolsa de cuero _____

6. un cinturón _____

7. una bufanda de lana _____

8. un libro sobre esta universidad _____

6-37   **¿Y tus regalos?** Your friend wants to know what gifts you bought for your friends and family. Listen to the questions and answer, using the cues given.

MODELO: You hear: ¿Tienes un regalo para tu mamá?
           You see: (unos aretes)
           You write and say: *Sí, le voy a regalar unos aretes.*

1. (un paraguas) _____

2. (unas bufandas) _____

3. (unos zapatos de tenis) _____

4. (unas pulseras) _____

5. (algo interesante) _____

4.   The verb *dar*

6-38   **¿Presente o pasado?** Listen to the sentences and decide whether these events belong to the present (**presente**) or the past (**pasado**).

	PRESENTE	PASADO
1.		
2.		
3.		
4.		
5.		
6.		
7.		
8.		

5. *Gustar* and similar verbs

6-39 Las preferencias de Susana. Susana Agustín, a third-year Venezuelan student, talks about her preferences with regards to academics and leisure-time activities. Listen to her once to get the gist: Are her preferences similar to or very different from those of most college students you know? Then listen again and select what Susana likes and does not like.

	LE GUSTA(N)	NO LE GUSTA(N)
los estudios		
la química		
la biología		
conversar con los amigos		
hablar de política		
mirar la televisión		
la música popular		
la música clásica		
la música rock		
bailar		

Now write about one school or leisure activity you like and one you dislike.

_____

_____

_____

_____

6-40 **Una encuesta sobre la universidad.** Your friend works for the university newspaper, and he is conducting a survey of opinions on some aspects of college life. He has some answers recorded, but he does not remember the order of his questions. Can you help him? Listen to each response and match it with the appropriate question.

1. ¿Qué piensa usted sobre las fiestas en el campus? _____

2. ¿Qué dicen sus amigos sobre la comida de la cafetería? _____

3. ¿Qué opina usted de la clase de economía? _____

4. ¿Qué piensan los estudiantes sobre los exámenes? _____

5. ¿Qué les parece a ustedes la vida en la universidad? _____

6-41 **Más ayuda con la encuesta.** Your friend asks you for another favor because he is running late with the survey for the newspaper: he noted some of the answers only partially, and they need to be completed. Note that the missing verbs are not only **gustar** but also other similar verbs such as **caer bien/mal** and **parecer** and that you will need two words in each space.

1. Sí, _____ mis clases.

2. Sí, _____ bien.

3. No, no _____ mal.

4. Sí, creo que a los profesores _____ enseñar sus clases.

5. No, no _____ escuchar la radio.

6. Sí, a nosotros _____ la residencia.

ALGO MÁS: SOME MORE USES OF *POR* AND *PARA*

6-42 **El regalo perfecto.** Different types of gifts are usually given for different occasions. For instance, you would not give the same gift for a birthday that you would for a wedding. Think for a moment about different occasions and gifts that would be appropriate.

Now you will listen to three conversations about different celebrations and gifts. Listen to each conversation and fill in the chart with the following information: the gift (**regalo**), the recipient (**para...**), and the occasion (**por...**).

	EL REGALO...	ES PARA...	POR...
Conversación 1			
Conversación 2			su aniversario
Conversación 3	un traje de bautizo	el bebé	

MOSAICOS

 6-43   En la tienda. You go to the store to buy some new clothes. What events might take place? What will the sales assistant ask or say to you? What might you ask or say to him or her?

Your side of the conversation with the sales assistant is written out below. Look at your statements and think about which will come earlier or later during the conversation. Then listen to the sales assistant and choose your appropriate reply. Respond orally as well, reading your reply out loud. After you finish, it would be a good idea to go through the dialogue again for further practice.

1. _____   a. Muchas gracias. Adiós.

2. _____   b. Lo prefiero rojo o verde, de lana.

3. _____   c. Muy bien, lo compro.

4. _____   d. El suéter rojo me queda bien. ¿Cuánto cuesta?

5. _____   e. Sí, me gustan mucho. Me los voy a probar.

6. _____   f. En efectivo, por favor. Aquí tiene.

7. _____   g. La talla mediana, por favor.

8. _____   h. Necesito un suéter de invierno (*winter*).

PRONUNCIACIÓN

Stress and the written accent

The combination of unstressed **u** or **i** with another vowel forms a diphthong, which is pronounced as one syllable. **Repitan las siguientes palabras.**

baile   fiesta   bueno   bebiendo   sirviendo   precioso

When a written accent is needed because of the rules of accentuation, it is not placed over the **i** or **u**. **Repitan las siguientes palabras.**

Dios   adiós   bien   también   seis   dieciséis

As you read the following words, make sure to pronounce the diphthong as one syllable. You will hear a confirmation after you read each word.

1. pienso

2. viejo

3. contrario

4. medias

5. pañuelo

6. cuero

7. guapo

8. canción

9. decisión

10. aire

When the **i** or **u** is stressed, the vowels form two syllables, and no diphthong results. A written accent is required over the **i** or **u**. **Repitan las siguientes palabras.**

cafetería   país   frío   Raúl   reírse   día

As you read the following words, make sure you pronounce each vowel separately. You will hear a confirmation after you read each word.

1. economía

2. geología

3. librería

4. tío

5. reúne

6. baúl

The combinations **iu** and **ui** form diphthongs, with the stress on the second vowel. **Repitan las siguientes palabras.**

    ciudad   cuidado   jesuita   veintiuno   ruina

Lección 7

Nombre: _____

Fecha: _____

El tiempo y los deportes

A PRIMERA VISTA

7-1   Los deportes. Indicate what sport you associate with the following names.

MODELO: New York Yankees   *béisbol*

1. Kobe Bryant   _____

2. Tour de France   _____

3. Tiger Woods   _____

4. New York Mets   _____

5. Wimbledon   _____

6. La Copa Mundial   _____

7-2   Equipo deportivo. Indicate which of these items you do not need to practice the following sports.

1. baloncesto: a. cesto   b. pelota   c. bate

2. natación: a. piscina   b. cancha   c. traje de baño

3. tenis: a. palos   b. raqueta   c. red

4. béisbol: a. guante   b. bate   c. cesto

5. golf: a. campo   b. red   c. palos

7-3   El tiempo y las estaciones. Sports and activities are in many cases correlated with the weather and the seasons. Typically, you would not go to the beach when it is snowing in the middle of January. Read the following statements and indicate what season or weather correlates best with each activity or sport.

1. A muchas personas les gusta ir a la playa en esta estación.
    a. invierno   b. verano   c. otoño

2. Esta estación se asocia con el fútbol americano.
    a. invierno   b. primavera   c. verano

3. En esta estación muchas veces hace viento, y las personas celebran el Día de Acción de Gracias.

   a. otoño   b. primavera   c. verano

4. Cuando hace este tiempo en San Francisco, muchas personas van a pasear al parque.

   a. calor   b. fresco   c. mucho frío

5. En esta estación muchas personas van a las montañas para esquiar.

   a. primavera   b. verano   c. invierno

6. En Nueva York en invierno, cuando juegan los Jets, hace este tiempo.

   a. hace calor   b. hace frío   c. hace fresco

7-4   **El tiempo.** Look at the following pictures and indicate their most accurate descriptions.

1. _____

2. _____

3. _____

4. _____

5. _____

6. _____

a. Miguel se pone el impermeable porque llueve mucho.

b. Hace viento, y por eso no vamos a jugar al golf.

c. Está nublado, y parece que va a llover.

d. Hace muy buen tiempo hoy.

e. Lleva pantalones cortos porque hace calor.

f. Hace mucho frío, y por eso Marta no se quita los guantes.

EXPLICACIÓN Y EXPANSIÓN

Síntesis gramatical

1. Preterit tense of -er and -ir verbs whose stem ends in a vowel

yo	leí	**nosotros/as**	leímos
tú	leíste	**vosotros/as**	leísteis
Ud., él, ella	leyó	**Uds., ellos/as**	leyeron
yo	oí	**nosotros/as**	oímos
tú	oíste	**vosotros/as**	oísteis
Ud., él, ella	oyó	**Uds., ellos/as**	oyeron

2. Preterit tense of stem-changing -ir verbs (e → i) (o → u)

yo	preferí	**nosotros/as**	preferimos
tú	preferiste	**vosotros/as**	preferisteis
Ud., él, ella	prefirió	**Uds., ellos/as**	prefirieron
yo	dormí	**nosotros/as**	dormimos
tú	dormiste	**vosotros/as**	dormisteis
Ud., él, ella	durmió	**Uds., ellos/as**	durmieron

3. Reflexive verbs and pronouns

yo	me lavo	*I wash (myself)*
tú	te lavas	*you wash (yourself)*
Ud.	se lava	*you wash (yourself)*
él	se lava	*he washes (himself)*
ella	se lava	*she washes (herself)*
nosotros/as	nos lavamos	*we wash (ourselves)*
vosotros/as	os laváis	*you wash (yourselves)*
Uds.	se lavan	*you wash (yourselves)*
ellos/as	se lavan	*they wash (themselves)*

4. Pronouns after prepositions

After **a, de, para, sin**		After **con**	After **entre**
mí	nosotros	conmigo	tú y yo
ti	vosotros	contigo	
usted, él, ella	ustedes, ellos, ellas	él/ella/usted	
		nosotros	
		vosotros	
		ustedes	

5. Some irregular preterits

INFINITIVE	NEW STEM	PRETERIT FORMS
hacer	hic-	hice, hiciste, hizo, hicimos, hicisteis, hicieron
querer	quis-	quise, quisiste, quiso, quisimos, quisisteis, quisieron
venir	vin-	vine, viniste, vino, vinimos, vinisteis, vinieron
decir	dij-	dije, dijiste, dijo, dijimos, dijisteis, dijeron
traer	traj-	traje, trajiste, trajo, trajimos, trajisteis, trajeron
traducir	traduj-	traduje, tradujiste, tradujo, tradujimos, tradujisteis, tradujeron
estar	estuv-	estuve, estuviste, estuvo, estuvimos, estuvisteis, estuvieron
tener	tuv-	tuve, tuviste, tuvo, tuvimos, tuvisteis, tuvieron
poder	pud-	pude, pudiste, pudo, pudimos, pudisteis, pudieron
poner	pus-	puse, pusiste, puso, pusimos, pusisteis, pusieron
saber	sup-	supe, supiste, supo, supimos, supisteis, supieron

1. Preterit tense of -er and -ir verbs whose stem ends in a vowel

7-5 **El periódico y la radio.** Answer the following questions about your preferences and those of your best friend, regarding newspaper and radio programs.

1. ¿Qué periódico leyó usted ayer? ¿Y su mejor amigo?

    _____

2. ¿Qué secciones leyeron (deportes/vida social/vida cultural/noticias internacionales)?

    _____

3. ¿Cuándo oyó usted un programa de radio? ¿Qué programa oyó?

    _____

4. ¿Oyeron usted y su mejor amigo el mismo (*same*) programa?

    _____

Now, based on your answers about you and your friend, circle a number on the following scale that best reflects the similarity of your habits with respect to newspapers and radio (5 is completely the same, and 0 is completely the opposite).

      0   1   2   3   4   5

2. Preterit tense of stem-changing -ir verbs (e → i) (o → u)

7-6 **Celebración.** Unscramble the sentences and conjugate the verbs to reveal what your Uruguayan friends did when they heard that their soccer team had won the World Cup.

1. la buena noticia muchas veces/Rodrigo/repetir

    _____

2. el triunfo/ellos/servir cerveza/para celebrar

    _____

3. vino/Teresa/preferir tomar

    _____

4. con los colores del equipo/vestirse/Víctor

    _____

5. esa noche/no dormir/ellos

    _____

7-7   Los amigos. Using the following information, indicate what Jorge, Alejandra, and Susana did last Saturday. Then indicate whether you did the same thing.

	JORGE	ALEJANDRA Y SUSANA
por la mañana	bañarse a las 7:00 tomar un café leer el periódico	dormir hasta tarde servirle cereal a su hermanito beber un vaso de leche
por la tarde	preferir estudiar en la biblioteca volver a casa a las 6:30	almorzar en el centro comercial oír un CD en el auto jugar al tenis
por la noche	vestirse rápidamente salir a cenar acostarse tarde	pedir una pizza bañarse leer una novela

¿y usted?

Sí   *No*

1. ¿Qué hicieron Alejandra y Susana por la mañana?

    Alejandra y Susana _____   ❏   ❏

2. ¿Qué hizo Jorge por la tarde?

    Jorge _____   ❏   ❏

3. ¿Qué hicieron las muchachas por la tarde?

    Alejandra y Susana _____   ❏   ❏

4. ¿Qué hizo Jorge por la noche?

    Jorge _____   ❏   ❏

5. ¿Qué hicieron las chicas por la noche?

    Alejandra y Susana _____   ❏   ❏

3. Reflexive verbs and pronouns

7-8   El día de Maribel. Below are Maribel's typical daily activities. Put them in chronological order, conjugating them to describe her routine in the morning and at night.

Por la mañana: *Por la noche:*

despertarse   ponerse el camisón

secarse   lavarse los dientes

bañarse   acostarse

vestirse

levantarse

Por la mañana Maribel...   *Por la noche Maribel...*

1. _____   6. _____

2. _____   7. _____

3. _____   8. _____

4. _____

5. _____

7-9   De vacaciones. Primera fase. En Punta del Este. A group of your friends are spending a week in Punta del Este, a famous resort in Uruguay. Make up questions for your friends to find out what they are doing there.

1. levantarse/a qué hora _____

2. ropa informal para estar en el hotel/ponerse _____

3. muy tarde por la noche/acostarse _____

4. en la piscina del hotel o en el mar/bañarse _____

5. irse de Punta del Este/qué día _____

Segunda fase. En casa. You and your boyfriend or girlfriend could not go to Punta del Este with your friends because you have to attend summer school. Describe your routine to your friends.

1. levantarse

   Mi novio/a y yo _____ (temprano/tarde).

2. ponerse

   Mi novio/a y yo _____ (ropa informal/ropa formal) para ir a clase.

3. lavarse

   Mi novio/a y yo _____ los dientes (después de desayunar/tan pronto [*as soon as*] nos levantamos).

4. acostarse

   Mi novio/a y yo _____ (temprano/tarde).

4. Pronouns after prepositions _____

7-10   Los regalos de Navidad. Your friend has been shopping for Christmas presents, and she has asked you to wrap and label them according to their recipients. Use the notes she has left to help you identify each present's recipient.

Notas:

- A mis primas les encanta la ropa.
- A mi papá le gusta mucho la música clásica.
- A mi abuela le gustan las novelas de misterio y de miedo.
- A mis primos les encanta jugar al tenis.
- Mi hermano juega al béisbol en el equipo de la escuela.
- A mi hermana le gusta mucho dibujar.

MODELO: ¿Para quién son las pinturas de colores, para su hermano o su hermana?
          Son para ella.

1. ¿Para quién es el libro de Stephen King, para su papá o para su abuela? _____

2. ¿Para quién son las raquetas, para su tía o para sus primos? _____

3. ¿Para quién es el CD de Mozart, para su mamá o para su papá? _____

4. ¿Para quién es el bate, para su hermana pequeña o para su hermano? _____

5. ¿Para quién son los suéteres, para su hermana o para sus primas? _____

7-11   Crucigrama. Complete the following crossword puzzle with the appropriate pronouns and prepositions.

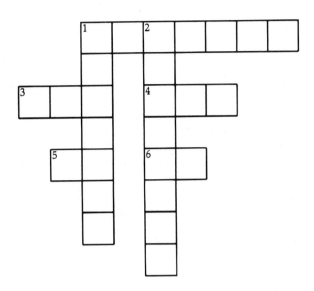

Horizontales

1. No quiero ir sola al dentista. Mi amiga Catalina va _____.

3. A Ramón no le gusta comer solo; por eso va al restaurante _____ Ana.

4. María no tiene auto. Yo la voy a buscar para ir al partido de fútbol. Ella no puede ir al estadio _____ mí.

5. A _____ me encanta el helado de vainilla.

6. Compré estos discos de Plácido Domingo para _____.

Verticales

1. Como te sientes mal, prefiero ir al médico _____; te acompaño.

2. Julio y yo vamos a ir a buscar a Anita para ir a ver una película. Ella va a venir al cine con _____.

5. Some irregular preterits

7-12   La noche de Esther. Esther did the following activities last night. Indicate what object or place is associated with each activity.

1. volvió a casa del trabajo _____   a. *Cien años de soledad*

2. fue al gimnasio _____   b. la televisión

3. se duchó _____   c. ejercicio aeróbico

4. vio *Friends* _____   d. cama

5. hizo la cena _____   e. la bañera

6. leyó un libro _____   f. la oficina

7. se acostó tarde _____   g. pollo a la barbacoa con vegetales

7-13   Descubriendo Uruguay. What could you do on vacation in Uruguay? Select from the following verbs to complete the paragraph about Catalina's family vacation in Uruguay. (One verb will be used twice.)

ver	ponerse	tener	poder
ser	ir	tomar	estar

Nuestra familia fue a Uruguay el año pasado. Nosotros (1) _____ en avión y (2) _____ una semana allí. El primer día en Montevideo (3) _____ la Ciudad Vieja y también la Puerta de la Ciudadela, que conecta el centro de Montevideo con la Ciudad Vieja. (4) _____ un paseo muy interesante. El segundo día (5) _____ un taxi para ir al mercado del Puerto. Nos encantó, pues es un lugar muy divertido y un poco bohemio. También (6) _____ al edificio donde están los Museos del Gaucho y de la Moneda, dos museos muy interesantes. No (7) _____ tiempo de ver todo lo que tienen en el Museo del Gaucho, y no (8) _____ ver el Museo de la Moneda porque era (*was*) muy tarde. El último día en Montevideo (9) _____ ropa muy informal para ir a Punta del Este y descansar el resto de la semana en la playa.

Now, based on what you learned from Catalina's description, do you think you would like to vacation in Uruguay? Why or why not?

_____

_____

7-14 **¿Qué hizo el fin de semana pasado?** Think about what you did last weekend. Write complete sentences to indicate whether you did the following activities.

MODELO: volver a casa tarde
Volví a casa tarde. OR *No volví a casa tarde.*

1. ir al cine

   _____

2. ponerse ropa elegante

   _____

3. querer ir a la playa

   _____

4. descansar

   _____

5. hacer la tarea

   _____

6. estar en casa

   _____

7. bañarse

   _____

8. tener mucho trabajo

   _____

ALGO MÁS: *HACE,* MEANING *AGO*

7-15 **¿Cuánto tiempo hace?** Complete the following sentences to indicate how long ago you did the following actions. Use **hace** + time expression (**horas, días, semanas, meses, años**) and additional personal information.

MODELO: *Hace seis meses* que llegué *a esta ciudad.*

1. _____ que comí _____.

2. _____ que conocí a _____.

3. _____ que fui _____.

4. _____ que empecé a _____.

5. _____ que visité _____.

7-16   Los famosos. As of the year 2005, how long ago have these famous people experienced or passed the following events? Complete the sentences using **hace** + time expression.

1. _____ que Melanie Griffith y Antonio Banderas se casaron. (1996)

2. _____ que Arnold Schwarzenegger se convirtió en gobernador. (2003)

3. _____ que Nixon se fue de la Casa Blanca. (1974)

4. _____ que se estrenó *El sonido de la música*. (1965)

5. _____ que John Lennon fue asesinado. (1980)

MOSAICOS

A leer

7-17   Antes de leer. Chile. Primera fase. Based on your own knowledge of Chile, indicate whether the each of the following statements is **cierto (C)** or **falso (F)**.

1. C F   Chile está muy cerca de México.

2. C F   En agosto en Chile normalmente hace frío porque es invierno.

3. C F   Uruguay es un país vecino (*neighboring*) de Chile.

4. C F   En Chile no hay desiertos.

5. C F   Chile es un país muy seco; no llueve casi nunca.

Segunda fase. Now look at the following answer key and see how many answers you got correct. Then read the evaluation that corresponds to the number of your correct answers.

Answers: 1. F; 2. F; 3. F; 4. F; 5. F

   0–2 respuestas correctas: Sabes muy poco de Chile; tienes que leer más sobre este interesante país.

   3–4 respuestas correctas: Sabes bastante de Chile; se ve que te interesa este país. Es buena idea leer más sobre él para conocerlo mejor.

   5 respuestas correctas: ¡Perfecto! Eres un gran conocedor de Chile; sabes mucho sobre este país.

7-18   **A leer. Medio país bajo el agua.** Read this article from the international section of an Uruguayan newspaper. Then indicate whether each of the statements that follow is **cierto (C)** or **falso (F)**.

MEDIO CHILE BAJO EL AGUA

Después de un invierno suave y temperaturas agradables, el frío y el agua azotan desde hace quince días buena parte del territorio chileno. El temporal, que es especialmente intenso en el sur del país, donde se encuentran decenas de pueblos aislados y numerosos caminos y carreteras cerrados al tráfico, se extiende también al centro y norte del país, especialmente al Desierto de Atacama, el más seco del mundo.

A altas horas de la noche, los escuadrones de rescate pudieron llegar en botes y lanchas a sacar de los techos de sus casas a cientos de damnificados —mujeres y niños— que esperaban angustiosamente la ayuda de las autoridades. Las zonas más afectadas son las poblaciones más adyacentes al río Bío-Bío en el sur del país.

Para hoy no se esperan cambios significativos en el clima; se esperan más heladas, lluvia y fuertes vientos.

---

1. C   F   El mal tiempo afecta sólo a una región del país.

2. C   F   Hace una semana que está nevando.

3. C   F   Las personas no pueden usar sus carros en el sur del país.

4. C   F   En el Desierto de Atacama hay tormentas de arena.

5. C   F   El tiempo va a mejorar.

6. C   F   Se esperan vientos de gran velocidad.

7-19   **Después de leer. Recomendaciones.** Make a list of recommendations for people who suffer from flooding. Indicate what they should do before the bad weather, during the flooding, and after the waters recede.

ANTES	DURANTE	DESPUÉS

7-20 **Antes de escribir. Inundación.** Think about a flood like the one described in "Medio Chile bajo el agua" and list the consequences of the flood and the actions that should be taken by people and by authorities.

CONSECUENCIAS	ACCIONES DE LA GENTE	ACCIONES DE LAS AUTORIDADES

7-21 **A escribir. Una carta desde Chile.** Imagine that you were in Chile during the terrible flood described in the article. Write a letter to your family explaining what the weather is like in Chile and its effect on the country. Use your list from exercise 7-20 to explain to your family the consequences of the flooding, what you and the people who suffered the flood did, and what the authorities did to cope with the situation.

_____

_____

_____

_____

_____

_____

_____

_____

_____

_____

7-22   Después de escribir. El tiempo donde vivo. In one of your classes, a Chilean exchange student has just arrived from Chile. You start talking to him about the recent floods in Chile. He wants to know about the weather where you live. Answer his questions as explicitly as possible.

1. ¿Qué tiempo hace en tu ciudad en invierno? ¿Nieva mucho? ¿Cuál es la temperatura media (*average*)?

   _____

   _____

2. En la primavera ¿llueve mucho? ¿hace buen tiempo? ¿Cuál es la temperatura media?

   _____

   _____

3. En el verano ¿hace mucho calor? ¿Cuál es la temperatura media? ¿Hay mucha humedad o es un clima seco? ¿Hay muchas tormentas eléctricas?

   _____

   _____

4. En el otoño ¿hace mucho viento? ¿De qué color son las hojas? ¿Cuál es la temperatura media? ¿Hace fresco?

   _____

   _____

5. ¿Hay algunos desastres metereológicos típicos de esta área? ¿Hay tornados, huracanes, inundaciones? ¿En qué estaciones son típicos estos eventos?

   _____

   _____

6. ¿Qué estación es ahora en tu ciudad? ¿Qué deportes son típicos de esta época?

   _____

   _____

ENFOQUE CULTURAL

7-23   Los deportes y conociendo la Argentina y el Uruguay. Indicate whether each of the following sentences about sports in Hispanic countries and about Uruguay and Argentina is **cierto (C)** or **falso (F)** according to the **Enfoque Cultural** on pages 273–278 in your textbook.

1. _____ El deporte más popular en el mundo hispano es el ciclismo.

2. _____ En el área del Caribe, el deporte más popular es el béisbol.

3. _____ Nicolás Scortichini es uno de los jugadores más conocidos de polo.

4. _____ El equipo de polo uruguayo ganó varios campeonatos mundiales.

5. _____ En Montevideo hay un museo dedicado a los gauchos.

6. _____ La capital del Uruguay es Punta del Este.

7. _____ Cuando los uruguayos quieren decir que una persona tuvo una F en un examen, dicen que perdió el examen.

8. _____ A los argentinos se les llama también porteños.

9. _____ Los argentinos pueden ir a una de las numerosas playas en el Mar de la Plata.

10. _____ Los argentinos llaman al trabajo *morocho*.

A PRIMERA VISTA

7-24 **¿Qué deporte practican?** Do you remember some of the popular sports in Hispanic countries? What about the equipment they require and the places they are practiced?

You are visiting some Hispanic countries during your winter vacation, and many people seem to enjoy sports here: you overhear four conversations about sports in one day! Identify the sports they are discussing.

	FÚTBOL	ESQUÍ	BALONCESTO	BOLOS	VOLEIBOL	GOLF	CICLISMO	TENIS
1.								
2.								
3.								
4.								

7-25 **El tiempo en Montevideo.** It is January 9 and you are in Montevideo, Uruguay, for the weekend. You want to make plans for the weekend. Listen to the weather report and indicate when the following weather conditions will happen. Note that one of the conditions will happen on two days. Remember: you are in the southern hemisphere!

	VIERNES	SÁBADO	DOMINGO
1. lluvia			
2. viento			
3. sol			
4. nublado			
5. fresco			
6. calor			

7-26   El entrenador personal. It is hard to stay in shape during the holidays, but as a personal trainer, you want to make sure your clients stay active. You call your trainees to encourage them, but you encounter some resistance. Listen to them and suggest a sport to try from the ones listed below. Give your recommendation both orally and in writing, as in the model.

el esquí   los bolos   el golf   el voleibol de playa

MODELO: You say and write: *Te recomiendo el tenis.*

1. Te recomiendo _____

2. Te recomiendo _____

3. Te recomiendo _____

4. Te recomiendo _____

7-27   ¿Qué necesito? One of your clients is unfamiliar with sports, so you need to help him. Listen to his statements and respond, both orally and in writing, letting him know when he is correct and correcting him when he is not, as in the Model.

MODELO: You hear: Necesito un bate para el béisbol, ¿verdad?
          You say and write: *Sí, para el béisbol necesitas un bate.*

          You hear: Necesito una bicicleta para el béisbol, ¿verdad?
          You say and write: *No, para el ciclismo necesitas una bicicleta.*

1. _____

2. _____

3. _____

4. _____

5. _____

EXPLICACIÓN Y EXPANSIÓN

1. Preterit tense of -*er* and -*ir* verbs whose stem ends in a vowel
_____

7-28   Planeando un partido de fútbol. César, Nicanor, and Santiago are organizing an informal soccer match, and there seems to be some disagreement on the weather. After you listen to their conversation, you call another friend to tell him about it. Complete the story with appropriate forms of **leer** and **oír.**

Fue muy cómico. César (1) _____ que el viernes va a llover, pero Nicanor (2) _____ que va a hacer buen tiempo, y Santiago y su hermano también (3) _____ eso... ¿Sabes qué fue? ¡Que César (4) _____ el periódico de la semana pasada!

2. Preterit tense of stem-changing -*ir* verbs (e → i) (o → u)
_____

7-29   El fin de semana. You are taking a weekend trip with your friends Lidia, Marcelo, and Francisco. Lidia is recounting now about what you all did last night. Listen to her and indicate to whom she is referring.

	LIDIA (YO)	TÚ	MARCELO	MARCELO Y FRANCISCO
1.				
2.				
3.				
4.				
5.				
6.				

3. Reflexive verbs and pronouns

7-30 **Rutinas diferentes.** Diego and Arturo are college students. Their routines are quite similar, but there are some differences too. Listen to their conversation and indicate whether the information on the left column refers to Diego, Arturo, or both (**los dos**).

	DIEGO	ARTURO	LOS DOS
1. levantarse temprano			
2. bañarse por la noche			
3. afeitarse			
4. lavarse los dientes			
5. irse al trabajo			
6. quitarse el traje			
7. dormirse mirando la televisión			
8. acostarse tarde			

7-31 **Un nuevo horario.** Diego has been having a hard time keeping up with his school work because of his demanding schedule. His advisor gave him some tips about stress and time management. Listen to him once for the gist; can you tell if the changes are helping him?

A common friend asks about Diego, and you tell her what he said about yesterday's activities. Remember to use the preterit to talk about yesterday. Note that **poner** is irregular (see the section on irregular preterits in this chapter).

irse (2)	bañarse	afeitarse	acostarse
dormirse	ponerse	quedarse	levantarse

Diego (1) _____ a las siete de la mañana. Fue a correr, y después
(2) _____, (3) _____ y (4) _____ la ropa. A las ocho
(5) _____ al trabajo. Desde allí fue a la universidad, comió y (6) _____
en la biblioteca tres horas para estudiar. Después de sus clases, Diego (7) _____
a casa. A las once de la noche (8) _____ y dice que (9) _____
rápidamente.

7-32   **¿Y tú?** Are your days as busy as Diego's? Listen to the following questions about what you did yesterday and answer with complete sentences. Remember to use preterit forms to talk about yesterday.

1. _____

2. _____

3. _____

4. _____

5. _____

4. Pronouns after prepositions

7-33   **¡Increíble!** You call your best friend from high school, and she tells you about a party where she saw some of your former classmates. You cannot believe what she is telling you! React to her news, both orally and in writing, as in the model.

MODELO: You hear: Mario está interesado en mí.
            You say: *¿En ti?*

Avoid repetition of nouns (Pedro, Linda) by substituting with a pronoun (**él, ella**).

MODELO: You hear: Mario está interesado en Ángela.
            You say: *¿En ella?*

1. _____

2. _____

3. _____

4. _____

5. _____

6. _____

Nombre: _____   Fecha: _____

5. Some irregular preterits

7-34   El trabajo de Isabel. Listen to Isabel describe her day at work yesterday. First listen for the gist: did she have a good day or a bad day? Then read the following statements and indicate whether each is **Cierto** or **Falso.** Listen again to check your answers. Finally, correct the false statements to make them true.

		Cierto	*Falso*
1.	Isabel estuvo muy ocupada ayer.	_____	_____
2.	Isabel no hizo nada en su casa; sólo fue a trabajar.	_____	_____
3.	Su primera clienta estuvo en la tienda poco tiempo.	_____	_____
4.	Su supervisora trajo a unos clientes a la tienda.	_____	_____
5.	Isabel tuvo que traducir del español al francés.	_____	_____
6.	Isabel pudo descansar después de comer.	_____	_____
7.	En casa Isabel tuvo que cocinar la cena.	_____	_____

7-35   Dictado. Complete the following statements about Isabel's day with appropriate preterit forms of the verbs below. Then listen to her again to check your answers.

venir   querer   poder   estar   tener   traducir

1. Ayer Isabel _____ muy ocupada.
2. Una clienta _____ a las diez y un minuto.
3. La clienta no _____ decidir rápidamente.
4. Isabel _____ de español a inglés para unos clientes.
5. Isabel no _____ tiempo libre por la tarde.
6. El marido de Isabel _____ hacer la cena para ellos.

7-36   **¿Qué hizo el profesor de español el fin de semana?** Can you imagine what your Spanish instructor did last weekend? Listen to the questions and answer negatively or affirmatively; in the latter case complete your sentence with more specific information, as in the model.

MODELO: You hear: ¿Leyó un libro?
            You say and write: *No, no leyó un libro.*
                                 OR *Sí, leyó* El código de Da Vinci.

1. _____

2. _____

3. _____

4. _____

5. _____

6. _____

In your next class ask your instructor whether he or she did any of these activities yesterday. Did you guess correctly?

7-37   **Demasiado tarde.** Your friend is always a bit behind everybody else: everything she wants to do today was already done yesterday! Listen to her questions and reply using the cues below, as in the model. Try to avoid repetition by substituting direct objects with pronouns in your answers.

MODELO: You hear: ¿Estudiamos los verbos irregulares?
            You see: (yo)
            You say and write: *Yo los estudié ayer.*

1. (Elena) _____

2. (nosotros) _____

3. (Juan) _____

4. (yo) _____

5. (Elena y Juan) _____

ALGO MÁS: *HACE,* MEANING *AGO*

7-38   Llegada a Buenos Aires. A few friends and you have been home for the first part of your vacation, but you plan to meet in Buenos Aires, Argentina, for the rest of it. You are all flying from different cities, so when you get off your plane, you check the automated arrivals information service.

It is 10:00 a.m. right now. Have your friends arrived? If so, how long ago? After determining this information, answer the questions that follow.

MODELO: You see: Juan/Philadelphia
            You hear: Vuelo 732, procedente de Philadelphia, llegada a las 9:40.
            You say and write: *Juan llegó hace veinte minutos.*

1. Elvira/Miami _____

2. Agustín y Carmen/Chicago _____

3. Ignacio/Nueva York _____

4. Lea y Sonia/Los Ángeles _____

5. Manuel/San Juan _____

6. ¿Llegaron todos tus amigos? _____

7. ¿Quién llegó primero? _____

MOSAICOS

 7-39 **El torneo.** You play on your school's volleyball team. This weekend you went to a tournament out of town, and you won! Your teammate Alejandro was not feeling well and could not go, but he wants to know all the details of your activities. Since you do not remember everything exactly, look at the following schedule to answer his questions. Remember to include the appropriate verb in your replies, as in the model.

Torneo de voleibol universitario: Sábado, 12 de abril

7:00   Levantarse

7:15   Ponerse el uniforme

7:30   Desayuno (en el hotel)

8:00   Autobús a las canchas

9:00   Partido 1

10:00   Partido 2

11: 00   Partido 3

12:00   Comida

3:00   Partido final (sólo los equipos finalistas)

5:00   Autobús al hotel

7:00   Cena

8:00   Celebración (sólo si ganamos el torneo)

¡Atención! Tienen que acostarse antes de las 11:30.

MODELO: You hear: ¿A qué hora desayunaron?
                You say and write: *Desayunamos a las 7:30.*

1. _____

2. _____

3. _____

4. _____

5. _____

6. _____

7. _____

8. _____

Lección 8

Nombre: _____

Fecha: _____

Fiestas y tradiciones

A PRIMERA VISTA

8-1 De fiesta. Read the following descriptions of holidays in the United States and Hispanic countries, and indicate the holiday being described.

1. Un día especial para los novios y esposos. _____
2. Una fiesta muy importante en algunas ciudades como Nueva Orleáns y Río de Janeiro. _____
3. Día especial para recordar a los parientes muertos. _____
4. La noche antes de la Navidad. _____
5. Hay desfiles con banderas (*flags*) y bandas. _____
6. Los niños norteamericanos van a las casas de sus vecinos (*neighbors*) y les piden algo. _____

a. el Día de los Muertos/ Difuntos
b. la Nochebuena
c. el Día de la Independencia
d. el Día de las Brujas
e. el Carnaval
f. el Día de los Enamorados

8-2 Crucigrama. Complete the following sentences about holidays to solve the crossword puzzle. When you complete the puzzle, the vertical row will contain the name of a holiday. HINT: **celebrar** = *to celebrate*; **celebrarse** = *to be celebrated*.

1. Los países celebran su libertad y soberanía (*sovereignty*) el Día de la _____.

2. Santa Claus les trae regalos a los niños en _____.

3. El cuarto jueves de noviembre se celebra en Estados Unidos el Día de Acción de _____.

4. Los adultos se disfrazan y se divierten mucho en el _____.

5. El primer día del año es el Día de Año _____.

6. En el mes de mayo se celebra en muchos países el Día de la(s) _____.

8-3   Las fiestas tradicionales de los Estados Unidos. Alberto is a Mexican student who is visiting the United States. Answer his questions about the holidays and traditions in the States.

ALBERTO: En mi país no tenemos el Día de Acción de Gracias. ¿Me puedes explicar qué es, cuándo y cómo lo celebran ustedes?

TÚ: _____

    _____

    _____

ALBERTO: Me parece una tradición estupenda. Aquí seguramente celebran el día del cumpleaños igual que nosotros. ¿Cuándo es tu cumpleaños, y qué tipo de regalos prefieres recibir (*to get*)?

TÚ: _____

    _____

    _____

ALBERTO: Ahora dime (*tell me*) algo de las fiestas en este país. ¿Qué tipo de fiestas te gustan a ti?

TÚ: _____

    _____

    _____

ALBERTO: ¡Qué bien! Me tienes que avisar (*let know*) la próxima vez para ir a una fiesta contigo.

8-4 **Invitaciones. Primera fase.** You are having a Super Bowl party in your apartment, and you invite a few friends. Write the invitation you will send to your friends.

1. Propósito de (*Reason for*) la fiesta: _____

2. Día: _____

3. Hora: _____

4. Dónde: _____

Segunda fase. Since you are very popular, you have received several invitations too. Accept or reject the following invitations depending on whether you have time to attend. If you accept, offer to help; if you do not, offer an excuse.

1. Tu amigo te invita a una fiesta en su casa para el Super Bowl:

   _____

   _____

2. Tu mejor amiga te invita a su fiesta de cumpleaños:

   _____

   _____

3. Un amigo te invita a su fiesta de graduación:

   _____

   _____

EXPLICACIÓN Y EXPANSIÓN

Síntesis gramatical

1. The imperfect

- express habitual or repeated actions in the past
- tell time in the past
- express an action or state that was in progress in the past
- tell age in the past
- describe characteristics and conditions in the past

2. Imperfect of regular and irregular verbs

	HABLAR	COMER	VIVIR
yo	hablaba	comía	vivía
tú	hablabas	comías	vivías
Ud., él, ella	hablaba	comía	vivía
nosotros/as	hablábamos	comíamos	vivíamos
vosotros/as	hablabais	comíais	vivíais
Uds., ellos/as	hablaban	comían	vivían

SPANISH HAS THREE IRREGULAR VERBS IN THE IMPERFECT:

ir:	iba, ibas, iba, íbamos, ibais, iban
ser:	era, eras, era, éramos, erais, eran
ver:	veía, veías, veía, veíamos, veíais, veían

3. The preterit and the imperfect

IMPERFECTO

- to talk about customary or habitual actions or states in the past.

- to talk about an ongoing part of an event or state.

PRETÉRITO

- to talk about the beginning or end of an event or state.

- to talk about an action or state that occurred over a period of time with a definite beginning and end.

- to narrate a sequence of completed actions in the past; note that there is a forward movement of narrative time.

4. Comparisons of inequality

más + *adjective/noun* + **que**

menos + *adjective/noun* + **que**

más/menos + *adverb* + **que**

5. Comparisons of equality

tan + *adjective/adverb* + como	as . . . + as
tantos/as + *noun* + como	as many . . . + as
tanto/a + *noun* + como	as much . . . + as
tanto como	as much as

6. The superlative

definite article + *noun* + **más/menos** + *adjective* + **de**

La procesión **más** importante de la ciudad.

adjective + -**ísimo**

grande + -**ísimo** = **grandísimo**

fácil + -**ísimo** = **facilísimo**

1. The imperfect

8-5   ¿Cuándo? Read the following sentences that describe Laura's routine in the present and in the past and indicate each activity's time frame (**presente** or **imperfecto**).

a. presente   b. imperfecto

1. Laura bailaba en las discotecas. _____

2. Va de compras al centro comercial. _____

3. Tenía un chihuahua muy gracioso (*cute*). _____

4. Trabaja en una oficina muy grande. _____

5. Visitaba a su abuela todos los veranos. _____

6. Comía en Wendy's frecuentemente. _____

7. Vive con sus padres. _____

8. Estudia los domingos por la noche. _____

9. Tocaba el piano. _____

10. Iba con su novio al cine. _____

2. Imperfect of regular and irregular verbs

8-6   En la escuela primaria. These are some things Amaya and her friends used to do in elementary school. Indicate who used to do each of the activities.

Hola. Me llamo Amaya. Mis amigas y yo éramos muy activas en la escuela primaria:

1. _____ hacíamos la tarea.

2. _____ jugaban al fútbol por las tardes.

3. _____ cuidaba (*took care of*) a su hermana pequeña.

4. _____ ayudabas a tu mamá.

a. Mi amiga Raquel

b. Mis amigas y yo

c. Mis amigas Raquel y Susana

d. Tú

8-7   Tu vida de niño. Think of your life as a child. Did you like vegetables, did you hate (**odiar**) them? Did you have a dog? Read the following statements and complete the sentences with the appropriate word. Then indicate whether they apply to you or not.

	Sí	*No*
MODELO: _____ la tarea: *Hacía* la tarea.	☑	☐

ser	practicar	tener	odiar
jugar	vivir	leer	ir

	Sí	*No*
1. _____ un perro.	☐	☐
2. _____ las verduras.	☐	☐
3. _____ a la iglesia los domingos.	☐	☐
4. _____ a los videojuegos.	☐	☐
5. _____ muchos cuentos.	☐	☐
6. _____ en una casa grande.	☐	☐
7. _____ buen/a estudiante.	☐	☐
8. _____ un deporte.	☐	☐

8-8   Amanda y su familia. Complete the following sentences that describe what Amanda and her family used to do when she was a child. Then indicate whether the sentences apply to you (**Es el caso**) or not (**No es el caso**).

ser	cocinar	jugar	estar
mirar	ir	reunirse	

	Es el caso	*No es el caso*
1. Mi familia y yo _____ de vacaciones todos juntos en el verano.	❏	❏
2. Siempre _____ para celebrar las fiestas más importantes.	❏	❏
3. El Día de Acción de Gracias _____ pavo (*turkey*) y puré de (*mashed*) papas.	❏	❏
4. A veces _____ la televisión todos juntos.	❏	❏
5. Mis padres _____ muy felices.	❏	❏
6. Mis hermanos y yo _____ a los videojuegos todo el tiempo.	❏	❏
7. Toda la familia _____ muy contenta.	❏	❏

Now select the statement that best applies to your family in comparison with Amanda's.

a. La rutina de la familia de Amanda y la rutina de mi familia eran muy diferentes.

b. La rutina de la familia de Amanda y la rutina de mi familia eran similares.

c. La rutina de la familia de Amanda y la rutina de mi familia eran iguales.

3. The preterit and the imperfect

8-9   La vida de Paula. Paula is always very busy and is always doing different things. Read the following sentences about Paula's life and indicate whether she most likely did (or does) these activities last weekend (**el fin de semana pasado**), when she was a child (**cuando era niña**), or now (**ahora**).

a. ahora   b. el fin de semana pasado   c. cuando era niña

1. Hablaba con su madre mucho. _____

2. Fue de vacaciones a Disney World. _____

3. Sale de paseo con su hermano los domingos por la mañana. _____

4. Estuvo muy enferma. _____

5. Tenía muchos amigos. _____

6. Preparó una cena especial para sus amigos. _____

8-10   Las fiestas. Read these statements about how Carolina and her family celebrate some holidays and choose the most logical ending for each sentence.

1. La familia de Carolina siempre pasa la Navidad en su casa, pero el año pasado...
   a. fueron a casa de sus abuelos en Monterrey.
   b. iban a casa de sus abuelos en Monterrey.
   c. van a casa de sus abuelos en Monterrey.

2. Carolina y su familia preparan pavo con puré de papas para el Día de Acción de Gracias, pero cuando Carolina era niña siempre...
   a. preparan un asado de cerdo.
   b. prepararon un asado de cerdo.
   c. preparaban un asado de cerdo.

3. A la madre de Carolina solo le gusta la música clásica, pero el año pasado para el Día de las Madres Carolina...
   a. lleva a su madre a un concierto de rock.
   b. llevó a su madre a un concierto de rock.
   c. llevaba a su madre a un concierto de rock.

4. Para sus fiestas de cumpleaños cuando eran niños, el papá de Carolina siempre...
   a. compraba piñatas.
   b. compró piñatas.
   c. compra piñatas.

5. Todos los años para celebrar el Año Nuevo, Carolina y su familia iban a casa de los Solís y...
   a. bailaron hasta las dos o tres de la mañana.
   b. bailaban hasta las dos o tres de la mañana.
   c. bailan hasta las dos o tres de la mañana.

8-11   En la escuela secundaria. Read the paragraph about Myriam's life during high school. Then indicate whether the following statements refer to events she did on a regular basis or to an event that happened only once.

Hola. Soy Myriam. Mi vida en la escuela secundaria fue excelente. Tenía muchos amigos. Iba a clase por las mañanas, y por las tardes practicaba natación. También estaba en el equipo de animadoras (*cheerleaders*) de mi escuela. Un día, después de un partido del equipo, comí una pizza con mis amigas en un restaurante de mi pueblo. Estudiaba por las noches y sacaba buenas notas. Mi sorpresa más grande fue una vez que saqué F en todos mis exámenes. ¡Por suerte fue un error administrativo! Cuando estaba en mi último año, conocí a un chico muy simpático en una fiesta. El fin de semana después fuimos juntos al cine. Pero al final del año él tuvo que irse del pueblo para vivir en otra ciudad con su familia.

  a. habitualmente   b. una vez

1. nadar en el equipo de la escuela secundaria _____

2. comer pizza _____

3. estudiar _____

4. sacar una F en los exámenes _____

5. ir al cine con un amigo _____

6. ser animadora _____

8-12   ¿Y su vida en la escuela secundaria? Write three things you used to do when you were in high school and three things you did that were memorable.

tres cosas que usted hacía regularmente:

1. _____

2. _____

3. _____

tres cosas que usted hizo que fueron memorables:

1. _____

2. _____

3. _____

4. Comparisons of inequality

8-13   Otras personas y yo. Compare yourself to other people by completing the following statements. Use **más... que** or **menos... que** and identify the other person.

MODELO: Yo soy _____ atlético _____.
Yo soy *más* atlético *que mi hermano.*

1. Hago _____ ejercicio _____.

2. Soy _____ fuerte _____.

3. Participo en _____ deportes _____.

4. Soy _____ activo _____.

5. Me gustan _____ los carnavales _____.

6. Como _____ verduras _____.

8-14   Personalidades famosas. You and your friends are talking about famous people and giving your opinions on who is more intelligent, who is prettier, and so on. Using complete sentences compare these famous people according to your own opinion about them.

MODELO: ¿Quién es más rico, Oprah o Michael Jordan?
Oprah es más rica que Michael Jordan. OR *Michael Jordan es más rico que Oprah.*

1. ¿Quién es más inteligente, Tom Brokaw o Regis Philbin?

   _____

2. ¿Quién es menos guapa, Salma Hayek o Penélope Cruz?

   _____

3. ¿Quién es más apasionado, Antonio Banderas o Chayanne?

   _____

4. ¿Quién es más divertido, Adam Sandler o Jim Carrey?

   _____

5. ¿Quién es mejor director, Steven Spielberg o Quentin Tarantino?

   _____

6. ¿Quién es más interesante, Jackie Kennedy o Hillary Clinton?

   _____

8-15   Cosas de la vida. Complete the sentences comparing how you feel about the following things.

1. ¿Cuál es más sabrosa?

   La comida mexicana _____ la comida china.

2. ¿Cuál es más interesante?

   La historia _____ la sociología.

3. ¿Cuál es más importante?

   Mi familia _____ mis amigos.

4. ¿Cuál es más divertido?

   El béisbol _____ el fútbol americano.

5. ¿Cuál es menos difícil?

   La química _____ la contabilidad.

8-16   Mi familia, mis amigos y yo. Compare yourself to family members and friends. Use **más/menos, mayor/menor, mejor/peor** and words from the list.

fiestas	discos	amigos	relojes	aretes	casas
hablar	comprar	bailar	ser	tener	celebrar

MODELO: *Yo tengo más aretes que mi hermana.*
            Yo bailo mejor que mi madre.

1. _____

2. _____

3. _____

4. _____

5. _____

6. _____

5. Comparisons of equality

8-17   Comparaciones. Look at the description of the families of Susana and Adela and indicate whether each of the following statements is **cierto (C)** or **falso (F)**.

Hola. Me llamo Susana. Mi familia es bastante grande: tengo dos hermanos y una hermana. Mi hermana Anabel está casada con Michel. Mi cuñado Michel es muy divertido. Ellos tienen dos hijos. Mis sobrinos se llaman Roberto y Carlos. Tengo muchos tíos y tías porque mi mamá tiene seis hermanos y mi papá tiene cuatro hermanos. Todos los hermanos de mi mamá y de mi papá están casados y tienen hijos. Tengo muchos primos; en total tengo veinticinco primos.

Hola. Me llamo Adela. Mi familia es pequeña. Tengo sólo una hermana pequeña. Mi hermana está en la escuela secundaria, así que no está casada. No tengo sobrinos. Tengo varios tíos y tías. Mi mamá tiene dos hermanas, y mi papá tiene cuatro hermanos. La hermana mayor de mi mamá está casada y tiene un hijo, mi primo Javier. La otra hermana de mi mamá es viuda y tiene una hija, mi prima Irene. Los hermanos de mi papá también están casados. En total tengo ocho primos.

1. _____ La familia de Adela es tan grande como la familia de Susana.

2. _____ Adela tiene tantos sobrinos como Susana.

3. _____ El papá de Adela tiene tantos hermanos como el papá de Susana.

4. _____ Adela no tiene tantos tíos como Susana.

5. _____ Susana no tiene tantos primos como Adela.

6. _____ Adela tiene tantas hermanas como Susana.

8-18   Los famosos. The following sentences describe famous people. Complete the sentences with the appropriate word.

a. tan   b. tanta   c. tanto   d. tantas   e. tantos

1. George Bush no es _____ aventurero como Indiana Jones.

2. Nicole Kidman no tiene _____ problemas como Michael Jackson.

3. Anna Nicole Smith no trabaja _____ como Oprah Winfrey.

4. Julia Roberts no es _____ simpática como Catherine Zeta Jones.

5. Bill Gates no tiene _____ amigas como Hugh Hefner.

Now indicate whether you agree or disagree with each statement.

a. estoy de acuerdo   b. no estoy de acuerdo

1. _____   4. _____

2. _____   5. _____

3. _____

8-19   En las décadas pasadas. Rebeca is a college student and is thinking about how life was when her parents were in college. Complete the following sentences in which Rebeca compares life now to life then.

tanto   tan   tantas   tantos   tanta

La vida entonces y la vida ahora son un poco diferentes. No había (1) _____ divorcios como ahora. Además, no había (2) _____ pornografía como ahora. Muchas cosas han cambiado. Antes no había (3) _____ madres solteras como ahora ni (4) _____ problemas con las drogas. Antes tenían (5) _____ enfermedades como ahora. A veces las personas no tenían (6) _____ dinero, pero eran (7) _____ felices como las personas hoy en día. Los jóvenes antes no eran (8) _____ liberales como los jóvenes ahora. ¡Ah! Muchas cosas han cambiado.

En la opinión de Rebeca en general:

a. Hoy en día hay más problemas que en décadas anteriores.

b. Hoy en día hay menos problemas que en épocas anteriores.

6. The superlative

8-20   El mundo. Do you know about the world's geography? Indicate what is being described in each sentence. Here is some basic geographical vocabulary:

agua dulce	*freshwater*	**montaña**	*mountain*
catarata	*waterfall*	**poblado/a**	*populated*
caudaloso/a	*big, large (river)*	**río**	*river*

1. el río más largo del mundo _____   a. Ártico

2. el río más caudaloso del mundo _____   b. Pacífico

3. la montaña más alta del mundo _____   c. Amazonas

4. las cataratas más altas del mundo _____   d. Nilo

5. el país más grande del mundo _____   e. Superior

6. el país más poblado del mundo _____   f. Everest

7. el lago de agua dulce más grande del mundo _____   g. Alaska

8. el océano más grande del mundo _____   h. China

9. el océano más pequeño del mundo _____   i. Salto del Angel

10. el estado más grande de Estados Unidos _____   j. Rusia

8-21   México Lindo. Antonio is a writer for a popular food magazine. Each week he selects a restaurant and writes a review in the magazine. Complete Antonio's excerpt with the appropriate words and then answer the question that follows.

buenísimo	fresquísimos	grandísimas
las más caras	las mejores	la mejor

Queridos lectores. Ayer comí en el restaurante México Lindo. En este restaurante sirven (1) _____ comida mexicana de la ciudad. Los vegetales son (2) _____ y los sirven con una salsa deliciosa. El queso es (3) _____, especialmente con los tacos y las fajitas. Las tortillas son (4) _____ de la ciudad. Las quesadillas de pollo son (5) _____, pero son tan buenas que no importa pagar un poco más. Es mejor pedir un plato solamente porque las porciones son (6) _____.

7. De acuerdo con el artículo de Antonio, el restaurante México Lindo:
   a. no es recomendable porque es muy caro y la comida no es buena.
   b. es un restaurante excelente, donde sirven comida mexicana exquisita.
   c. es un restaurante bueno, pero lo mejor es que la comida es muy barata.

8-22   Isabel, Juan y Felipe. Isabel, Juan, and Felipe live in the same apartment complex. They have all applied for a job as a lifeguard, but only one position is open. You are in charge of evaluating their physical condition and reporting to your boss. Look at the chart below and write sentences to compare them and report who is the tallest, who is in the best physical condition, and so on.

	JUAN	FELIPE	ISABEL
Edad	22 años	39 años	19 años
Estatura	1 m 85 cm	1 m 72 cm	1 m 55 cm
Peso	72 kilos	61 kilos	48 kilos
Condición física general	buena	muy buena	excelente

MODELO: Isabel/edad: *Isabel es la más joven.* OR *Isabel es la menor.*

1. Felipe/edad _____

2. Juan/estatura _____

3. Isabel/estatura _____

4. Juan/peso _____

5. Isabel/peso _____

6. Isabel/condición física _____

Based on the information above, who do you think should get the job?

a. Juan   b. Felipe   c. Isabel

MOSAICOS

8-23 Antes de leer. Primera fase. ¿Fiesta o no? Indicate whether each of the following occasions is a holiday.

      sí   no

1. Nochebuena _____
2. Nochevieja _____
3. Día de la Independencia _____
4. Pascua de Resurrección _____
5. Aniversario de matrimonio _____
6. Día de los Enamorados _____
7. Día de Acción de Gracias _____
8. Navidad _____
9. Año Nuevo _____
10. Día de la Madre _____
11. Januká _____
12. Día de las Brujas _____
13. Ramadán _____
14. Día de los Muertos _____

Segunda fase. ¿Religiosa, secular o personal? Indicate whether each of these events is a religious, secular, or personal celebration.

	RELIGIOSO	SECULAR	PERSONAL
1. Nochebuena			
2. Navidad			
3. Nochevieja			
4. Año Nuevo			
5. Día de la Independencia			
6. Pascua de Resurrección			
7. Aniversario de matrimonio			
8. Día de la Madre			
9. Januká			
10. Día de las Brujas			
11. Día de los Enamorados			
12. Día de Acción de Gracias			
13. Día de los Muertos			
14. Ramadán			

Nombre: _____   Fecha: _____

8-24   A leer. Fiestas de México. Now read these paragraphs about Mexican holidays and answer the questions that follow.

Sin duda México es un país con una naturaleza privilegiada. Si a eso agregamos el carácter amigable de los mexicanos y el gran número de fiestas y celebraciones locales y nacionales, tenemos la imagen de una nación con una riqueza humana y cultural extraordinaria.

En México hay muchos días festivos en los cuales se rinde (*pay*) homenaje a figuras históricas nacionales como a Benito Juárez, el 21 de marzo, o a santos, como en la celebración de San Antonio Abad, el 17 de enero. También se realizan procesiones religiosas de diversos santos o de la Virgen. Un ejemplo es la visita a la Basílica de la Virgen de Guadalupe, el 12 de diciembre.

Otro ejemplo de la religiosidad del pueblo mexicano es la celebración del Día de los Muertos. Esta ocasión fusiona (*mixes*) creencias precolombinas con ritos católicos. La Navidad se celebra el 25 de diciembre, igual que en el resto del mundo cristiano. Sin embargo (*However*), las Posadas son las festividades religiosas más interesantes. Del 16 al 23 de diciembre, los mexicanos celebran las Posadas, representaciones (*performances*) de la peregrinación de José y María hacia Belén. El 6 de enero, día de la Epifanía, se celebra el día de los Santos Reyes. Ese día los niños mexicanos reciben regalos de los tres Reyes Magos (*Wise*).

Otra festividad de gran interés, tanto (*both*) para niños como (*and*) para adultos, son las famosas Pastorelas, la expresión más antigua del teatro mexicano. En éstas la figura del diablo adquiere especial relevancia en las magníficas representaciones en plazas públicas, teatros y otros escenarios (*venues*).

México, además de (*besides*) ser un país muy católico, es una nación de grandes tradiciones históricas. Por ejemplor, el 5 de Mayo, los mexicanos celebran su triunfo sobre los franceses en la batalla de Puebla (1862). El 16 de septiembre, el Día de la Independencia mexicana, conmemora el día en que su héroe nacional, Miguel Hidalgo, "dio" el Grito de Dolores.

Todas estas ocasiones son invitaciones para aprender y disfrutar de la herencia histórico-cultural del país.

Indique:

1. dos festividades religiosas y la fecha de celebración.

   _____

2. una festividad en la que se fusionan costumbres europeas e indígenas.

   _____

3. una festividad de tipo artístico y el lugar donde se celebra.

   _____

4. dos festividades históricas de México y la fecha de celebración.

   _____

8-25   Después de leer. Tradiciones familiares. Describe two of your favorite family
traditions for each of the following holidays.

1. el Día de Año Nuevo

   _____

   _____

2. El Día de la Independencia

   _____

   _____

3. El Día de Acción de Gracias

   _____

   _____

8-26   Antes de escribir. Las fiestas. Complete the following chart with information about your favorite holiday.

Nombre de la fiesta	
Tipo de fiesta (religiosa, secular, personal)	
Qué se celebra	
Cuándo se celebra	
Cómo se celebra	

8-27   A escribir. De fiesta. Think of the last time you celebrated your favorite holiday. Who was there? Did you follow all the family traditions? Did you do something different? Write a paragraph describing the celebration. (If necessary consult your textbook to review the guidelines on how to narrate a story.)

_____

_____

_____

_____

_____

_____

Nombre: _____   Fecha: _____

_____

_____

_____

_____

_____

_____

_____

_____

_____

_____

_____

_____

_____

_____

_____

_____

8-28   **Después de escribir. Una nueva tración familiar.** If you could invent a holiday, what would it be? Write a paragraph describing the name of the holiday, the type of holiday it is, and what, when, and how it should be celebrated.

_____

_____

_____

_____

_____

_____

_____

ENFOQUE CULTURAL

8-29   **Primera fase. Tradiciones hispanas.** Indicate whether each of the following statements is **cierto (C)** or **falso (F)** according to the information in the **Enfoque cultural** on pages 311–316 in your textbook and the reading about Mexico in exercise 8-24.

1. _____ En México y Guatemala se celebran muchas fiestas de carácter religioso.

2. _____ La Quema de Diablo es parte de la tradición del Día de los Muertos en México.

3. _____ La fiesta religiosa más importante en Venezuela es la Navidad.

4. _____ En Guatemala en la Pascua de Resurrección, se celebran procesiones religiosas.

5. _____ En Guatemala y México se celebran las Posadas.

Segunda fase. ¿Qué sabe usted de México y Guatemala? There is much more to Mexico and Guatemala than their holidays. Complete this paragraph with the correct information about the two countries.

La Ciudad de México es una de las ciudades más grandes del mundo. Cuando hablan de su capital, muchos mexicanos usan la expresión Distrito Federal o (1) _____. La segunda ciudad más importante de México es (2) _____. Esta ciudad es el lugar de origen de los grupos musicales más populares de México, los (3) _____. En México también existen muchas ruinas mayas, como las ciudades de Chichén Itza y Uxmal, que se encuentran en la península de (4) _____.

El clima de Guatemala es muy agradable, y por eso llaman a este país la tierra de la eterna primavera. Su capital, la Ciudad de Guatemala, tiene museos muy interesantes. En Chichicastenango tiene lugar, dos veces a la semana, uno de los más famosos (5) _____ de artesanías del mundo. En Guatemala, al igual que en México, hay numerosas ruinas mayas. La más importante es (6) _____, la ciudad más grande de la civilización maya que se ha descubierto.

A PRIMERA VISTA

8-30 **Fiestas tradicionales hispanas.** Think about some of the popular Hispanic celebrations you have learned about. Can you recall details such as what they commemorate and what happens? You will hear some Hispanic people describing a few of those celebrations. Listen to the descriptions and match them with a celebration.

1. _____   a. la Nochebuena

2. _____   b. el Día de los Muertos

3. _____   c. el Día de la Independencia

4. _____   d. la Semana Santa

5. _____   e. el Carnaval

8-31 **Otras fiestas populares.** Now think about popular celebrations and holidays in North America. Listen to some people who are planning for those celebrations, can you identify them? Write the name of the celebration they are preparing for. Do not forget to include the definite article (el/la) in your answer.

1. _____   4. _____

2. _____   5. _____

3. _____

8-32 **De vacaciones en Mexico.** Both Ramón and Anita have recently vacationed in Mexico and had different experiences: one stayed with a Mexican family while the other went to the beach on a family trip. Listen to their phone conversation once for the gist, and select the answers for questions 1 through 3.

Then look at questions 4 through 8. Try to answer them by recalling the conversation you just heard. Listen to Ramón and Anita again, concentrating on the information you need to answer the remaining questions.

1. ¿Quién visitó a una familia mexicana?
   a. Ramón   b. Anita   c. Ramón y Anita

2. ¿Quién fue a la playa con su familia?
   a. Ramón   b. Anita   c. Ramón y Anita

3. ¿Cómo se llama la fiesta en la que participó Anita?
   a. el Día de los Muertos   b. el Día de la Independencia   c. la charreada

4. ¿Qué ciudad mexicana visitó Anita?

    a. Cancún   b. Acapulco   c. Guadalajara

5. ¿Qué tipo de música había en la fiesta en que Anita participó?

    a. mariachis   b. músicas indígenas   c. música moderna

6. ¿Qué es la charreada?

    a. un baile   b. una comida tradicional   c. un espectáculo

7. ¿Qué hacen los charros?

    a. tocan instrumentos musicales   b. hacen bailes folclóricos   c. participan en un rodeo

8. ¿Qué complementos del traje charro le gustan a Anita?

    a. sus grandes cinturones   b. sus sombreros coloridos   c. sus botas decoradas

8-33   Un día especial. Anita has also learned about other types of celebrations in Mexico and Hispanic countries, and now Ramón is asking about them. First look at Anita's answers to Ramón, which are listed below. Try to guess what type of celebration they are discussing. Then listen to Ramón's questions and match them with Anita's answers.

_____ 1. Son las personas que acompañan al novio y a la novia. Normalmente son el padre de la novia y la madre del novio, pero pueden ser otros parientes o buenos amigos.

_____ 2. Generalmente hay una recepción con comida, bebida y música de una orquesta o mariachis.

_____ 3. Generalmente las celebran en la iglesia porque la mayoría de los mexicanos son católicos.

_____ 4. La familia y los amigos, y a veces tienen otros invitados como compañeros de trabajo, etcétera.

_____ 5. Sí, los padres de los novios las envían para anunciar el día y el lugar de la ceremonia.

EXPLICACIÓN Y EXPANSIÓN

1. The imperfect

8-34   Cuando iba a la escuela. Listen to Silvia talk about her days as a schoolgirl. Decide whether each statement refers to an event that happened repeatedly or habitually (**acción habitual**), an event that was in progress in the past (**acción en progreso**) or a description of characteristics or conditions in the past (**descripción**).

	ACCIÓN HABITUAL	ACCIÓN EN PROGRESO	DESCRIPCIÓN
1.			
2.			
3.			
4.			
5.			

2. Imperfect of regular and irregular verbs

8-35   En la secundaria. Silvia is now reminiscing about her high school days and the things she and other people used to do. Listen to her and select her subject: Silvia herself (**yo**), her friend Raquel (**ella**), all the students (**nosotros**), or the teachers (**ellos**). Remember that **yo** and **él/ella/usted** have the same form, so you will need to pay attention to the context or any pronouns mentioned to avoid ambiguity.

	SILVIA (YO)	RAQUEL (ELLA)	LOS ESTUDIANTES (NOSOTROS)	LOS PROFESORES (ELLOS)
1.				
2.				
3.				
4.				
5.				
6.				

8-36   La universidad es diferente. Silvia and Raquel have finished college now, and they are comparing the experience to high school. Can you anticipate some of the similarities or differences they might mention?

First read the statements below. Then listen to the conversation between the two friends. Indicate whether each of the following statements is **Cierto** or **Falso**. Finally, correct the false statements to make them true.

	SÍ	NO
1. Caminaban a la universidad. _____		
2. En la secundaria hacían mucha tarea. _____		
3. En la universidad estudiaban en la biblioteca. _____		
4. En la secundaria los horarios eran flexibles. _____		
5. En la secundaria había más clases interesantes. _____		
6. Iban a más fiestas en la universidad. _____		
7. En la secundaria y en la universidad se divertían. _____		

Now think about your own experience and write about something you used to do in high school that you liked and something that you did not like.

_____

_____

8-37   Ahora y antes. Many things may have changed in your routine since childhood, but some things are probably similar. Listen to the statements and respond, stating whether each is true for you, as in the model.

MODELO: You hear: Ahora los niños tienen mucha tarea.
You say: *Yo también tenía mucha tarea.* OR *Yo no tenía mucha tarea.*

1. _____

2. _____

3. _____

4. _____

5. _____

3. The preterit and the imperfect

8-38   ¿Sabes qué le pasó a Margarita? Some days everything seems to go wrong. Estrella, Margarita's sister, is telling you about what caused her sister to be late for work. Anticipate common situations that may delay someone. Then listen to Estrella's story once for the gist. Note how she uses both the imperfect and the preterit to narrate what happened to Margarita.

Now listen to the story again and categorize each event mentioned as a completed action (**acción completa**), a habitual action (**acción habitual**), or background information (**descripción/situación**).

MODELO: You see: salir para la oficina
You hear: Cuando mi hermana Margarita salió para la oficina...
You choose "**a**" because Margarita's act of "leaving for the office" in this story was a completed action.

a. acción completa   b. acción habitual   c. descripción/situación

1. llover mucho _____

2. hacer frío _____

3. ir a la oficina a las ocho de la mañana _____

4. recibir una llamada de una amiga _____

5. usar transporte público _____

6. estar preocupada _____

7. ver (que un auto...) _____

8. (Pamela) trabajar en su edificio _____

9. haber mucho tráfico _____

10. llegar media hora tarde _____

8-39   ¿Y sabes qué me pasó a mí? Another friend, Álvaro, is listening to Estrella's story, and he tells you of a similar experience he had recently. Read his story below and try to understand what happened, despite the verbs in infinitive form.

Now, keeping in mind the context, decide whether the verbs refer to completed events, events in progress, or background information. Based on your assessment, complete the story with appropriate forms of the imperfect or the preterit.

After you finish listen to Álvaro to check your predictions and make any necessary changes.

El lunes yo también tuve un mal día. Cuando (1. despertar) por la mañana todo parecía normal. En realidad (2. ser) un día muy bonito: (3. hacer) buen tiempo, y no (4. haber) nubes. (5. Mirar) mi reloj: (6. ser) las ocho de la mañana. (7. Levantarme) y (8. ir) al baño. Mientras (9. bañarme) el agua caliente se terminó. ¡Qué frío! (10. Ir) a la cocina para tomar el desayuno; (11. tener) cereales pero no (12. haber) leche, así que no (13. tomar) nada. Después de vestirme (14. ver) que la camisa (15. estar) sucia y tuve que buscar otra rápidamente. Finalmente (16. salir) de casa y (17. tomar) el autobús. (18. Haber) pocas personas en los pasillos de la facultad, y me pareció extraño. Al entrar en la cafetería para desayunar (19. ver) el reloj: no (20. ser) las nueve menos cuarto sino las ocho menos cuarto! Esa noche empezó el horario de invierno, y yo no había cambiado la hora en mi reloj.

1. a. me desperté	b. me despertaba	11. a. tuve	b. tenía
2. a. fue	b. era	12. a. hubo	b. había
3. a. hizo	b. hacía	13. a. tomé	b. tomaba
4. a. hubo	b. había	14. a. vi	b. veía
5. a. Miré	b. Miraba	15. a. estuvo	b. estaba
6. a. fueron	b. eran	16. a. salí	b. salía
7. a. Me levanté	b. Me levantaba	17. a. tomé	b. tomaba
8. a. fui	b. iba	18. a. Hubo	b. Había
9. a. me bañé	b. me bañaba	19. a. vi	b. veía
10. a. Fui	b. Iba	20. a. fueron	b. eran

4. Comparisons of inequality

8-40   **Preparativos de boda.** Amelia and Javier are planning their wedding day, and they need to finalize the arrangements today so that everything will be ready. As their good friend, you are helping them get this done.

First they want to decide on a restaurant for the reception. Javier is still a bit confused, so Amelia has drawn a chart with the important details.

	RESTAURANTE Miramar	*RESTAURANTE* París	*RESTAURANTE* Torres las
Precio por persona	50 pesos	53 pesos	58 pesos
Camareros	17	15	20
Menú	Bueno	Muy bueno	Excelente
Espacio	Grande	Pequeño	Muy grande

Listen to Javier and let him know whether his understanding is **Cierto** or **Falso**. If he is not right, correct his statement based on the information in the chart.

	CIERTO	**FALSO**	
1.			_____
2.			_____
3.			_____
4.			_____
5.			_____

8-41   **La luna de miel.** Amelia and Javier have to decide on their honeymoon too. They are going to Cozumel, and they have a choice between two hotels. Look at Amelia's chart and listen to her comment on the different hotels. Indicate the hotel she is discussing in each statement.

MODELO: You hear: Este hotel es más barato que ese.
                You say and write: *Es el Hotel Miramar.*

	HOTEL MIRAMAR	HOTEL SOL
Número de habitaciones	135	280
Precio por noche	10.000 pesos	17.000 pesos
Restaurantes	1 restaurante, 1 bar	2 restaurantes, 1 cafetería
Piscinas	2 piscinas	3 piscinas
Servicios	gimnasio	gimnasio, salón de belleza, masajes
Calidad (quality)	***	*****

1. _____
2. _____
3. _____
4. _____
5. _____

8-42   La música. Amelia and Javier are counting on you to help them choose the music for the reception. You have gathered information about two choices: Orquesta Celeste and Mariachi Veracruz. Listen to your friends' questions and respond, both orally and in writing.

MODELO: You hear: ¿Qué grupo tiene menos músicos?
           You say and write: *El Mariachi Veracruz tiene menos músicos que la Orquesta Celeste.*

	ORQUESTA CELESTE	MARIACHI VERACRUZ
Precio	60.000 pesos	45.000 pesos
Calidad	excelente	bueno
Número de músicos	7 personas: 5 músicos, 2 cantantes	4 músicos
Número de canciones (songs)	20 canciones	12 canciones

1. _____
2. _____
3. _____
4. _____

5. Comparisons of equality

8-43   ¡Son diferentes! Your friend misjudges Guillermo and Héctor: she thinks they are very similar. Listen to her statements and indicate whether she is right (**Sí**) or not (**No**). Then correct her incorrect statements to make them true.

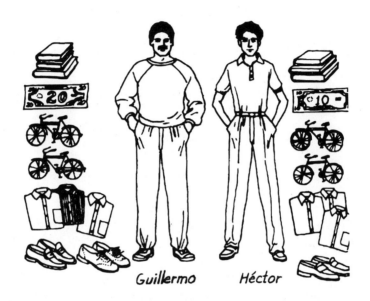

Guillermo   Héctor

MODELO: You hear: Héctor tiene tanto dinero como Guillermo.
          You select: No
          You say and write: *Héctor tiene más dinero que Guillermo.*

	SÍ	NO	
1.			_____
2.			_____
3.			_____
4.			_____
5.			_____
6.			_____

8-44   ¡Yolanda también! You and some other friends who like music want to form a band, but you still need another female singer. One of the members wants Lucía to join the band, but you think your friend Yolanda is as good a choice and should be considered. Listen to the arguments he offers for Lucía, and tell him Yolanda can do the same.

MODELO: You hear: Lucía tiene mucho tiempo para practicar.
           You say and write: *Yolanda tiene tanto tiempo para practicar como Lucía.*

1. _____

2. _____

3. _____

4. _____

5. _____

8-45   ¿Y usted, qué opina? Listen to the statements about a number of famous people, and express who is comparable in your opinion.

MODELO: You hear: Madonna es muy creativa.
           You say and write: *Sí, pero Prince es tan creativo como Madonna.*

1. _____

2. _____

3. _____

4. _____

5. _____

6. The superlative

8-46 **¡Mucho más!** Your friends and you are talking about your favorite things at school: classes, professors, and so on. You are really excited about everything! Listen to your friends and agree with them, emphasizing your response with the superlative, as in the model.

MODELO: You hear: La clase de historia es muy interesante.
         You say and write: *Sí, la clase de historia es interesantísima.*

1. _____

2. _____

3. _____

4. _____

5. _____

8-47 **Una encuesta.** A student organization has carried out a survey of students' opinions on their professors. Listen to the summary of the survey and mark the results in the chart below. Note that not all categories will be checked.

	POPULAR + −	ARROGANTE + −	INTELIGENTE + −	SIMPÁTICO + −	BUENO + −
Vega					
Sánchez					
Muñoz					
Domínguez					
Bernal					
Tejada					

8-48   ¿Y en su universidad? Now it is your turn to share your opinions about your own experience. Listen to the questions and answer both orally and in writing.

1. _____

2. _____

3. _____

4. _____

5. _____

6. _____

MOSAICOS

8-49   La historia de mi mamá. Many Hispanics in the United States and Canada still celebrate Hispanic festivities or experience celebrations with a Hispanic flavor. If you come from a bicultural background, you may have a similar experience; otherwise you may have a friend who does. Recall examples of celebrations with a different cultural influence that you have enjoyed or heard about.

You will listen to José talk about celebrating a Hispanic Christmas. Listen once to get the gist. Then listen again, paying attention to whether José is describing the situation, the background, or the actions that were in progress. Finally, complete the following statements with an appropriate imperfect or preterit form of the verb in parentheses.

1. La mamá de José _____ a San Antonio cuando _____ joven. (llegar, ser)

2. _____ allí sólo cuatro meses; después _____ a Iowa. (vivir, irse)

3. Allí _____ con el papá de José, y ellos _____ dos hijos. (casarse, tener)

4. Todos los años _____ la Navidad juntos, y _____ una cena tradicional mexicana. (celebrar, tener)

5. José y su hermana siempre _____ regalos dos veces. (recibir)

Lección 9

El trabajo

A PRIMERA VISTA

9-1   **¿Dónde trabajan?** Every occupation takes you to a different workplace. Look at the following occupations and indicate where these people work.

1. _____ cajero   a. en un laboratorio

2. _____ científico   b. en una limosina

3. _____ enfermera   c. en un banco

4. _____ chofer   d. en una tienda

5. _____ dependienta   e. en un hospital

6. _____ mujer de negocios   f. en una oficina

9-2   **¿A qué se dedica?** Isidro is telling you about what his friends do for a living. Write the name of the profession next to each statement.

1. Ernesto ayuda a las personas con problemas psicológicos y de comprensión humana.

    _____

2. Erica defiende a las personas con problemas legales enfrente del juez.

    _____

3. Sergio repara electrodomésticos.

    _____

4. Mario actúa en películas o en la televisión.

    _____

5. José repara el fregadero, el lavabo y el inodoro.

    _____

9-3   ¡Ayuda! Read these people's problems and tell them what professional they need to call to solve the situation.

1. Me acabo de despertar, y hay un incendio en la casa de enfrente. _____

2. Hay mucha agua en el piso de mi cuarto y del baño. _____

3. Mi pelo está demasiado (*too*) largo y no tiene forma. _____

4. Hoy tengo que entrevistar a alguien que no sabe español ni inglés. _____

5. Estoy en una tienda de ropa, y quiero pagar. _____

6. Tengo muchos problemas con el IRS. _____

9-4   Su trabajo ideal. A reporter from the school newspaper is writing an article on ideal jobs for college students, and he has asked to interview you about the ideal post-graduation job. Answer the reporter's questions so that he can write his article.

PERIODISTA: ¿Cómo es su trabajo?

USTED: _____

PERIODISTA: ¿A qué hora va a llegar al trabajo?

USTED: _____

PERIODISTA: ¿A qué hora va a salir del trabajo, probablemente?

USTED: _____

PERIODISTA: ¿Cuántas personas trabajan allí?

USTED: _____

PERIODISTA: ¿Qué va a hacer en su trabajo?

USTED: _____

PERIODISTA: ¿Cuál es su sueldo?

USTED: _____

PERIODISTA: Muchas gracias por la entrevista.

EXPLICACIÓN Y EXPANSIÓN

Síntesis gramatical

1. Se + verb constructions

Se + **usted, él, ella** verb form + *singular noun*
Se necesita un vendedor. *A salesman is needed.*

Se + **ustedes, ellos, ellas** verb form + *plural noun*
Se necesitan unos vendedores. *Salesmen are needed.*

Se + **usted, él, ella** verb form
Se trabaja mucho en esta oficina. *One/You work(s) a lot in this office.*
Se dice que recibió un aumento. *They/People say that he got a raise.*

---

2. More on the preterit and the imperfect

Verbs whose meaning in English depends on whether the Spanish preterit or imperfect is used: **saber, querer, conocer, poder**

Expressing intentions in the past: imperfect of **ir** + **a** + infinitive
   Iba a salir, pero era tarde. *She was going to go out, but it was late.*

Imperfect progressive: imperfect of **estar** + present participle (**-ando** or **-iendo**)
   El secretario **estaba hablando** con un cliente. *The secretary was talking to a client.*

---

3. Direct and indirect object pronouns

Ella me dio la solicitud. *She gave me the application.*

Ella **me la** dio. *She gave it to me.*

4. Formal commands

		USTED	USTEDES	
hablar:	hablo	hable	hablen	*speak*
comer:	como	coma	coman	*eat*
escribir:	escribo	escriba	escriban	*write*

---

1. *Se* + verb constructions

9-5   ¡Mmm, qué rico! Miami is famous for its variety of Latin food. Numerous restaurants serve many delicious plates. Indicate the best way to complete each of the following sentences.

1. En la cafetería cubana se venden...
   a. café cubano   b. pastelitos   c. arroz con pollo

2. En el restaurante La Carreta, se come...
   a. comida latina   b. hamburguesas   c. papas fritas

3. En el restaurante Delicias de España, se preparan...
   a. langosta   b. paella   c. mariscos

4. En los restaurantes puertorriqueños siempre se sirven...
   a. arroz con gandules   b. camarones al ajillo   c. caldo de pollo con mofongo

5. En el restaurante chileno se prepara...
   a. empanadas   b. pastel de choclo   c. mariscos

9-6   ¿Qué se hace? Indicate what people in the following workplaces do on the job.

hacer experimentos	escribir noticias
guardar dinero	cocinar platos exquisitos
preparar informes	vender ropa

1. en la cocina de un restaurante: _____

2. en una oficina: _____

3. en un periódico: _____

4. en una tienda: _____

5. en un banco: _____

6. en un laboratorio: _____

9-7 **Los anuncios.** You are an intern at the newspaper *El Mercurio* in Chile, and you are in charge of organizing the ad section. You have received several ads, but no one has written a heading for their ad. Write a heading for each of these ads using the passive **se.**

MODELO: *Se alquila una casa*

LIQUIDADORA
vende a precios bajísimos material
deportivo
(patines, raquetas y pelotas de tenis)
San Francisco 749, 5541956

1. _____

CICO LTDA., vende oficina
52 m alfombrada,
dividida en dos ambientes
20 millones
Paseo Bulnes 1395, 695 7878

2. _____

TÉCNICOS REPARAN

electrodomésticos:
refrigeradores, congeladores, estufas,
lavaplatos, lavadoras, secadoras
Teléfono 5542012

3. _____

VENDO COMPUTADORA

Compatible IBM,
Pentium III, 20 GB
Pantalla color
5577842

4. _____

LAVAMOS ALFOMBRAS

Trabajo garantizado.
2747483

5. _____

9-8   En mi casa. Write a paragraph to a friend, describing your family's general habits. Use the "se pasivo" with at least six of the expressions from the list and any you wish to add.

poner la televisión	ver una película
llamar al médico	celebrar fiestas
comprar el periódico	ir al mercado
cenar	limpiar la casa
sacar la basura	recoger las hojas
lavar el auto	cortar el césped

MODELO: *En mi casa se almuerza a la una de la tarde.*

_____

_____

_____

_____

_____

_____

2. More on the preterit and the imperfect

9-9   El accidente. Primera fase. Josefina went to Santiago last year in an exchange program. Complete the following statements about her life in Santiago.

1. Cuando Josefina estudiaba en Santiago _____, un centro de esquí cerca de la capital.
   a. quería ir a Portillo   b. quiso ir a Portillo   c. quiere ir a Portillo

2. Josefina _____ a Juan Manuel en su primer día en Santiago.
   a. conocía   b. conoció   c. conoce

3. Juan Manuel tuvo un accidente, y Josefina se enteró cuando una amiga la _____.
   a. llamaba   b. llama   c. llamó

4. Josefina _____ la dirección del hospital.
   a. supo   b. sabía   c. sabe

5. Josefina tenía muchos amigos que _____ allí.
   a. trabajaban   b. trabajaron   c. trabajan

Segunda fase. Now answer the following questions about what happened to Josefina and Juan Manuel.

1. ¿Quién tuvo un accidente?
   a. Josefina   b. Juan Manuel   c. una amiga de Josefina

2. ¿Conocía Josefina el hospital?
   a. sí   b. no

3. ¿Qué tipo de accidente fue?
   a. de esquí   b. no sabemos

9-10   ¿Qué tiene la vecina? The paramedics took your neighbor away in an ambulance. A policeman is asking her daughter, who was at the house, what happened. Complete their conversation with the appropriate preterit or imperfect form of the verb.

estar	empezar	decir	ser
poder	deber	abrir	entrar

POLICÍA: ¿Qué hora era cuando usted llegó a la casa de su madre?

HIJA: (1) _____ las siete más o menos cuando llegué.

POLICÍA: ¿Quién le abrió la puerta?

HIJA: Mi mamá me (2) _____ la puerta.

POLICÍA: ¿Ella le dijo algo?

HIJA: Primero no me (3) _____ una palabra.

POLICÍA: ¿Por qué?

AMIGA: Porque (4) _____ llorando.

POLICÍA: ¿Qué pasó después?

HIJA: Mi mamá me dijo, "Me siento muy mal. Llama a los paramédicos".

POLICÍA: ¿Y qué hizo usted?

HIJA: (5) _____ en la casa y llamé a los paramédicos.

POLICÍA: ¿Qué pasó después?

HIJA: Cuando mi mamá llegó al hospital (6) _____ muy débil.

POLICÍA: ¡Oh!

HIJA: Casi no (7) _____ respirar.

POLICÍA: ¿Qué hicieron los médicos?

HIJA: Los médicos le dieron una medicina y le dijeron que (8) _____ descansar.

POLICÍA: ¿Cómo está su madre ahora?

HIJA: Bien, gracias a Dios, está bien. Ayer por la tarde ya (*already*) (9) _____ a sentirse mucho mejor. Sólo necesita descansar.

10. Which of these sentences best summarizes the situation described?

    a. La señora Ruiz tuvo un accidente muy grave y está en situación crítica en el hospital.

    b. La señora Ruiz se encontraba mal, pero con medicina y descanso ya está mejor.

    c. La señora Ruiz se cayó en su casa y se rompió una pierna. En el hospital los médicos le dieron medicina, y ya está mejor.

9-11   Su niñez. Remember when you were a child? Complete these sentences and then indicate how often you used to do the following activities.

     a. siempre   b. frecuentemente   c. a veces   d. nunca

1. _____ música. _____

2. _____ de vacaciones con mis padres. _____

3. _____ los dibujos animados (*cartoons*) en la televisión. _____

4. _____ en restaurantes. _____

5. _____ a los videojuegos. _____

3. Direct and indirect object pronouns

9-12   ¿Quién lo hace? Read the following conversations and answer the questions about each dialog in complete sentences using the appropriate object pronouns.

MODELO:

      ANA: Hola. Tengo la gripe. Me siento fatal.

ROBERTO: Lo siento. ¿Puedo hacer algo por ti?

      ANA: Necesito un pañuelo; ¿alguien tiene uno?

     LUIS: Yo no, lo siento.

ROBERTO: Sí, toma. Aquí lo tienes.

¿Quién le da el pañuelo a Ana? *Roberto se lo da.*

    MAMÁ: Juan, ¡saca al perro!

    JUAN: Ahora no puedo. Tengo que hacer la tarea.

    MAMÁ: Bueno, termina la tarea y después sacas al perro.

    JUAN: Bien, Mamá.

1. ¿Quién saca el perro? _____

MANOLO: Hola, Patricia. ¿Quieres ir al concierto de U2?

PATRICIA: ¿Vas a ir?

MANOLO: No. Tengo dos entradas, pero no puedo ir porque tengo que trabajar.

RICARDO: Yo también tengo una entrada para el concierto.

MANOLO: ¿Quieres las entradas Patricia?

PATRICIA: Sí, claro. Muchísimas gracias.

RICARDO: ¡Qué bien! Así puedes venir conmigo.

PATRICIA: Lo siento, Ricardo, voy a ir con mi novio.

2. ¿Quién le da las entradas a Patricia? _____

MARCELO: Hola, chicas. Estoy vendiendo mi auto.

SANDRA: Yo estoy buscando uno.

VIRGINIA: Yo también. ¿Qué auto es?

MARCELO: Es éste: un Camaro del 99 de color rojo. Está como nuevo.

SANDRA: Me encanta. ¿Cuánto pides?

MARCELO: $10.000

VIRGINIA: ¡Oh! me encantan los Camaros, pero no tengo tanto dinero.

SANDRA: Me parece un precio excelente. Ese auto tiene que ser para mí.

3. ¿Quién le compra el carro a Marcelo? _____

MARTA: Felicidades, Andrea. Gracias por invitarme a tu fiesta de cumpleaños.

ANDREA: De nada. Espero que te diviertas.

LORENA: Gracias por invitarme a mí también.

ANDREA: Gracias por venir.

MARTA: Tengo un regalo para ti. Aquí lo tienes.

ANDREA: Es una billetera, la que yo quería. Muchas gracias. Es preciosa.

LORENA: Yo también tengo un regalo.

ANDREA: ¡Ah! Dos discos compactos de REM. Estupendo, me encantan. Gracias a las dos.

4. ¿Quién le regala a Andrea la billetera? _____

5. ¿Quién le regala a Andrea los CDs? _____

9-13 Viaje de negocios. Your boss is going on a business trip and has asked you to prepare certain things. He is just about to leave and is double checking that you did everything necessary. Reassure your boss by letting him know you did all the things he asked.

MODELO: ¿Me preparó el informe de gastos? *Sí, se lo preparé.*

1. ¿Nos compró el boleto de avión a mí y a mi secretaria personal? _____

_____

2. ¿Me preparó la presentación? _____

3. ¿Nos hizo las reservaciones en el hotel? _____

4. ¿Le trajo Alfonso los informes a usted? _____

5. ¿Le di yo a usted el número de teléfono del presidente de la compañía? _____

_____

9-14 ¿Qué me recomiendas? Your brother has just started this semester at your college, and he has many questions about campus life. Answer your brother's questions, using direct object pronouns.

1. ¿Me recomiendas a tu profesor de español?

_____

2. ¿Me recomiendas la cafetería de la universidad?

_____

3. ¿Me recomiendas el gimnasio de la universidad?

_____

4. ¿Me recomiendas los grupos de estudio para la clase de biología?

_____

5. ¿Me recomiendas las fiestas de las fraternidades?

_____

6. ¿Me recomiendas la profesión de abogado?

_____

4. Formal commands

9-15   ¿Qué hago? Read the following statements and indicate the most logical answer for each situation.

1. Un arquitecto tiene que mandar un proyecto a casa de un cliente. Habla con el dibujante (*draftsman*) que está haciéndolo y le dice:
   a. Termine hoy.   b. Compre la casa.   c. No venga mañana.

2. Juan tiene mucha sed. Ve a un hombre que vende bebidas y le dice:
   a. Déme su camisa.   b. Déme agua.   c. Déme dinero.

3. Los sobrinos de Carlota están jugando en la sala de Carlota. Carlota tiene unos objetos antiguos muy caros, y los niños están corriendo por la sala. Carlota les dice:
   a. Tomen el helado aquí. b. Cierren la puerta.   c. No jueguen aquí.

4. Amanda va a entrevistar a una persona que quiere trabajar en su empresa. Cuando el entrevistado llega Amanda lo saluda y le dice:
   a. Abra la ventana.   b. Siéntese, por favor.   c. No trabaje más.

5. El profesor de literatura de Erica da tarea todos los días. Al terminar la clase dice:
   a. Hagan la tarea.   b. No hablen.   c. Cambien los libros.

9-16   En la oficina. A new person in your office does not know what to do. Your boss asks you to help him. Answer your coworker's questions by using formal commands.

1. ¿Debo estudiar para la presentación de la empresa?
   a. Sí, estudió.   b. Sí, estudie.   c. Sí, estudiaré.

2. ¿Compro todos estos materiales en la papelería?
   a. No los compre.   b. Los compraré.   c. Los va a comprar.

3. López y yo vamos a ver al cliente. ¿Recogemos el contrato en la oficina esta tarde?
   a. Lo recogeremos.   b. Lo recogíamos.   c. Sí, recójanlo.

4. ¿Hago las fotocopias de los contratos?
   a. Sí, las hace.   b. Sí, hágalas.   c. Sí, las hacía.

5. ¿Preparo el informe para la firma del contrato?
   a. No, no lo prepare.   b. No, no lo preparó.   c. No, no lo preparaba.

9-17   Consejos. You are working for a radio program, and you have to answer callers' questions and give them advice. Advise the following people who have called you.

1. Estoy un poco gordo. Quiero perder peso, pero no me gusta correr ni hacer ejercicio fuerte.
   a. Camine por las mañanas.   b. Nadas en la piscina.   c. Hace dieta.

2. No tengo muchos amigos, y me aburro mucho en las fiestas.
   a. Bailas en todas las fiestas.   c. Hable con todas las personas.
   b. Inviten a una chica especial.

3. Quiero encontrar un buen trabajo después de graduarme.
   a. Estudias mucho.   c. Compra un traje elegante para las entrevistas.
   b. Saque buenas notas.

4. Tengo problema con mi clase de matemáticas: estudio mucho pero siempre suspendo.
   a. Busque un tutor.   c. Va a las horas de oficina del profesor.
   b. Vas a un grupo de estudio.

5. Mi esposo y yo tenemos muchos problemas. No puedo hablar con él porque siempre discutimos.
   a. Le pides el divorcio.   c. Vayan a un consejero matrimonial.
   b. Habla con él de sus problemas.

9-18   Por favor. While you and your parents are on vacation, you will have someone house sit for you. Your mother asks you to write instructions on what to do. Write five commands to the house sitter.

MODELO: *Abra las ventanas por la mañana.*
             Active la alarma de la casa por las noches.

1. _____

2. _____

3. _____

4. _____

5. _____

MOSAICOS

9-19   Antes de leer. Los anuncios. Think of some typical job ads and list the information they should include.

_____   _____

_____   _____

_____   _____

_____   _____

_____   _____

9-20   A leer. Los anuncios. Read the following ads and give the information requested regarding each one.

A. Read the ad and analyze the information it includes.

> ## Secretaria ejecutiva bilingüe
>
> **_Importante empresa minera_** solicita secretaria ejecutiva bilingüe (español, inglés) con experiencia mínima de 4 años, con conocimientos de procesador de palabras. Indispensable: excelentes relaciones interpersonales y buena presencia.
>
> _Interesadas enviar currículum,
> foto reciente y pretensiones de sueldo a
> Oficina de Personal Mineral el Teniente, Morandé 938_

1. Puesto: _____

2. Experiencia: _____

3. Cualidades importantes: _____

4. Información que se debe mandar por correo: _____

5. Dirección donde se debe enviar la información: _____

B. Indicate whether the following statements are true (**C**) or false (**F**) according to the ad.

> **SE BUSCA PERSONAL**
> **JÓVENES DINÁMICOS DE AMBOS SEXOS**
> REQUISITOS:
> • Facilidad de palabra
> • Aptitud para las ventas
> • Buena presencia
> Disposición para entrenamiento.
> Trabajo no requiere tiempo completo.
> **INTERESADOS LLAMAR AL TEL. 223-23-44**
> Pedir hablar con Jefe de Contrataciones
> Horario de 9 a 13 hrs. y de 14 a 18 hrs.

1. _____ Los puestos son sólo para hombres.

2. _____ Las personas interesadas deben saber expresarse bien.

3. _____ Es necesario trabajar a tiempo completo.

4. _____ Para este trabajo no importa la ropa de las personas.

5. _____ Las personas interesadas van a recibir preparación para el puesto.

6. _____ Los interesados pueden llamar a cualquier hora.

C. Read the following ad and analyze the information it includes.

> **Tienda especializada en computadoras**
> **y comunicaciones necesita**
>
> **VENDEDORA**
>
> Soltera, menor de 45 años, con experiencia en
> programación, interés en comenzar una carrera en
> venta de computadoras y viajar por el extranjero,
> buena presencia y dinamismo: Se prefiere
> candidata con conocimiento de idiomas. Enviar
> currículum vitae con fotografía a:
>
> **CONTRATACIONES IBM,**
> **Avenida Costanera 1075, Providencia, Santiago**

1. Puesto: _____

   _____

2. Límite de edad: _____

   _____

3. Estado civil: _____

   _____

4. Requisitos: _____

   _____

5. Conocimiento que se prefiere: _____

   _____

6. Documentos que se requieren: _____

   _____

7. Se debe mandar esta información a: _____

   _____

9-21   Después de leer. La información. Now look at your list of the information that should be present in a job ad (see exercise 9-19). Do the ads in exercise 9-20 include all the information you listed? Is there anything they include that you did not list?

INFORMACIÓN EN LOS ANUNCIOS QUE NO ESTABA EN LA LISTA	INFORMACIÓN EN LA LISTA QUE NO ESTABA EN LOS ANUNCIOS
_____	_____
_____	_____
_____	_____
_____	_____
_____	

9-22   Antes de escribir. En busca de trabajo. You are preparing your résumé to apply for your dream job. Which of the following types of information would you include in your résumé? Place the items below in order of importance, with 1 being the most important. In the final space include and prioritize one additional piece of information.

_____ nacionalidad   _____ dirección de correo electrónico

_____ nombre   _____ historial de salud (*health*)

_____ educación   _____ profesión, oficio/ocupación

_____ edad   _____ pasatiempos preferidos

_____ sexo   _____ experiencia

_____ _____

9-23   A escribir. Su profesión ideal. What is your post-graduation dream job? Write a composition explaining your ideal profession and why you would be good at it. Describe the characteristics that make you good for this profession. Explain also your ideal job within the profession, its location, the work schedule, the responsibilities, and the salary.

_____

_____

_____

_____

_____

_____

_____

_____

_____

_____

_____

_____

_____

_____

_____

9-24   Después de escribir. El anuncio. Now write an ad for your dream job. You may wish to use format and information from the ads in exercise 9-20.

_____
_____
_____
_____
_____
_____
_____
_____
_____
_____

ENFOQUE CULTURAL

9-25   Primera fase. La economía de los países hispanos. Indicate whether the following statements are true (**C**) or false (**F**) according to the information in the **Enfoque cultural** on pages 349–354 of your textbook.

1. _____ En los países hispanos los jóvenes de la clase media generalmente trabajan cuando están en la escuela secundaria.

2. _____ Algunos jóvenes de las clases pobres que necesitan trabajar pueden limpiar zapatos o vender periódicos en la calle.

3. _____ La economía de Chile está en peores condiciones que la de otros países hispanos.

4. _____ Los jóvenes hispanos se independizan pronto.

5. _____ Uno de los productos más importantes para la economía de Chile es el vino.

Segunda fase. ¿Qué sabe de Chile? Complete this paragraph with the correct information about Chile.

La capital de Chile es (1) _____. Debido a su situación geográfica, las personas que viven en esta ciudad pueden (2) _____ en la montañas o disfrutar del sol y el mar en la (3) _____. El esquí se puede practicar en Chile desde el mes de (4) _____ hasta (5) _____.

El puerto más importante de Chile es (6) _____. Cerca de esta ciudad se celebra uno de los festivales más conocidos del mundo hispano, el famoso Festival de la (7) _____. También se encuentra allí la casa museo del poeta (8) _____, ganador del Premio Nobel de Literatura en 1971.

A PRIMERA VISTA

9-26   Servicios profesionales. This summer you have an internship at a hotel in Valparaíso, Chile, and some of the guests require professional services. Listen to their situations and select a professional you can recommend among those listed below. Note that the masculine form is often used to refer to a person generically, without regard to a specific gender (man or woman).

un peluquero	un vendedor	un bombero	un psicólogo	un actor
un periodista	un arquitecto	un técnico	un intérprete	un electricista
un abogado	un locutor	un doctor	un gerente	un contador

1. Los señores Hurtado necesitan _____.

2. El señor Taylor necesita _____.

3. La señora Fernández necesita _____.

4. Pepito necesita _____.

5. La señora López Miranda necesita _____.

6. Los señores Álvarez necesitan _____.

7. El señor Ramos necesita _____.

9-27   Su profesión. You work at the Career Counseling Center, and tonight you attend a session where professionals come to talk about their jobs. You arrive after the introductions have been made, so you must try to guess the speakers' professions. Remember that the names of many professions have masculine and feminine forms.

MODELO: Marta Delgado es *cajera*. PERO Pedro Ruiz es *cajero*.

1. Josefina Pedraza es _____.

2. Roberto Jiménez es _____.

3. Ana Luisa Poey es _____.

4. Reinaldo Vázquez es _____.

5. Rosalía Camacho es _____.

9-28   **Consejero profesional.** You have interviewed five women at the Career Counseling Center today. You wrote a card with three recommendations for each person, but the cards fell on the floor and are now out of order. Listen to your recordings of the interviews and match the recommendations with the person.

1. _____   a. chef, científica o artista

2. _____   b. intérprete, locutora o periodista

3. _____   c. mujer policía, bombera o profesora de educación física

4. _____   d. técnica, electricista o plomera

5. _____   e. psicóloga, doctora o enfermera

9-29   **Buscando trabajo.** One of the people you are helping at the Center is Arturo Castillo. You will hear his phone call to Compañía Salcedo. First listen to get the gist of the conversation and answer questions 1 and 2. Then read questions 3 through 5, which ask about details. This will help you focus on the specific information you need when you listen again.

1. ¿Por qué llama Arturo a la Compañía Salcedo?
   a. Porque quiere preguntar sobre un puesto de trabajo.
   b. Porque quiere hablar con la gerente.
   c. Porque compró unos electrodomésticos de esta compañía.

2. ¿Con quién habla Arturo?
   a. Con una recepcionista y una vendedora.
   b. Con una ejecutiva de ventas y una jefa de ventas.
   c. Con una recepcionista y una jefa de personal.

3. ¿Tiene Arturo experiencia como vendedor?
   a. Sí, es vendedor desde hace cuatro años.
   b. Sí, trabajó como vendedor en el pasado.
   c. No, nunca fue vendedor. Reparaba electrodomésticos y computadoras.

4. ¿Qué necesita Arturo para solicitar el puesto?
   a. Tiene que llenar una solicitud y entregarla con su currículum.
   b. Tiene que enviar su currículum.
   c. Tiene que ir a entrevistarse esta tarde.

5. ¿La señora Alonso va a entrevistar a Arturo?
   a. Sí, ella entrevista a todos los solicitantes.
   b. No, necesita sólo el currículum.
   c. En este momento no lo sabe.

EXPLICACIÓN Y EXPANSIÓN

1. *Se* + verb constructions

9-30   ¿Qué se recomienda para encontrar un puesto de trabajo? At the Career Counseling Center, you and your colleagues are putting together a brief brochure outlining the process of looking for a job. The brainstorming session has been recorded; listen to your colleagues' ideas and put them in order.

1. _____   3. _____   5. _____   7. _____

2. _____   4. _____   6. _____   8. _____

9-31   ¿Dónde estoy? Tonight you and your friends are competing on a television game show! Your friends are taken to different places around the city. When they get there, they will give you three clues about what people usually do at that place; your task is to guess where they are. Listen carefully and guess where they are, both orally and in writing.

MODELO: You hear: Estoy en un lugar donde se come y se bebe por
                                        poco dinero. También se conversa con los amigos.
                                        Normalmente se viene aquí entre clases. ¿Dónde estoy?
                   You say and write: *Estás en una cafetería.*

1. _____

2. _____

3. _____

4. _____

5. _____

9-32   Publicidad. Your relatives own a small store, and business is slow. You appoint yourself as their advertising agent and plan to make a few interesting signs to attract clients. But first you need more details about the store. Listen to them and transform their statements into lines that could go on a sign, as in the model.

MODELO: You hear: Reparamos vestidos.
                   You write: *Se reparan vestidos.*

1. _____

2. _____

3. _____

4. _____

5. _____

2. More on the preterit and the imperfect

9-33   El nuevo jefe. Pedro and Luis are coworkers at a bank. Listen to their conversation once to get the gist. Who are they talking about? Then listen again, paying attention to verbs that express a different meaning in preterit and imperfect forms. Select the statements that correctly convey what you hear in the conversation.

1. a. Pedro ya conocía al señor Bermúdez.
   b. Pedro conoció al señor Bermúdez.

2. a. Pedro dijo que el nuevo jefe tenía mucha experiencia en negocios.
   b. Pedro dijo que el nuevo jefe aprendió mucho de negocios.

3. a. Luis intentó ir a la reunión pero fue imposible.
   b. Luis no quiso ir a la reunión.

4. a. Esa mañana Luis ya tenía la información sobre la reunión.
   b. Esa mañana Luis recibió la información sobre la reunión.

5. a. El nuevo jefe no quería hablar mucho.
   b. El nuevo jefe tenía la intención de hablar más, pero no pudo.

9-34   El robo. There has been a robbery at the bank, and Mrs. Jiménez, one of the bank officers, is reconstructing the scene for the police. She is telling them what various people were doing at the time of the robbery. Match each person with the appropriate action, according to the information you hear.

1. La señora Jiménez _____   a. estaba cambiando un cheque.

2. La secretaria de la señora Jiménez _____   b. estaba leyendo unos documentos.

3. la señora Iglesias _____   c. estaba buscando algo en la computadora.

4. los señores Martínez _____   d. estaba pagando unas cuentas.

5. Raúl _____   e. estaban hablando con el director.

9-35 **¿Recuerda o imagina?** Now you are going to hear questions about what you and other people were doing at certain times. If you do not remember or know, make a guess.

1. _____

2. _____

3. _____

4. _____

5. _____

3. Direct and indirect object pronouns

9-36 **¡Bienvenida!** Graciela is a new coworker in your office. Everybody has tried to do something to make her feel welcome, and she is surprised and moved by the gesture. She is asking you who did all these things before her arrival. Listen to her and select the appropriate response.

1. a. Sí, se las trajo.　　b. Sí, nos la trajo.　　c. Sí, te la trajo.　　d. Sí, te las trajo.

2. a. Sí, se la puso.　　b. Sí, te la puso.　　c. Sí, me lo puso.　　d. Sí, se las puso.

3. a. Sí, me los hizo.　　b. Sí, te los hizo.　　c. Sí, nos lo hizo.　　d. Sí, se lo hizo.

4. a. Sí, se lo limpiaron.　　c. Sí, te lo limpiaron.
   b. Sí, me lo limpiaron.　　d. Sí, te la limpiaron.

5. a. Sí, te lo dio.　　b. Sí, te la dio.　　c. Sí, se las dio.　　d. Sí, se lo dio.

6. a. Sí, te los trajo.　　b. Sí, nos los trajo.　　c. Sí, te las trajo.　　d. Sí, te lo trajo.

9-37 **¿Me ayudas?** Graciela is adapting well to her new position, but she has many questions for you. Listen to her questions and select the appropriate answer.

1. a. Se las puedes llevar a Luis.
   b. Me la puede llevar a mí.
   c. Se la puedes llevar a Luis.

2. a. Tienes que pedírsela a Clara.
   b. Tienes que pedírmela a mí.
   c. Tienes que pedírselo a Clara.

3. a. Se lo debes decir a tu secretaria.
   b. Se la debes decir a tu secretaria.
   c. Se lo debes decir a tu hermana.

4. a. Tienes que dárselas al jefe.
   b. Tienes que dárselos al jefe.
   c. Tienes que dárselo al jefe.

5. a. Debes traérmelo a mí.
   b. Debes traérsela a ella.
   c. Debes traérmela a mí.

9-38   ¿Quién lo tiene? Everybody at the office is looking for something that you already gave to someone else. Listen to your coworkers' questions and respond, both orally and in writing, using the following cues.

MODELO: You hear: ¿Tienes el contrato?
           You see: (a Marta)
           You say and write: *No, se lo di a Marta.*

1. (a Luis) _____

2. (a ti) _____

3. (a ustedes) _____

4. (a Graciela) _____

5. (a usted) _____

4. Formal commands

9-39   Buenos consejos. Tomorrow will be a day of new experiences for Lidia. In the morning she has a job interview for a manager position at a restaurant, and in the evening she will attend a formal party for a charity event. She has received advice for both situations, but she is confused now. Listen to what people told her and select the event for which each suggestion was meant.

	ENTREVISTA DE TRABAJO	FIESTA FORMAL
1.		
2.		
3.		
4.		
5.		
6.		
7.		

9-40   La entrevista. Lidia is now arriving at her job interview. She talks with the receptionist first and then with the interviewer. Listen to them once to get the gist, and complete item 1. Then look at items 2 through 6 and listen again, this time paying special attention to the information you need. Indicate whether each of these statements is **Cierto** or **Falso.**

	CIERTO	FALSO
1. La entrevista va bien.		
2. Lidia no tiene que esperar antes de la entrevista.		
3. Lidia tiene mucha experiencia como gerente.		
4. Lidia piensa que está calificada para el puesto.		
5. Lidia dice que no tiene características negativas.		
6. Lidia va a trabajar unos días de prueba.		

9-41   Instrucciones al chef. It is Lidia's first day at the restaurant. First she wants to talk to the chef. She has noted some instructions, but she wants to sound professional. Listen to her ideas and help her express them as formal commands. Remember, she will be speaking to only one person.

MODELO: You hear: Comprar frutas muy frescas.
          You say and write: *Por favor, compre frutas muy frescas.*

1. _____
2. _____
3. _____
4. _____
5. _____

9-42   Instrucciones a los camareros. Now Lidia wants to prepare her instructions for the server staff. As in exercise 9-41, listen to her ideas and help her transform them into commands. Remember that in this case she will be speaking to more than one person.

MODELO: You hear: Contestar las preguntas de los clientes.
          You say and write: *Por favor, contesten las preguntas de los clientes.*

1. _____
2. _____
3. _____
4. _____
5. _____

Nombre: _____   Fecha: _____

9-43   Trabajando en el restaurante. The first day is going well, but a young server is asking a lot of questions. Listen to his questions and respond as Lidia would. Answer affirmatively and use direct object pronouns to avoid repetition.

MODELO: You hear: ¿Cierro la puerta?
           You say and write: *Sí, ciérrela.*

1. _____   3. _____   5. _____

2. _____   4. _____

MOSAICOS

9-44   La señorita Consejo. You are listening to the student radio station, and it is time for *señorita Consejo*, the daily advice segment. Today señorita Consejo is giving advice to "Esperanza de Amor," who has a crush on a classmate and does not know what to do. First listen to señorita Consejo for the gist, but also pay attention to the verb forms she uses for advice and suggestions. Then listen again and write the verb forms you hear. Keep in mind that some pronouns may be attached to the word.

Querida "Esperanza de Amor":

Si está usted enamorada, (1. ser) valiente y no (2. perder) su oportunidad de ser feliz. (3. olvidar) su timidez y (4. actuar). Claro que esto puede ser difícil, pero las cosas importantes requieren valentía. Con estas estrategias va a escuchar "Te amo" antes del final de semestre: (5. sentarse) cerca de ese chico para poder hacer ejercicios en pareja con él. (6. poner) atención a sus objetos personales para conocer sus gustos. Después (7. hablar) de estos temas con él. Si su Romeo tiene problemas con los verbos irregulares, (8. ofrecer) su ayuda y, al mismo tiempo, su número de teléfono. Antes de los exámenes (9. ir) con el chico a la biblioteca para revisar las conjugaciones juntos. Pero su ayuda tiene un límite: ¡no le (10. dejar) copiar en el examen! Y si esto no funciona, seguro que hay algún estudiante guapo en la clase de química...

Un afectuoso saludo,

Srta. Consejo

1. _____   6. _____

2. _____   7. _____

3. _____   8. _____

4. _____   9. _____

5. _____   10. _____

Lección 10

La comida y la nutrición

A PRIMERA VISTA

10-1   A comer. Ileana is telling you about some of her favorite foods. Read Ileana's descriptions and indicate what food she is describing.

1. _____ espinacas

2. _____ pimienta

3. _____ uva

4. _____ carne molida

5. _____ aguacate

6. _____ zanahorias

a. Se usa para hacer hamburguesas.

b. Popeye es fuerte porque come este vegetal verde.

c. Se necesita esta fruta para hacer vino.

d. A Bugs Bunny le gustan mucho.

e. Se pone en la mesa con la sal.

f. Se usa para hacer guacamole.

10-2   Los ingredientes. Can you cook? Do you know what ingredients are part of each meal? Look at each of the following meals and indicate which ingredient should not be used to make it.

1. una ensalada de frutas:
    a. las uvas   b. la manzana   c. la banana   d. el pollo

2. una sopa de verduras:
    a. las zanahorias   b. la langosta   c. el maíz   d. los pimientos verdes

3. una hamburguesa:
    a. la carne picada   b. el tomate   c. la mostaza   d. el pomelo

4. un pastel de cumpleaños
    a. la mantequilla   b. los huevos   c. la pimienta   d. el azúcar

5. un sándwich
    a. el pavo   b. el queso   c. los churros   d. la lechuga

10-3   Los utensilios. Indicate what utensils you need to eat each of the following food items.

1. bistec _____   a. cuchara

2. sopa _____   b. cuchillo

3. café _____   c. taza

4. vino _____   d. platillo

5. un pastel _____   e. copa

10-4   A la hora de comer. Belinda likes several different foods. Read the following sentences about Belinda's favorite foods and indicate what types of food they are.

1. La zanahoria es _____.
   a. un producto lácteo   c. una verdura
   b. una carne   d. un condimento

2. Los camarones son un tipo de _____.
   a. verdura   c. carne
   b. fruta   d. marisco

3. El pavo es un tipo de _____.
   a. carne   c. postre (*dessert*)
   b. verdura   d. pescado

4. El aderezo es un tipo de _____.
   a. postre   c. pescado
   b. carne   d. condimento

5. Las galletas son un tipo de _____.
   a. pescado   c. postre
   b. marisco   d. verdura

10-5   Tus preferencias. A reporter is writing a news story about the eating habits of college students. Answer his interview questions about your food preferences and eating habits.

1. ¿Qué verduras compras regularmente?

   _____

2. ¿Cuál es tu comida favorita?

   _____

3. ¿Qué condimentos usas normalmente?

   _____

4. ¿Qué almuerzas normalmente cuando vas a la universidad?

   _____

5. ¿Cuáles son las comidas que comes regularmente para la cena?

   _____

EXPLICACIÓN Y EXPANSIÓN

Síntesis gramatical

Present subjunctive

yo	habl **e**	com **a**	viv **a**
tú	habl **es**	com **as**	viv **as**
Ud., él, ella	habl **e**	com **a**	viv **a**
nosotros/as	habl **emos**	com **amos**	viv **amos**
vosotros/as	habl **éis**	com **áis**	viv **áis**
Uds., ellos/as	habl **en**	com **an**	viv **an**

1. The present subjunctive

10-6   El médico. Primera fase. Complete the following statements to find out the advice a doctor gave Susana on nutrition and health.

El médico...

1. quiere que _____ (como, come, coma) dulces todos los días.

2. prefiere que _____ (como, come, coma) muchas verduras.

3. prefiere que _____ (bebo, beba, bebía) agua y no refrescos.

4. piensa que es importante que no _____ (desayuno, desayuna, desayune) nunca.

5. quiere que _____ (fumo, fuma, fume) muchos cigarrillos todos los días.

6. quiere que _____ (tomo, tome, toma) muchas bebidas alcohólicas.

Segunda fase. Now indicate whether the advice the doctor gave Susana is logical (**lógico**) or illogical (**ilógico**).

     a. lógico   b. ilógico

1. _____   4. _____

2. _____   5. _____

3. _____   6. _____

10-7   La buena salud. It is very important to eat healthful foods. Indicate the best ending for each of these sentences about eating habits.

1. Es muy importante que...
   a. almuerces bien todos los días.
   b. no comes muchos dulces.
   c. bebes refrescos.

2. Tu madre quiere que...
   a. almuerzas espinacas.
   b. comas frutas variadas.
   c. desayunas leche y huevos.

3. Queremos que los estudiantes universitarios...
   a. no beben tantas cervezas.
   b. cocinan pescado una vez a la semana.
   c. coman menos grasas.

4. Los expertos prefieren que la gente joven...
   a. no coma muchas hamburguesas y papas fritas.
   b. prepara comidas al vapor (*steamed*).
   c. usa menos condimentos.

5. Es importante que los estudiantes...
   a. tienen una dieta equilibrada (*balanced*).
   b. preparen comida con pocas grasas.
   c. usan aceite de oliva para cocinar.

2. The subjunctive used to express wishes and hopes

10-8   Cuidando la casa. You are taking care of your neighbor's house while he is on vacation. He has left one-word notes on the refrigerator so that you will know what to do. Can you figure out what he wants you to do? Write sentences using the subjunctive to express the chores you have to do.

MODELO: los muebles: Mi vecino *quiere que saque el polvo de los muebles.*

pasear	lavar	cerrar
encender	sacar	comprar

1. el perro: Mi vecino _____

2. la ropa: Mi vecino _____

3. las ventanas: Mi vecino _____

4. la alarma: Mi vecino _____

5. la basura: Mi vecino _____

6. el periódico: Mi vecino _____

10-9   La fiesta. You and your classmates are preparing a party for the last day in your Spanish class. You are in charge of making the arrangements. Tell everyone in your class what you want them to do.

MODELO: Quiero que *Elena traiga unos CDs de música latina.*

1. Necesito que _____

2. Quiero que _____

3. Prefiero que _____

4. Te pido que _____

5. Deseo que _____

6. Quiero que _____

10-10   Ana María. A new year has just started, and Ana María is full of good wishes for her loved ones. Unscramble the sentences and conjugate the verbs properly to find out what Ana María wishes for her family and friends.

1. tener un hijo/mi hermana/Quiero que

   _____

2. para estudiar en México/mi prima/conseguir una beca/Deseo que

   _____

3. mi novio/me pedir en (*propose*) matrimonio/Deseo que

   _____

4. tener buena salud/mi madre/Quiero que

   _____

5. con honores/mi mejor amiga/graduarse/Deseo que

   _____

10-11   Los buenos deseos. What do you wish for your loved ones in the new year? Write sentences to express what you wish for them.

MODELO: *Deseo que mi hermano consiga un trabajo bueno este año.*
          Quiero que mi madre sea feliz.

1. su hermano/a:

   _____

2. su madre:

   _____

3. su padre:

   _____

4. sus abuelos:

   _____

5. su mejor amigo/a:

   _____

6. el mundo:

   _____

7. su equipo favorito (de algún deporte):

   _____

3. The subjunctive with verbs and expressions of doubt

10-12   Tu futuro. Have you thought much about your own future? Complete these sentences and indicate whether they apply to you (**sí**) or not (**no**).

1. Es probable que _____ (hable, habla, habló) español dentro de (*in*)   a. sí   b. no
   cinco años.

2. Dudo que _____ (estaba, estuvo, esté) casado/a dentro de tres años.   a. sí   b. no

3. Es posible que no _____ (viva, vivía, vivo) en este estado.   a. sí   b. no

4. No creo que _____ (soy, sería, sea) millonario en el futuro.   a. sí   b. no

5. Dudo que _____ (tengo, tenga, tuve) muchos hijos en el futuro.   a. sí   b. no

6. No es probable que _____ (peso, pesaba, pese—*weigh*) 350 libras   a. sí   b. no
   en el futuro.

10-13   El futuro del mundo. Do you think a lot about the world's future? Do you think life in 50 years will be very different? Complete these sentences about the future. Then indicate whether you agree or disagree by writing **sí** or **no** at the end of each statement.

andar   ir   haber

desaparecer   ser   usar

1. Dudo que los hombres _____ a la luna de vacaciones. _____

2. No creo que las casas _____ inteligentes. _____

3. Es difícil que los autos _____ por sí solos. _____

4. No pienso que en el mundo _____ paz. _____

5. Es posible que los autos del futuro _____ energía nuclear. _____

6. Dudo que _____ las enfermedades (*illnesses*) del mundo. _____

10-14   Ecuador. Carmen, a young Ecuadorian student, expresses her opinions about tourism in her country. Complete the sentences to understand her opinion, and then answer the question that follows.

Me llamo Carmen Romero Salazar, y vivo en Quito, la capital de Ecuador. Los turistas que visitan Ecuador saben que mi país (1) _____ (ser) uno de los países más interesantes de la América del Sur, pero las personas que no lo conocen dudan que aquí (2) _____ (haber) lugares tan interesantes. Por eso quiero darles más información sobre mi país. En Ecuador, y especialmente en Quito, la arquitectura religiosa colonial es extraordinaria. Es posible que los turistas (3) _____ (poder) ver iglesias con decoraciones de oro (*gold*) en otras ciudades de América Latina, pero no creo que estas ciudades (4) _____ (tener) tantas iglesias tan cerca una de otra como en Quito. Además es cierto que desde Quito las excursiones (5) _____ (llevar) a los turistas a ver el volcán activo más alto del mundo, el Cotopaxi, en menos de dos horas. Asimismo es posible que los turistas (6) _____ (tomar) excursiones para visitar la región de las selvas (*jungles*) en el occidente del país y que allí (7) _____ (ver) la gran variedad de animales y plantas tropicales. Ahora bien, para los amantes de la naturaleza, el lugar ideal está fuera del continente, en las Islas Galápagos. Dudo que (8) _____ (existir) un lugar en el mundo tan interesante como éste. Espero que las personas de otros países (9) _____ (venir) a visitarnos, y así (10) _____ (poder) comprobar que no exagero cuando hablo de mi país con tanta admiración.

11. Now choose which of the following sentences best describes Carmen's opinion about Ecuador.

   a. Si quieres disfrutar de turismo ecológico de aventura, el mejor lugar del mundo es Ecuador.

   b. Ecuador es un país muy interesante por su ecología y su tradición histórica.

MOSAICOS

10-15   Antes de leer. Ingredientes de la comida hispana. Do you know much about Hispanic foods? Look at the following foods and indicate, based on your knowledge, whether they are Hispanic foods. Add to the list two items generally associated with Hispanic food.

_____ tortillas	_____ hamburguesas	_____ paella
_____ papas	_____ pavo	_____ tacos
_____ arroz	_____ mariscos	√ _____
_____ pasta	_____ bistec	√ _____

10-16   A leer. La cocina hispana. Read the following article and answer the questions that follow.

La cocina hispana en el mundo hispano

La variada cocina del mundo hispano posee varias características semejantes, heredadas de la cocina de España. La cocina española se caracteriza por el uso del arroz y el azafrán, los mariscos y pescados y el ajo. Se dice que el plato clásico nacional español es el cocido (*stew*). Sin embargo, este varía de región a región e incluso recibe nombres diferentes. En España las numerosas cordilleras y valles contribuyen a la división del país en distintas regiones que mantienen sus propias costumbres y tradiciones, incluidas las culinarias. Se puede afirmar, entonces que una de las características más importantes de la cocina española es su variedad. Uno de los placeres de viajar por España es la oportunidad que se le ofrece al viajero de probar platos y bocadillos diferentes en cada lugar.

Con el descubrimiento y la colonización de América, la cocina española pasa a este continente. Se pone en contacto con la cocina de las distintas culturas indígenas y sufre un proceso de adaptación. En primer lugar muchos de los ingredientes de los platos españoles no existen en América, y la dificultad de las comunicaciones impedía que se pudieran obtener con regularidad. Esto obligó a los españoles a sustituir estos ingredientes por otros semejantes. En segundo lugar los españoles probaron los platos típicos de las culturas indígenas —preparados con productos desconocidos en Europa, como el maíz, la papa y el tomate— y estos platos influyeron en la cocina española.

Si en España la topografía influyó en la diversidad culinaria del país, el mismo fenómeno, pero en una escala mucho mayor, ocurrió en América. La existencia de diferentes pueblos indígenas con una gran variedad de culturas, y las barreras naturales formadas por ríos, montañas, selvas y desiertos contribuyeron a la división y subdivisión del mundo hispanoamericano. Dentro de cada una de estas comunidades va a desarrollarse una cocina con características propias, y aunque se habla de una comida mexicana, colombiana, peruana, boliviana, etcétera, lo cierto es que las diferentes regiones de estos países tienen, hasta cierto punto, su propia cocina.

Entre las cocinas hispanoamericanas, la cocina mexicana goza de una gran fama mundial. Uno de sus platos más típicos, la tortilla, se remonta a la época de los aztecas. Hoy en día hay máquinas que hacen las tortillas, pero en algunos lugares apartados, muchas mujeres todavía preparan y cocinan las tortillas con los mismos utensilios que se usaban hace más de dos siglos. Para realizar esta labor lenta y pesada, la mujer se arrodilla (*kneels*) detrás de una piedra rectangular llamada metate, donde se coloca el maíz hervido. Lo muele, pasándole por encima un cilindro de piedra. Cuando la masa tiene la consistencia deseada, toma una pequeña porción y con las palmas de las manos, le da la forma de círculo. Después cocina las tortillas en el comal, un disco de barro colocado sobre el fuego. Como en América no existía el trigo (*wheat*), la tortilla era para los aztecas algo similar al pan para los europeos. Pero además, las tortillas se usaban como cubiertos (*eating utensils*), ya que los aztecas no conocían esos instrumentos. Se colocaban pedacitos de carne, frijoles, etcétera sobre las tortillas, se enrollaban y se comían. Estos platos son, con algunas variaciones, los tacos y las enchiladas ya bastante bien conocidos en los Estados Unidos.

Cuando los españoles llegaron a América del Sur, el Imperio Inca se extendía desde el Ecuador hasta la parte norte de Chile. La papa era entonces, y todavía es, un elemento básico en la dieta de estas regiones. Una gran variedad de platos, como las papas chorreadas de Colombia y las papas a la huancaína del Perú, constituyen un ejemplo más de la unión de la cocina española y la indígena: la papa —producto americano— y el queso, que los españoles les enseñaron a preparar a los indios.

Más al sur, Chile y la Argentina ofrecen dos tipos de cocinas diferentes. En las costas de Chile existe una riqueza extraordinaria de pescados y mariscos debido a la corriente fría del Pacífico. Se puede decir que Chile es el país hispanoamericano que consume más productos del mar. En cambio en la Argentina la carne es el producto básico, pues la pampa, esa gran extensión de tierra llana y fértil, constituye el medio ideal para el desarrollo de una ganadería (*cattle*) de primera calidad.

Las comidas de los pueblos son parte de su cultura. La variedad y la calidad de la cocina de España e Hispanoamérica muestran un aspecto más de la riqueza de la cultura hispana.

A. Indicate whether the following sentences are true (**C**) or false (**F**) according to the reading.

1. _____ La cocina de América tiene mucho en común con la española.

2. _____ Se dice que el cocido es el plato nacional de México.

3. _____ Es evidente que la topografía española influye en la cocina del país.

4. _____ Al llegar los españoles a América, la cocina de los españoles se vio influenciada por la de las culturas indígenas.

5. _____ Se puede afirmar que la cocina hispanoamericana es una sola.

6. _____ La tortilla de maíz es de origen español.

7. _____ Los españoles trajeron la papa a América.

8. _____ La carne es un producto importantísimo en la cocina de Chile.

B. Identify the following information from the article:

1. tres productos alimenticios indígenas desconocidos en Europa:

   _____

2. nombre del utensilio donde se prepara la tortilla de maíz:

   _____

3. lugar donde se cocina la tortilla:

   _____

4. un plato típico peruano:

   _____

5. el nombre de la tierra llana y fértil en la Argentina:

   _____

10-17   Después de leer. Los ingredientes. Primera fase. Look back at your answers in exercise 10-15. Did you select the correct items? Were you missing any? Did you select any that are not Hispanic foods?

_____

_____

Segunda fase. Now you have learned a lot about Hispanic food. Indicate with what countries you associate these products.

1. carne _____   a. México

2. papas _____   b. Chile

3. mariscos _____   c. España

4. tortillas _____   d. Colombia

5. cocido _____   e. Argentina

10-18   Antes de escribir. La comida americana. Do you think food in the United States is similar to Hispanic food? List some of the foods typical of the diet of people in the United States.

1. _____   6. _____

2. _____   7. _____

3. _____   8. _____

4. _____   9. _____

5. _____   10. _____

10-19   A escribir. Comparación. Now write a letter to a friend in Mexico, comparing Hispanic food and the food in the United States. Explain what the typical meals are in the United States and how these are similar to and different from Hispanic food. For example, you might compare ingredients, preparation methods, healthfulness, and so on. Be sure to mention what the typical American eats normally and during special holidays.

_____

_____

_____

_____

_____

_____

_____

_____

_____

_____

_____

_____

_____

_____

_____

10-20   Después de escribir. La receta. Your Mexican friend is very interested in your description of foods in the United States, and he would like to try one of the meals. Tell your Mexican friend your favorite meal and give him the recipe so that he can try it.

_____

_____

_____

_____

_____

ENFOQUE CULTURAL

10-21   Primera fase. Los mercados artesanales. Indicate whether the following statements are true (**C**) or false (**F**), according to the information in the **Enfoque cultural** on pages 385–390 in your textbook.

1. _____ En general hay muchos mercados artesanales en los países hispanos.

2. _____ Hay menos mercados artesanales en los países donde gran parte de la población es indígena.

3. _____ En los mercados se pueden comprar sólo ropas artesanales y productos para la casa.

4. _____ El mercado de Otavalo es uno de los mercados más famosos de Ecuador.

Segunda fase. Ecuador, Paraguay y Bolivia. Do you know much about these Hispanic countries? Indicate whether the following statements are true (**C**) or false (**F**), according to the information in the **Enfoque cultural** in your textbook.

5. _____ Muchas personas visitan Paraguay para disfrutar de sus maravillosas playas.

6. _____ Las Galápagos son unas islas ecuatorianas donde se pueden encontrar especies de animales únicas en el mundo.

7. _____ Una parte muy importante de la economía de Bolivia es la minería.

8. _____ El guaraní es un tipo de música tradicional muy famoso en Paraguay.

9. _____ Para decir que un alumno estudia mucho, los ecuatorianos dicen que es "buena nota".

10. _____ Para decir que una persona es perezosa, en Paraguay dicen que es "caigue".

A PRIMERA VISTA

10-22   Una cena especial. You and your roommates are giving a dinner party tonight. Alex is going to cook, and he has made a list of the ingredients he needs. Diana and you are in charge of shopping. Before you go, Diana checks the fridge and cabinets (**el/los armario/s**) in case you already have any of the ingredients. Listen to Diana and check off any items you already have and do not need to buy.

SOPA	ENSALADA
zanahorias _____	lechuga _____
pollo _____	pepino _____
ajo _____	tomates _____
patatas _____	aguacate _____
espinacas _____	aderezo _____
cebolla _____	
PASTA	**POSTRE (*DESSERT*)**
camarones _____	fresas _____
espaguetis _____	naranjas _____
crema _____	yogur _____
mantequilla _____	azúcar _____
aceite _____	**TAMBIÉN**
pimienta _____	pan _____
sal _____	refrescos _____

10-23   La lista de la compra. Diana and you are getting ready to go to the supermarket. To save time there, you want to organize the shopping list by category. Listen to Diana read the list for you, and write the name of each ingredient under the appropriate category. Use the singular or plural forms you hear. The first one has been done for you to use as a model.

VERDURAS	FRUTAS	CARNES	PESCADOS	LÁCTEOS	CONDIMENTOS	OTROS
zanahorias						

10-24 **¿Cómo se pone la mesa?** You are going to set the table for dinner. You want to do it properly, so you ask your mother. She shows you a drawing of a formal setting and explains where everything goes. Listen to her, find each object she mentions in the drawing, and write its name in the space provided next to the corresponding number.

1. _____

2. _____

3. _____

4. _____

5. _____

6. _____

7. _____

8. _____

9. _____

10. _____

10-25   Preparativos para la cena. Your guests will be arriving soon, and Alex and Diana are going over the preparations to make sure everything is ready. Listen to their conversation once to get the gist of it. Then read the statements below and listen again, for specific information. Indicate whether the statements are **Cierto** or **Falso**.

	CIERTO	FALSO
1. Compraron comida y flores en el supermercado.		
2. Van a comprar una botella de vino.		
3. Alex limpió la cocina.		
4. Van a poner tazas de café después de cenar.		
5. No tienen aderezo para la ensalada.		

10-26   Consejos de nutrición. One of your friends at your dinner party wants to lose some weight, and he asks for your advice. Listen to his questions and respond appropriately. Use a direct object pronoun in your answer to avoid repetition.

MODELO: You hear: ¿Puedo comer peras?   You say & write: *Sí, puedes comerlas.*
            You hear: ¿Puedo comer helado?   You say & write: *No, no puedes comerlo.*

1. _____

2. _____

3. _____

4. _____

5. _____

Your friend could use some more advice. Tell him three other things he should eat and three things he should not eat.

Puedes comer _____, _____ y _____. Pero no puedes

comer _____, _____ ni _____.

EXPLICACIÓN Y EXPANSIÓN

1. The present subjunctive

 10-27   Una fiesta sorpresa. It is Claudia's birthday today, and her mother, Mrs. Villa, and sister Natalia are preparing a surprise party for her. Listen to their conversation once for the main ideas and select the answer for question 1 below. Then look at items 2 through 9 and select the correct subjunctive form. Listen to the conversation again to check your answers.

1. Según Natalia, ¿qué problema tiene la señora Villa?
   a. No tiene tiempo para comprar el pastel, llamar a los invitados y preparar todo.
   b. No quiere llamar a los amigos de Claudia.
   c. Tiene tiempo pero está demasiado nerviosa.

2. Espero que todo _____ bien.
   a. sale   b. salgo   c. salga

3. ¿Quieres que te _____?
   a. ayudo   b. ayude   c. ayudo

4. Quiero que _____ al supermercado.
   a. vayas   b. vas   c. voy

5. Necesito que _____ el pastel de cumpleaños.
   a. compres   b. compra   c. compras

6. Quiero que _____ servilletas de papel.
   a. traigas   b. traes   c. traigo

7. ¿No quieres que _____ algo más?
   a. haces   b. haga   c. hago

8. Espero que no _____ demasiado tarde.
   a. soy   b. es   c. sea

9. Es importante que _____ tranquila.
   a. estás   b. estés   c. estoy

10-28   La hora de la fiesta. It is almost time for the party and, being a family friend, you arrive early to help with the final details. Mrs. Villa calls with some last-minute instructions for Natalia. Natalia cannot come to the phone right now, so you write down what Mrs. Villa wants her to do.

MODELO: You hear: Tiene que abrir las botellas.
          You say and write: *Dice que abras las botellas.*

1. _____

2. _____

3. _____

4. _____

5. _____

2. The subjunctive used to express wishes and hope

10-29   La noche de Bolivia. The Hispanic Student Association at your university is organizing a "Bolivian Night" with music, dance, and a "Taste of Bolivia." You and other students are volunteering to help with the event. You have a list of the tasks involved, but the association's president is going to decide who will do each. Listen to his instructions, paying attention to the verb forms, and indicate who will be doing each task.

	EL PRESIDENTE (YO)	TÚ	JORGE	TODOS NOSOTROS	RAMÓN Y LORENZO
1.					
2.					
3.					
4.					
5.					
6.					
7.					

10-30   Preparando unas salteñas. Antonio Suárez is an exchange student from Bolivia, and he wants to prepare **salteñas,** small meat pies that are very popular in his country, for "La noche de Bolivia." Salteñas are made of ground beef, potatoes, onions, eggs, and peas (**arvejas**). Ramón, Lorenzo, and you are going to help him. Listen to Antonio. Then tell

Ramón what Antonio wants, both orally and in writing. NOTE: The perspective, and therefore the subjects, will change when Antonio expresses his ideas and when you address Ramón:

MODELO: You hear Antonio say: Yo: cortar las papas.
           You tell Ramón: *Antonio quiere cortar las papas.*

           You hear Antonio say: Tú: cortar las papas.
           You tell Ramón: *Antonio quiere que yo...*

           You hear Antonio say: Ramón: cortar las papas.
           You tell Ramón: *Antonio quiere que tú...*

1. _____

2. _____

3. _____

4. _____

5. _____

6. _____

7. _____

3. The subjunctive with verbs and expressions of doubt

10-31   Un viaje a Ecuador. Marina is planning a trip to Ecuador and is telling you about it. Listen to her and indicate what she thinks is true, probable, or unlikely.

	VERDAD	PROBABLE	IMPROBABLE
1. Va a Ecuador en verano.			
2. Va a visitar las Islas Galápagos.			
3. Va a hablar mucho español.			
4. Va a enfermarse (*get sick*).			
5. Va a ir a la playa en Guayaquil.			
6. Va a comer humitas ecuatorianas.			
7. Va a viajar a Bolivia.			
8. Va a aburrirse en Ecuador.			

10-32   Hablando sobre Ecuador. Lucas and Margarita are talking about Marina's trip to Ecuador. Listen to their conversation and select whether each of the following statements is **Cierto** or **Falso**.

	CIERTO	FALSO
1. Marina está en Ecuador ahora.	_____	_____
2. No es probable que Marina esté en Ecuador dos semanas.	_____	_____
3. Es muy posible que a Marina le guste Quito.	_____	_____
4. Lucas duda que Marina compre mucho en el mercado de Otavalo.	_____	_____
5. Lucas no cree que a Marina le guste la artesanía.	_____	_____
6. Margarita está segura de que a Marina le va a gustar la artesanía.	_____	_____

10-33   No lo creo. When Marina told Carmen about her trip, Carmen said that she is going to travel in South America all summer. You have heard Carmen brag about things that were not true before, so you question what she said. Listen to Marina and respond both orally and in writing, as in the model.

MODELO: You hear: Carmen dice que va a visitar diez países.
           You say and write: *Dudo que visite diez países.*

1. _____

2. _____

3. _____

4. _____

5. _____

MOSAICOS

10-34   Nutrición con el Dr. Bernabé. You are listening to *Nutrición con el Dr. Bernabé*, a radio program during which listeners call to ask nutrition questions. Listen once for the gist and answer questions 1 and 2 below. Then look at questions 3 through 6 and listen again, this time focusing on the information you will need to select your answers.

1. La señora Beltrán está preocupada porque...
   a. su familia tiene muy mala salud.
   b. a su familia no le gusta ninguna fruta o verdura.
   c. su familia tiene malos hábitos de alimentación (*nutricion*).

2. El doctor Bernabé recomienda que...
   a. no coman pizza o hamburguesas nunca más.
   b. hagan una dieta estricta de verduras y pescado.
   c. coman los platos que les gustan, pero con cambios de algunos ingredientes.

3. El doctor Bernabé piensa que la alimentación de la familia Beltrán...
   a. es muy saludable.
   b. va a traer problemas de salud en el futuro.
   c. es terrible para su salud ahora.

4. El doctor Bernabé quiere que...
   a. coman mucha verdura y fruta.
   b. no coman carne ni dulces.
   c. que coman verdura y fruta unos días, y carne y dulces otros días.

5. La señora Beltrán duda que...
   a. a su familia le gusten las verduras.
   b. su familia acepte comer frutas y verduras todos los días.
   c. su familia quiera verduras en la pizza.

6. La señora Beltrán está segura de que...
   a. sus hijos siempre quieren un postre (*dessert*).
   b. sus hijos no quieren comer fruta.
   c. sus hijos no van a poder comer chocolate.

Now give two more recommendations, as in the model:

MODELO: *No es bueno que beban muchos refrescos; es mejor que tomen agua y jugos de fruta.*

1. _____

   _____

2. _____

   _____

Lección 11

Nombre: _____

Fecha: _____

La salud y los médicos

A PRIMERA VISTA

11-1   El cuerpo humano. Your little brother is taking a basic anatomy class in school and has asked you to help him with his homework. He needs to classify body parts into three categories: head (**cabeza**), trunk (**tronco**), and extremities (**extremidades**).

	a. cabeza		b. tronco		c. extremidades		
1. _____ cintura		5. _____ pierna		9. _____ ceja		13. _____ espalda	
2. _____ rodilla		6. _____ cuello		10. _____ tobillo		14. _____ boca	
3. _____ oreja		7. _____ dedo		11. _____ pelo		15. _____ frente	
4. _____ nariz		8. _____ hombro		12. _____ brazo		16. _____ muñeca	

11-2   Las partes del cuerpo. Your friend does not know the vocabulary of the body in Spanish very well. He is writing a composition and needs several words. He gives you a description, and you tell him the word in Spanish to help him get a good grade.

1. Es el líquido rojo esencial para vivir. _____

2. Digiere la comida. _____

3. Nos permite escuchar la música. _____

4. Mueve la sangre por el cuerpo. _____

5. Los necesitamos para respirar. _____

6. Sostiene la cabeza. _____

7. Conecta la mano con el brazo. _____

8. Es una articulación (*joint*) en el brazo. _____

9. Es una articulación en la pierna. _____

10. Podemos ver con estos órganos. _____

11-3   Usted es el doctor. What do you recommend in these cases? Indicate the best advice for each problem.

1. Su paciente tiene una infección en los oídos.
   a. nadar en la piscina
   b. tomar antibióticos
   c. viajar en avión

2. Su paciente tiene artritis y le duelen las manos y las rodillas. ¿Qué debe hacer?
   a. hacer ejercicio moderado y tomar aspirinas
   b. tomar clases de baile
   c. correr en una maratón

3. A su paciente le duele mucho el estómago. ¿Qué debe hacer?
   a. comer mucho
   b. tomar bebidas alcohólicas
   c. comer con poco condimento

4. Su paciente se torció el tobillo. ¿Qué debe hacer?
   a. descansar
   b. ir a esquiar
   c. jugar al baloncesto

11-4   En la consulta del médico. Do you get sick often? Do you always know what to do when you get sick? Indicate whether the following sentences about illnesses are (a) logical or (b) illogical.

1. Una persona que tiene gripe muchas veces tiene fiebre alta. _____

2. Un paciente con indigestión debe comer mucho. _____

3. Es buena idea que una persona que tiene anemia tome vitaminas. _____

4. Una persona que sufre un ataque al corazón debe hacer ejercicio todos los días. _____

5. Una persona que no ve bien debe tomar antibióticos. _____

11-5   ¿Es buena su salud? Answer the following questions about your health.

1. ¿Tiene buena o mala salud? _____

2. ¿Con qué frecuencia ve al médico? _____

3. ¿Fuma? ¿Quiere dejar de (*quit*) fumar? _____

4. ¿Tiene alergias? ¿A qué cosas es alérgico/a? _____

5. ¿Qué come para mantenerse sano/a? _____

6. ¿Qué hace para estar en buena condición física? _____

EXPLICACIÓN Y EXPANSIÓN

Síntesis gramatical

1. The subjunctive with expressions of emotion

Me alegro de que **te sientas** mejor. *I am happy you are feeling better.*

¡Qué lástima que no **puedas** ir! *What a shame you cannot go!*

2. Informal commands

	PRESENT INDICATIVE	AFFIRMATIVE *TÚ* COMMAND
llamar:	llamas	llama
leer:	lees	lee
escribir:	escribes	escribe

	NEGATIVE *TÚ* COMMAND
llamar:	no llames
leer:	no leas
escribir:	no escribas

3. Por *and* para

	por	*para*
MOVEMENT	through or by	toward
TIME	duration	deadline
ACTION	reason/motive	for whom

4. *Other uses of* por *and* para

por

- exchange/substitution: Pagué $10 **por** la medicina. *I paid $10 for the medicine.*
- unit/rate: Camina 4 kms. **por** hora. *He walks 4 kms. per hour.*
- means of transportation: Van a ir **por** tren. *They are going to go by train.*
- object of an errand: Van a ir **por** pan. *They are going to pick up bread.*

para

- judgement: **Para** mí, la aspirina es mejor. *For me, aspirin is better.*
- intention/purpose (with infinitive):   Fue **para** comprar aspirinas. *He went to buy aspirin.*

5. *Relative pronouns*

que	persons or things
quien(es)	persons only

---

1. The subjunctive with expressions of emotion

11-6   Las opiniones de Ana. Complete the following sentences in which Ana expresses her opinion about different topics. Then indicate whether you agree (**estoy de acuerdo**) or disagree (**no estoy de acuerdo**) with each of Ana's statements.

	Estoy de acuerdo	*No estoy de acuerdo*

1. Me encanta que George W. Bush...
   a. ser presidente.
   b. sea presidente.
   c. fue presidente.

2. Me molesta que la gente...
   a. fuma en mi casa.
   b. fumar en mi casa.
   c. fume en mi casa.

3. Quiero que mi hermana...
   a. sea famosa cuando se gradúe.
   b. ser famosa cuando se gradúe.
   c. soy famosa cuando se gradúe.

4. Temo que...
   a. haya más atentados terroristas en el mundo.
   b. hay más atentados terroristas en el mundo.
   c. haber más atentados terroristas en el mundo.

5. Me molesta que mis amigos...
   a. me mienten.
   b. me mientan.
   c. mentirme.

6. Creo que los estudiantes...
   a. deben ser respetuosos con los profesores.
   b. deban ser respetuosos con los profesores.
   c. deber ser respetuosos con los profesores.

11-7   En las montañas. You have invited a friend to spend a week with you at a cabin your father owns in the mountains. Your father has left you very clear instructions about what he wants from you. Complete the following sentences so that your friend understands your father's wishes and feelings.

comer	limpiar	divertirse
hacer	ir	gastar

1. Mi padre quiere que nosotros _____ mucho.

2. Teme que nosotros _____ dinero en las pistas de esquí.

3. Prefiere que nosotros _____ en los restaurantes.

4. Le molesta que nosotros _____ muchas llamadas de teléfono desde la cabaña.

5. Se alegra de que yo no _____ solo a la cabaña.

6. Le molesta que nosotros no _____ la cabaña.

11-8   ¿Qué opinas? There has been a hurricane in southern Florida that has caused tremendous damage. Read the statements about events taking place there and write sentences to express how you feel about them. Use expressions from the list.

alegrarse de	encantar	sentir
molestar	gustar	temer

1. Miles de personas no tienen casa debido a un huracán.

   _____

2. El presidente George W. Bush envía dinero para ayudar.

   _____

3. La Cruz Roja está en el área afectada para ayudar.

   _____

4. Muchas personas no encuentran a sus familiares.

   _____

5. Algunos actores y actrices quieren visitar la zona para animar a los afectados.

   _____

6. Las pérdidas económicas en el área afectada son increíbles.

   _____

2. Informal commands

11-9   El ejercicio físico. You are a counselor at a gym, and a person who wants to start an exercise program comes to you. Tell this person what he or she needs to do.

1. El lugar:
   a. Ve a la biblioteca.   b. Ve al gimnasio.   c. Ve al baño.

2. Antes de hacer ejercicio:
   a. Come mucho.
   b. Nada en la piscina.
   c. Haz movimientos para calentar el cuerpo.

3. Para evitar accidentes:
   a. Habla durante los ejercicios.
   b. Empieza con movimientos fáciles.
   c. No practiques con un/a compañero/a.

4. Los ejercicios:
   a. Haz ejercicios muy difíciles la primera vez.
   b. Haz ejercicios intensos.
   c. Haz cada movimiento diez veces por lo menos.

5. El tiempo:
   a. No practiques demasiado la primera vez.
   b. Haz los ejercicios rápido.
   c. Lleva tu reloj para ver la hora.

6. Mientras haces los ejercicios:
   a. Respira por la boca.   b. No respires.   c. Respira por la nariz.

11-10   La enfermera. Your friend is going to start a job as a nurse in a hospital next week, and she is nervous about it. Complete the following sentences to advise her on what to do.

ser	llegar	poner	tomar
tratar	consultar	seguir	visitar

1. No _____ mal a los pacientes.

2. _____ a todos los pacientes con frecuencia.

3. _____ a los médicos cuando tengas dudas.

4. _____ amable con los pacientes.

5. _____ las inyecciones con cuidado.

6. No _____ tarde al trabajo.

7. _____ la tensión arterial de los enfermos.

8. _____ las instrucciones del médico.

11-11   La salud perfecta. Your friends are very concerned about their health, and they want to know what they need to do to be healthy. They have asked their older brother for advice, and now they want to know your opinion. Complete the sentences to find out what advice their brother has given them, and at the end of each sentence indicate whether it is (a) good or (b) bad advice.

fumar	beber	comer
hacer	dormir	controlar

1. _____ muchas grasas y carbohidratos. _____

2. _____ tu nivel de estrés. _____

3. _____ ejercicio frecuentemente. _____

4. _____ cigarrillos de vez en cuando. _____

5. No _____ bebidas alcohólicas. _____

6. No _____ más de seis horas por la noche. _____

11-12   Los consejos. Primera fase. This is some advice you might give your friend. Write sentences with informal commands.

1. no hablar: _____

2. comer con las manos: _____

3. nadar: _____

4. escuchar al profesor: _____

5. bailar: _____

Segunda fase. Decide in which situation you would give each of the five statements of advice to your friend.

1. _____   a. en el restaurante

2. _____   b. en la discoteca

3. _____   c. en clase

4. _____   d. en la piscina

5. _____   e. en la biblioteca

3. *Por* and *para* (review) and **4.** Other uses of *por* and *para*

11-13   **¿Cambiamos?** At a garage sale you decide that rather than offering to buy items, you would prefer to trade. Ask the sellers if they will trade the items you want for what you have to offer.

MODELO: una bicicleta/un estéreo: *Te cambio mi bicicleta por tu estéreo*

LO QUE VENDEN EN EL GARAJE	LO QUE USTED TIENE
1. una chaqueta←	→una mochila
2. un diccionario←	→una silla
3. una aspiradora←	→un televisor
4. una guitarra←	→una lámpara
5. una grabadora←	→un reloj

1. _____

2. _____

3. _____

4. _____

5. _____

11-14   **Visita al médico.** Your friend is spending a month in Mexico and has become sick. He has just come back from the doctor's office and calls to tell you about his experience. Your friend is so sick you can barely hear him over the phone. Complete his statements with the correct word (**por** or **para**) to fully understand his experience.

Fui a ver al médico (1) _____ el dolor de garganta y la fiebre que tenía. El médico era mexicano, pero hablaba inglés. En realidad (2) _____ ser extranjero hablaba inglés muy bien. Después de examinarme me recetó un antibiótico, y fui (3) _____ el antibiótico a la farmacia. En la farmacia pagué 40.000 pesos (4) _____ el antibiótico. Cuando salí de la farmacia tomé un taxi (5) _____ ir a casa. Dentro de poco (*In a little while*) me voy a acostar (6) _____ descansar.

11-15   **Un viaje a la República Dominicana.** Read about Mr. and Mrs. Ruiz's plan for a trip to the Dominican Republic and complete the paragraph with the correct word (**por** or **para**). Then answer the question at the end of the paragraph.

Mi esposa Elena y yo vivimos en Nueva York. Salimos (1) _____ la República Dominicana el lunes próximo. Vamos (2) _____ avión, y debemos llegar a Santo Domingo (3) _____ la tarde. Vamos a estar en el avión tres horas, lo que me parece un viaje corto (4) _____ llegar tan pronto al Caribe. Pero como el avión va a 600 millas (5) _____ hora, podemos llegar en tan poco tiempo. Realmente no tenemos mucho dinero (6) _____ hacer el viaje, pero lo quiero hacer (7) _____ Elena. Ella es dominicana, y no ve a su familia (8) _____ más de cinco años. Ella tiene muchos regalos (9) _____ sus padres y hermanos, y (10) _____ eso hay que llevar muchas maletas. En Santo Domingo quiero ir primero al Alcázar de Colón (11) _____ ver el lugar donde vivió. Después voy a caminar (12) _____ las calles de la parte antigua de la ciudad. Va a ser un viaje muy interesante, pero tengo que volver (13) _____ el día 25 porque tengo que terminar un proyecto muy importante en el trabajo.

14. What is the main purpose of Mr. and Mrs. Ruiz's trip to the Dominican Republic?
    a. Los señores Ruiz van a viajar por el trabajo del señor Ruiz.
    b. Los señores Ruiz van a viajar por razones familiares.
    c. Los señores Ruiz van a viajar porque la señora Ruiz quiere conocer la República Dominicana.

11-16   **Información personal.** A popular magazine has published a survey about people's attitudes and customs in relation to health care. Answer the survey questions in complete sentences using **por** or **para**.

1. ¿Cuántas veces por año va usted al médico?

   _____

2. ¿Prefiere hacer ejercicio por la mañana o por la noche?

   _____

3. ¿Qué piensa que es razonable pagar por una consulta con el médico?

   _____

4. ¿Para qué va usted a la farmacia?

   _____

5. ¿Para quién(es) son las recetas que lleva usted a la farmacia?

   _____

5. Relative pronouns

11-17   Su vida. Complete the following sentences about various aspects of your life.

MODELO: Soy una persona que *piensa mucho las cosas.*

1. Soy de una familia que _____

2. Vivo en una ciudad que _____

3. Prefiero las ciudades que _____

4. Soy un estudiante a quien _____

5. Respeto a las personas que _____

6. Me gusta mucho la comida que _____

11-18   Después de la crisis. Your friend is in the hospital recovering from an operation. As you walk down the hallway with him, he points out people he has met during his stay. Finish the sentences with the appropriate pronoun: **que, quien,** or **quienes.**

   a. que   b. quien   c. quienes

1. La señora _____ está allí es mi enfermera.

2. Este señor alto y rubio a _____ ven hablando con aquella señora es mi médico.

3. Estas señoras a _____ les están dando unos papeles trabajan como voluntarias en este piso.

4. El otro doctor _____ está con la enfermera es muy amigo de mi padre.

5. Ahora conozco a casi todas las personas _____ trabajan en este piso.

11-19   Preferencias personales. What is important for you in a date? Indicate which of the two options you prefer by using **que** or **quien**.

MODELO: alto/a y serio/a   bajo/a y simpático/a
Prefiero la chica que es alta y seria. OR *Prefiero la chica que es baja y simpática.*
OR
Prefiero el chico que es alto y serio. OR *Prefiero el chico que es bajo y simpático.*

1. simpático/a y no tiene dinero   antipático y tiene mucho dinero

_____

2. le gusta bailar y viajar   le gusta bailar y tocar la guitarra

_____

3. intelectual pero sin sentido del humor   normal pero con buen sentido del humor

_____

4. le interesan los autos y los deportes   le interesan los animales y el campo

_____

MOSAICOS

11-20   Antes de leer. El menú más sano. For each pair of food, indicate which is healthier.

1. a. el pan blanco   b. el pan integral

2. a. el pescado frito   b. el pescado asado

3. a. el aceite vegetal   b. el aceite de oliva

4. a. un pastel   b. una naranja

5. a. el yogur   b. el helado

11-21   A leer. Prevención de un ataque. Read the following article about health and nutrition and answer the questions that follow.

Prevenga un ataque al corazón

Para disfrutar de una vida sana más larga y mejor, se debe disminuir o eliminar ciertos vicios, y se deben comer alimentos más sanos.

1. El tabaco aumenta el ritmo cardíaco en veinte pulsaciones por minuto. El riesgo continúa presente en los ex-fumadores durante los primeros cinco años. Por eso evite el tabaco.

2. El colesterol, que se encuentra en las grasas de origen animal, como en cremas, charcutería (*cold cuts*), mantequilla y carnes en salsas, es otro factor de alto riesgo (*risk*) para la salud. Las carnes con más materia grasa son el cerdo y el cordero (*lamb*, 20 por ciento), res (2 a 10 por ciento), la ternera (*veal*, 2 a 10 por ciento), el conejo (*rabbit*, 5 a 10 por ciento) y las aves sin piel (no más de 2 a 8 por ciento). Para evitar el colesterol es necesario reducir las grasas en su dieta. También es necesario reducir los aceites o sustituir los comunes por los de soja (*soy*) o maíz.

    Comer pescado, verduras y frutas es lo recomendado porque estas comidas no perjudican las arterias. No es bueno consumir huevos en exceso ya que la yema (*yolk*) tiene un alto porcentaje de colesterol. Afortunadamente, en la actualidad el colesterol se puede combatir con medicamentos eficaces, entre ellos, al parecer, la aspirina.

3. El sobrepeso (*being overweight*) y la inactividad obligan al corazón a trabajar más. Para ello, no hay nada mejor que el deporte y una dieta sana. Se recomienda que las personas sedentarias practiquen algún deporte progresivamente. Aventurarse a un partido de tenis extenuante, por ejemplo, puede tener efectos peligrosos y a veces fatales. Agitar (*To work up*) demasiado el corazón causa hipertensión: el corazón realiza un doble trabajo. Manténgase activo, coma bien y cuide su peso.

4. El abuso de la sal en las comidas, el alcohol y el estrés también pueden ser causantes de un ataque. Acostúmbrese a cocinar o comer con poca sal. Usted va a notar que al hacerlo va a bajar de peso y va a sentirse saludable. Asimismo no cometa excesos con (*overdo*) la bebida. Se piensa que un vaso de vino con la cena o comida no hace daño a su salud.

5. Otro riesgo para su corazón es el estrés. Este puede ser provocado por el exceso de trabajo o problemas en su casa, en el trabajo o en los estudios. Aprenda a mantenerse en calma y a relajarse. Trate de ignorar lo que le produce la ansiedad, y por consiguiente el estrés. Recuerde que su vida vale más que todo lo demás.

A. Indicate whether the following sentences are true (**C**) or false (**F**) according to the article.

1. _____ El ritmo del corazón se acelera cuando una persona fuma.

2. _____ Las carnes que contienen menos colesterol son la de ternera y la de ave sin piel.

3. _____ Se piensa que la aspirina puede controlar el colesterol.

4. _____ La yema es la parte más saludable del huevo.

5. _____ La práctica de los deportes en moderación ayuda a evitar los ataques del corazón.

6. _____ La sal y el alcohol en grandes cantidades tienen efectos positivos en el cuerpo.

B. Complete the following sentences according to the information in the article.

1. Si una persona fuma, el...
   a. riesgo de un ataque es menor.
   b. corazón palpita más rápido.
   c. riesgo de un ataque es seguro durante cinco años.

2. Entre las comidas que más se recomiendan está...
   a. el pescado.
   b. el huevo.
   c. el cerdo.

3. Ahora se dice que la aspirina es buena para...
   a. controlar el apetito.
   b. bajar de peso.
   c. combatir el colesterol.

4. Para disminuir el estrés es bueno...
   a. comer más sal y no hacer ejercicio.
   b. evitar el trabajo.
   c. tratar de no darle mucha importancia a los problemas.

11-22   Después de leer. Consejos. You work as a counselor in a health clinic. A person has come to talk to you because he is worried about his health and the possibility of having a heart attack. He tells you that he smokes a pack of cigarettes each day and eats bacon and eggs every morning. Having the article you read, tell this person what he needs to do to stay healthy. Use phrases like **es evidente que...**, **es importante que...**, **es dudoso que...**, **es vital que...**, **(no) es bueno que...**, and so on.

_____

_____

_____

_____

_____

_____

11-23   Antes de escribir. La dieta de los estudiantes. Think about the eating habits of university students and list the foods a typical student eats or does not eat and things he does or does not do (e.g., eating habits, exercise, stress).

1. _____   6. _____

2. _____   7. _____

3. _____   8. _____

4. _____   9. _____

5. _____   10. _____

11-24   A escribir. El discurso. You work for the Health Department, and you have to give a speech to university students about the role of nutrition, exercise, stress, and all the factors affecting health. Address all the topics you mentioned in exercise 11-23 and all the factors mentioned in exercise 11-21 in your speech. You may use expressions in the following list.

para evitar... (*to avoid*)   es importante/necesario que...

asegúrese de que... (*make sure that*)   espero que...

_____

_____

_____

_____

_____

_____

_____

_____

_____

_____

_____

_____

_____

_____

11-25 **Después de escribir. Su salud.** It is not always easy to stay healthy on a university campus. Answer the following questions about your own health and eating habits.

1. ¿Mantiene usted un buen horario de comidas? ¿Desayuna, almuerza y cena, o se salta (*skip*) comidas?

   _____

   _____

2. ¿Come muchas cosas que contienen colesterol, como huevos en exceso o grasas?

   _____

   _____

3. ¿Come verduras y frutas frecuentemente? ¿Come mucha comida rápida?

   _____

   _____

4. ¿Hace ejercicio regularmente?

   _____

   _____

5. ¿Fuma? ¿Bebe bebidas alcohólicas?

   _____

   _____

ENFOQUE CULTURAL

11-26   **Primera fase. La salud en los países hispanos.** Indicate whether the following statements are true (**C**) or false (**F**) according to the information in the **Enfoque cultural** on pages 423–428 in your textbook.

1. _____ En la mayoría de los países hispanos, los centros de salud y los hospitales públicos son gratis.

2. _____ Las farmacias hispanas generalmente están en los mercados y almacenes grandes.

3. _____ En todas las farmacias hispanas, hay que tener recetas para comprar antibióticos.

4. _____ En las farmacias nunca venden artículos de belleza.

5. _____ Según la cultura popular hispana, los curanderos pueden curar muchas enfermedades.

6. _____ Las plantas medicinales se usan para el tratamiento de algunas enfermedades.

Segunda fase. El caribe. Do you know much about Caribbean countries? Indicate whether the following statements are true (**C**) or false (**F**) according to the information in the **Enfoque cultural** in your textbook.

7. _____ En la Habana hay muy pocas cosas que hacer para divertirse.

8. _____ Los puertorriqueños usan la palabra "macacoa" para referirse a la suerte.

9. _____ Para decir que algo es verdad, los dominicanos usan la expresión "eso es puro aguaje".

10. _____ En Cuba se usa la expresión "fulas" para referirse a los dólares.

A PRIMERA VISTA

11-27   ¿Con qué parte del cuerpo? Everything we do involves many body parts working together, but which body part do you mainly associate with the following activities? Listen to the activity description and write the name of the body part that is directly related to the activity. Include the appropriate definite article.

1. _____

2. _____

3. _____

4. _____

5. _____

11-28   ¿Qué les duele? Many of your friends are not feeling well today. Listen to them describe their ailments and identify the part of their body that hurts. Remember to include the appropriate definite article.

1. _____

2. _____

3. _____

4. _____

5. _____

11-29   ¿Adónde deben ir? Listen to the following people talk about certain medical situations they or other people have. Where should they go? Use the most appropriate place from the option list to express your opinion, as in the model.

el hospital   el consultorio del doctor   la farmacia

MODELO: You hear: Mi padre se cayó por una escalera, y le duele mucho la espalda.

You say and write: *Creo que debe ir al hospital.*

1. _____

2. _____

3. _____

4. _____

5. _____

6. _____

7. _____

11-30 **¿Qué recomienda el doctor?** At the doctor's office you overhear some recommendations to patients. Match these recommendations with the corresponding ailments.

1. un catarro o una gripe _____

2. una indigestión o dolor (*ache*) de estómago _____

3. debilidad (*weakness*) o cansancio (*fatigue*) _____

4. un tobillo torcido (*sprained*) _____

5. una infección en el oído _____

EXPLICACIÓN Y EXPANSIÓN

1. The subjunctive with expressions of emotion

11-31 **Una carta para Olga.** Olga is spending a semester studying in Santo Domingo, the Dominican Republic. She just received an e-mail from home and is reading it out loud. Listen to her once for the gist. Then listen again and identify how her relatives are feeling about the following things. Some items will have multiple answers.

1. A la abuela no le gusta que _____

2. Los papás se alegran de que _____

3. Para la mamá es una lástima que _____

4. La mamá teme que _____

5. A la mamá le preocupa que _____

6. A la mamá le encanta que _____

7. La mamá siente que _____

a. Olga no esté en el cumpleaños de la abuela.

b. Olga salga mucho por las noches.

c. Olga tenga muchas actividades.

d. Olga esté bien.

e. su familia le dé medicinas.

f. ellos (los padres) no puedan visitarla.

g. a Olga le guste la República Dominicana.

h. Olga tenga muchos amigos.

i. la abuela no esté con ellos mucho tiempo.

j. Olga olvide los estudios.

k. el médico venga.

l. Olga lo pase muy bien.

11-32   **¿Qué les dice?** Olga has met many nice people in Santo Domingo. She wants to express her support to her new friends, but she is unsure of how to do that in Spanish. Help Olga by listening to her friends, selecting an appropriate expression from the options, and then responding with a complete statement, both orally and in writing.

> Me alegro de que...   Siento que...

MODELO: You hear: Mis amigas vienen hoy.
          You say and write: *Me alegro de que tus amigas vengan hoy.*

1. _____

2. _____

3. _____

4. _____

5. _____

2. Informal commands

11-33   **La visita del pediatra.** You are studying to become a pediatrician, and today you accompany Dr. Castellano on a visit to Pablo Mariscal, a boy who has had surgery for a broken arm. Dr. Castellano is giving instructions to Pablo, his mother, and his nurses. Indicate the person to whom he directs each statement. Remember that the doctor will address the boy less formally than the mother or the nurses.

MODELO: You hear: 1. Levanta el brazo
          You indicate: Pablo

	PABLO	LA SRA. MARISCAL	LOS ENFERMEROS
1.	✓		
2.			
3.			
4.			
5.			
6.			
7.			
8.			

11-34   Un payaso en el hospital. Pablo does not like the hospital, and he has not been doing as the doctor and nurses tell him. You sometimes dress as a clown for the children, and the nurse suggests you talk to Pablo, since he may follow your instructions more happily. Listen to the nurse and then tell Pablo what to do, both orally and in writing, as in the model.

MODELO: You hear: Pablo debe comer más.
           You say and write: *Pablito, come más.*

1. _____

2. _____

3. _____

4. _____

5. _____

11-35   En clase de medicina. In today's class you are assisting the doctor. She gives you several commands, which are not very explicit. Figure out what you need to do by listening to the doctor and selecting the appropriate action.

1. a. Darle el informe a la doctora.
   b. Darle la medicina a la doctora.
   c. Darle el termómetro al paciente.
   d. Darle las pastillas al paciente.

2. a. Preguntarle la hora al paciente.
   b. Preguntarles la enfermedad a los otros estudiantes.
   c. Preguntarle los síntomas al paciente.
   d. Preguntarle las dudas a la doctora.

3. a. Buscar el informe para la doctora.
   b. Buscar a las enfermeras para el paciente.
   c. Buscar las medicinas para la doctora.
   d. Buscar los instrumentos para la doctora.

4. a. Mostrarle el informe a la doctora.
   b. Mostrarle el termómetro al enfermero.
   c. Mostrarle la medicina a la doctora.
   d. Mostrarles los resultados a los otros estudiantes.

5. a. Traerle el termómetro a la doctora.
   b. Traerle las pastillas a la doctora.
   c. Traerle las medicinas al paciente.
   d. Traerle la inyección al enfermero.

11-36   Las prácticas de medicina. Now you and your study partner are preparing for a test in which you have to simulate a surgery. Listen to your partner's questions and reply using affirmative or negative commands, as indicated in the cues.

Modelo: You hear: ¿Traigo los guantes?
            You see: Sí,   You say and write: *tráelos.*
            You see: No,   You say and write: *no los traigas.*

1. Sí, _____

2. No, _____

3. Sí, _____

4. Sí, _____

5. No, _____

3. *Por* and *para*

11-37   Un día especial para Angélica. You are going to hear about a special occasion at a hospital. Before you listen, think about what kind of special event could take place at a hospital. Then listen once for the gist; did you guess correctly?

Now look at the statements below and listen once again, paying attention to the information needed to complete these statements with **por** or **para**.

1. El hijo de Angélica es el niño más hermoso del mundo _____ su madre.

2. Muchos parientes y amigos van al hospital _____ conocer al niño.

3. Angélica recibe felicitaciones _____ el feliz acontecimiento (*happening*).

4. Llevan flores y regalos _____ ellos.

5. Lola va _____ su cámara _____ sacar fotos.

6. Es probable que madre e hijo salgan del hospital _____ el fin de semana.

7. Todos desean que Angélica y su bebé vayan pronto _____ la casa.

11-38   ¿Qué responden? Listen to the questions and choose the appropriate answer from the following options.

1. a. Voy caminando para el Parque de las Avenidas.
    b. Voy caminando por el Parque de las Avenidas.

2. a. Ese viaje a la Habana es para la próxima semana.
    b. El viaje a la Habana es por dos semanas.

3. a. Para el barco.

   b. Por barco.

4. a. Bueno, te doy cien dólares para la bicicleta.

   b. Bueno, te doy cien dólares por la bicicleta.

5. a. Sí, para Alfredo todo está muy bien.

   b. Sí, todo está muy bien por Alfredo.

11-39   Regalos para todos. It is Christmas time at the hospital. Presents were exchanged while your friend was busy with a patient, and now he wants to know who received each gift. Listen to his questions and respond both orally and in writing, based on what you see.

MODELO: You hear: ¿Para quién es el radio?

You see:

Susana

You say and write: _El radio es para Susana._

Pablito

Josefina

Ramiro

_Yo_

Irma

_Tú_

1. _____

2. _____

3. _____

4. _____

5. _____

6. _____

11-40   ¿Y a quién le regalas tú? You leave your Christmas shopping for the last minute, and now there are only a few things left in the store. You buy what you can and take home the odd gifts. Listen to your roommate's questions and tell her who will receive each gift and why.

MODELO: You hear: ¿Para quién es esta botella de aceite?
           You say and write: El aceite es para mi mamá porque ella siempre hace la
                                          comida.

1. _____

2. _____

3. _____

4. _____

5. _____

4. Relative pronouns

11-41   En el hospital. Your friend Enrique is recovering from surgery at the hospital, and you are visiting him. You have heard about some of the staff, and you tell Enrique about them. Listen to his replies and then summarize your ideas and his ideas to the other visitors, as in the model.

MODELO: You see and say: Aquí hay una secretaria muy simpática.
           You hear: Sí, esa secretaria está en la oficina.
           You say and write: *La secretaria que está en la oficina es muy simpática.*

1. Aquí hay un enfermero muy competente.

_____

2. Aquí hay un doctor excelente.

_____

3. Aquí hay un psiquiatra muy afectuoso.

_____

4. Aquí hay una recepcionista de Cuba.

_____

5. Aquí hay una enfermera muy seria.

_____

11-42   ¿Quién es? Many people visited Enrique at the hospital today. Their names sounded familiar, but you are not sure who each person was. After they leave you ask Enrique about them. Listen to him and match their names to their circumstances.

1. Enrique trabaja para _____   a. la señora Valverde.

2. Enrique va al cine con _____   b. el señor Ramírez.

3. Enrique me habló de _____   c. Carlos.

4. Enrique ayuda con las compras a _____   d. Gabriela.

5. Enrique cocinó comida cubana para _____   e. Marta.

6. Enrique hace la tarea de historia con _____   f. Raúl y Diego.

MOSAICOS

11-43   En el consultorio de la doctora Suárez. Today you are observing at Dr. Suárez's office. Mrs. Muñoz is here today because she has not been feeling well. After Mrs. Muñoz leaves, Dr. Suárez is going to ask you some questions, so you may want to take some notes.

Listen to the conversation once. Then listen to Dr. Suárez's questions and answer with as much detail as possible. You may listen to the conversation again to check and complete your answers.

1. _____

2. _____

3. _____

4. _____

5. _____

6. _____

Lección 12

Nombre: _____

Fecha: _____

Las vacaciones y los viajes

A PRIMERA VISTA

12-1   De viaje. These are some means of transportation and places related to traveling. Indicate what is being referred to in each statement.

1. _____ el avión
2. _____ el mostrador
3. _____ la aduana
4. _____ el autobús
5. _____ el barco

a. para declarar los productos que trae de otro país

b. para viajar por tierra

c. en un aeropuerto, para reservar o cancelar un vuelo

d. para viajar en el mar

e. para viajar por el aire

12-2   Las vacaciones. These are some of the things you need when you go on a trip. Write the name of each item described.

1. Documento personal necesario para poder viajar a otros países. _____

2. Tarjeta necesaria para abordar un avión. _____

3. Documentos que se compran en el banco y que se usan como dinero en los viajes. _____

4. Artículo donde se pone la ropa cuando se viaja. _____

5. Tipo de pasaje que se necesita para viajar a un país y regresar al punto de partida. _____

12-3   Un viaje en auto. Read the following sentences about cars and indicate whether they are true (**C**) or false (**F**).

1. _____ En la llanta ponemos las maletas cuando viajamos.

2. _____ Es necesario ponerse la guantera.

3. _____ El espejo retrovisor nos permite ver los autos que están detrás.

4. _____ Un auto no puede funcionar si no tiene batería.

5. _____ Algunos coches no tienen volante.

12-4   En el hotel. Write the word of the following objects, places, or actions associated with a hotel stay.

1. Un cuarto para una sola persona. _____

2. Lugar donde el cliente va para pedir información cuando llega al hotel. _____

3. Objeto que se necesita para abrir la puerta de la habitación. _____

4. Lugar donde los clientes guardan objetos de valor. _____

5. Pedir una habitación a un hotel por teléfono, fax o correo electrónico. _____

12-5   El agente de viajes. You are a travel agent, and you have many clients. Describe the ideal trip for each of your clients. Tell them where they should go, the best method of transportation, how long they should stay, and how much the trip will cost.

1. un matrimonio que celebra sus bodas de oro (*50th anniversary*)

_____

_____

_____

_____

_____

2. un grupo de estudiantes universitarios, para sus vacaciones de primavera

_____

_____

_____

_____

_____

EXPLICACIÓN Y EXPANSIÓN

Síntesis gramatical

1. Affirmative and negative expressions

AFFIRMATIVE		NEGATIVE	
todo	everything	nada	nothing
algo	something, anything		
todos	everybody, all	nadie	no one, nobody
alguien	someone, anyone, somebody		
algún, alguno/a (-os, -as)	some, any, someone, several	ningún, ninguno/a	no, not any, none
o...o	either . . . or	ni...ni	neither . . . nor
siempre	always	nunca	never, (not) ever
una vez	once		
alguna vez	sometime, ever		
algunas veces	sometimes		
a veces	at times		
también	also, too	tampoco	neither, not

2. Indicative and subjunctive in adjective clauses

Indicative (known antecedent)

Hay alguien aquí que **habla** ruso. *There is someone here who speaks Russian.*

Busco a la auxiliar que **va** en ese vuelo. *I am looking for the flight attendant who goes on that flight.*

Subjunctive (nonexistent or unknown antecedent)

No hay nadie aquí que **hable** ruso. *There is not anyone here who speaks Russian.*

Busco una auxiliar que **vaya** en ese vuelo. *I am looking for a flight attendant who goes on that flight.*

3. Stressed possessive adjectives

MASCULINE	FEMININE	MASCULINE	FEMININE	
mío	mía	míos	mías	*my, (of) mine*
tuyo	tuya	tuyos	tuyas	*your (familiar), (of) yours*
suyo	suya	suyos	suyas	*your (formal), his, her, its, their, (of) yours, his, hers, theirs*
nuestro	nuestra	nuestros	nuestras	*our, (of) ours*
vuestro	vuestra	vuestros	vuestras	*your (fam.), (of) yours*

4. Possessive pronouns

	Adjective	¿Tienes la mochila **suya?**
	Pronoun	Sí, tengo la **suya.**

5. The future tense

		HABLAR	COMER	VIVIR
	yo	hablaré	comeré	viviré
	tú	hablarás	comerás	vivirás
	Ud., él, ella	hablará	comerá	vivirá
	nosotros/as	hablaremos	comeremos	viviremos
	vosotros/as	hablaréis	comeréis	viviréis
	Uds., ellos/as	hablarán	comerán	vivirán

1. Affirmative and negative expressions

12-6   ¿Con qué frecuencia? Are you an active person? Do you travel often? Indicate how often you do the following activities.

a. algunas veces   b. siempre   c. a veces   d. nunca   e. todos los días

1. Viajo en autobús. _____

2. Voy de viaje solo/a. _____

3. Visito lugares históricos. _____

4. Como en restaurantes elegantes. _____

5. Paso una semana en las montañas. _____

6. Me acuesto a las nueve de la noche. _____

12-7   Una entrevista. A reporter is interviewing a famous person who is in a bad mood and is not forthcoming with her answers. Indicate the most logical answer to each question. Use each response only once.

1. ¿Viajó a México alguna vez antes? _____   a. Nadie lo sabe.

2. ¿Conoce a alguna amiga de Brad Pitt? _____   b. No, a nadie.

3. ¿Tiene algún plan de casarse o tener hijos? _____   c. No, nunca.

4. ¿Alguien sabe cuánto dinero tiene usted? _____   d. No, ninguno.

5. ¿Va a visitar a alguien cuando esté en México? _____ e. No, a ninguna.

12-8   Mi familia y amigos. Complete each of the following sentences about family and friends and indicate at the end of each sentence whether it is true (**C**) or false (**F**) for your family.

1. No tengo _____ prima que estudie español en la Universidad de Panamá. _____
   a. nadie   b. alguna   c. ningún   d. ninguna

2. No conozco a _____ que viva en Caracas. _____
   a. algún   b. nada   c. nadie   d. ningún

3. No tengo _____ miembro en mi familia que viaje a Nicaragua todos los años. _____
   a. alguien   b. ningún   c. nadie   d. nada

4. Hay varias personas que conocen el Canal de Panamá, pero yo no conozco a _____.
   a. ninguna   b. alguien   c. ningún   d. tampoco

5. No conozco a _____ que sea panameño. _____
   a. ninguna   b. nada   c. nadie   d. ninguno

12-9   Actividades. Are you always busy? Write complete sentences to indicate how often you do these activities.

algunas veces	siempre	a veces	nunca	nada
todos los días	nadie	ningún	ninguno/a	jamás

1. ir a la iglesia

   _____

2. bailar en una discoteca

   _____

3. levantarse temprano

   _____

4. ir de vacaciones

   _____

5. leer algún libro de terror

   _____

6. mirar algunas películas románticas

   _____

2. Indicative and subjunctive in adjective clauses

12-10   Un apartamento en la costa. Mr. and Mrs. Molina are looking for a condominium for their family. They have two children, ages two and four. Their children's nanny lives with them. Mr. and Mrs. Molina have extremely stressful jobs, so they need a place where they can relax. Based on the information you have of the Molinas, write five sentences describing what they are looking for. Finally, choose one of the condominiums for them.

PLAYA TAMARINDO
CONDOMINIOS DE LUJO FRENTE AL MAR

Dos tipos de apartamento

Condominio tipo A: 147 m²
- Sala
- comedor
- gran terraza con vista al mar
- 3 cuartos
- 2 baños
- closets grandes
- cocina moderna
- cuarto y baño de servicio
$220.000

Condominio tipo B: 98 m²
- Sala
- comedor
- terraza con vista al mar
- 2 cuartos
- 2 baños
- closets grandes
- cocina, baño de servicio
$175.000

☆ *Zona de juegos infantiles*
☆ *Piscina*
☆ *Antena parabólica*
☆ *Salida directa al mar*

PROYECTO Y CONSTRUCCIÓN
MENÉNDEZ Y CÍA.

Plaza del Mar
Playa Tamarindo
Guanacaste, Costa Rica

MODELO: *Buscan un apartamento que esté al lado del mar.*

1. _____

2. _____

3. _____

4. _____

5. _____

6. ¿Qué apartamento deben alquilar? _____

12-11   Buscando trabajo. You are looking for a job and are reading the classified ads in your newspaper. Complete the following ads and then indicate what kind of professional they are seeking.

A. Se busca una persona que (1) _____ (tener) experiencia en el campo de la medicina. Se necesita una persona que (2) _____ (trabajar) con los enfermos en un hospital y que (3) _____ (ser) paciente y amable. Es necesario que esta persona (4) _____ (tener) un título de médico de una universidad acreditada.

    a. buscan a un/a veterinario/a

    b. buscan a un/a médico/a

    c. buscan a un/a abogado/a

B. Se necesita una persona que (1) _____ (saber) hablar varios idiomas. Esta persona debe (2) _____ (tener) buena presencia. Se necesita una persona que (3) _____ (traducir) las conversaciones con nuestros clientes extranjeros. Es necesario que la nueva persona (4) _____ (estar) disponible para comenzar inmediatamente.

    a. buscan a un/a juez/a

    b. buscan a un/a intérprete

    c. buscan a un/a cajero/a

C. Se busca una persona que (1) _____ (tener) conocimientos del funcionamiento de aparatos electrodomésticos. Se necesita una persona que (2) _____ (reparar) refrigeradores, lavadoras y secadoras. Se busca una persona que (3) _____ (trabajar) bien en equipo y que (4) _____ (ser) trabajadora.

    a. buscan a un/a técnico/a

    b. buscan a un/a plomero/a

    c. buscan a un/a chófer

D. Se busca una persona que (1) _____ (vender) ropa en una tienda exclusiva. Es esencial que esta persona (2) _____ (vestirse) elegantemente y con mucho gusto (*taste*). Es necesario que esta persona (3) _____ (ser) amable y que (4)_____ (conocer) los estilos de moda más actuales. Se necesita una persona que (5) _____ (saber) expresarse y (6) _____ (tener) don de gentes (*interpersonal skills*).

    a. buscan a un/a enfermero/a

    b. buscan a un hombre/una mujer de negocios

    c. buscan a un/a dependiente/a

12-12   La universidad. Primera fase. Paola is telling you all about her university. Complete the sentences to learn about her school.

tener computadoras nuevas   donar dinero para una nueva biblioteca
publicar libros   no tener aire acondicionado
ir a España a estudiar por un semestre

1. Hay varios edificios que _____

2. Tenemos muchos profesores que _____

3. Necesitamos un laboratorio que _____

4. El rector (*president*) busca una persona que _____

5. Hay muchos estudiantes que _____

Segunda fase. Is your university the same? Indicate whether the previous statements apply to your university.

1. a. sí   b. no

2. a. sí   b. no

3. a. sí   b. no

4. a. sí   b. no

5. a. sí   b. no

12-13   Nueva vida. You won the lottery, and your lifestyle is changing! Write down a few things you would like to do.

1. Quiero comprar un auto que _____

2. Quiero conocer a una persona que _____

3. Quiero comer en restaurantes que _____

4. Quiero visitar países que _____

5. Quiero tener un trabajo que _____

6. Quiero vivir en una casa que _____

3. Stressed possessive adjectives and 4. Possessive pronouns

12-14   **¿Qué opina usted?** Look at the following objects and people and indicate your opinion about them. Complete the sentences with the possessive adjective and the word that best describes how you feel about the object or person.

MODELO: la música de U2
           La música (1) __c__ es (2) __a__
           (1) a. mía   b. tuyas   c. suya   d. nuestra
           (2) a. buena   b. mala

1. las novelas de Mary Higgins Clark

   Las novelas (1) _____ son (2) _____.
   (1) a. mía   b. mías   c. suyas   d. nuestra
   (2) a. entretenidas   b. aburridas

2. los hermanos de tu amigo

   Los hermanos (1) _____ son (2) _____.
   (1) a. míos   b. tuyas   c. suyos   d. nuestra
   (2) a. inteligentes   b. divertidos

3. el novio de tu amiga

   El novio (1) _____ es (2) _____.
   (1) a. tuyo   b. suyo   c. nuestro   d. mío
   (2) a. atractivo   b. cariñoso

4. tus clases en la universidad

   Las clases (1) _____ son (2) _____.
   (1) a. mío   b. suyo   c. mías   d. nuestra
   (2) a. aburridas   b. interesantes

5. tu abuelo

   El abuelo (1) _____ es (2) _____.
   (1) a. mío   b. suyo   c. mías   d. nuestra
   (2) a. extrovertido   b. serio

12-15   En el aeropuerto. A plane from Cancún has just arrived, and the passengers are waiting for their luggage. Complete the following conversation among a group of waiting people, and then indicate whether the statements that follow are true (**C**) or false (**F**).

SOFÍA: No veo mis maletas. ¡Ah! Ahí están.

RAQUEL: No Sofía, ésas no son las (1) _____.

SOFÍA: Sí, son ésas.

FERNANDO: Perdón, señora, está equivocada. Ésas maletas son (2) _____, de mi esposa y de mí.

SOFÍA: ¿(3) _____? ¿Está usted seguro?

FERNANDO: Mire bien los números, señora. Son los números (4) _____.

SOFÍA: Lo siento mucho, es que las maletas mías son iguales a las (5) _____.

¿Cierto o falso?

1. _____ Las maletas de la conversación son de Sofía.

2. _____ Las maletas de Sofía y las maletas de Raquel son iguales.

3. _____ Fernando es un buen amigo de Raquel.

12-16   ¿Quién lo dijo? Several people in an apartment complex have had a meeting. When they left the room, some things were left behind. Now everyone who left something has returned to get their things back. What would they say to reclaim their property? Write sentences using possessive adjectives.

MODELO: un profesor de matemáticas/calculadora: *La calculadora es mía.*

| bate | libro de español | raquetas |
| sartén | cartas | maletín |

1. unos cocineros: _____

2. una estudiante: _____

3. una mujer de negocios: _____

4. un cartero: _____

5. unos jugadores de tenis: _____

6. unos jugadores de béisbol: _____

12-17   En un viaje. You and a group of friends are traveling in Costa Rica. One of your friends wants your opinion about some things related to the trip. Answer your friend's questions with the appropriate form of **el mío, el tuyo, el suyo,** or **el nuestro.**

MODELO: ¿Qué habitación te gusta más, la de Ana o la tuya?

Me gusta más la suya. OR *Me gusta más la mía.*

1. ¿Qué hotel es más cómodo, nuestro hotel o el de ustedes?

   _____

2. ¿Quieres ir a San José en mi auto o en el de Víctor?

   _____

3. ¿Qué mapa de Costa Rica prefieres usar, tu mapa o el de Sara?

   _____

4. ¿Te gustan más mis fotos del volcán Irazú o las de Ana?

   _____

5. ¿Vas a usar mi mochila o tu mochila?

   _____

5. The future tense

12-18   Después de graduarse. Maricela is curious about her roommate's future and asks her a few questions. Complete the conversation with the appropriate questions.

a. ¿Cuándo te graduarás?   d. ¿Vivirás en este estado?

b. ¿Qué harás después de graduarte?   e. ¿Qué tipo de trabajo harás?

c. ¿Te casarás?

BELÉN: Hola, Maricela.

MARICELA: Hola, Belén. ¿Piensas mucho en el futuro?

BELÉN: Un poco. Tengo algunos planes, claro.

MARICELA: (1) _____

BELÉN: Dentro de un año.

MARICELA: (2) _____

BELÉN: Buscaré un trabajo.

MARICELA: (3) _____

BELÉN: No sé. Viviré donde encuentre un trabajo.

MARICELA: (4) _____

BELÉN: Quiero un trabajo de profesora de español en una escuela.

MARICELA: (5) _____

BELÉN: Sí, dentro de unos años. Mi novio y yo queremos hacer una carrera (*establish a career*).

BELÉN: Mucha suerte, Maricela.

MARICELA: Gracias.

12-19   Una carta de la abuela. A friend receives a letter from her grandmother, and she is reading it to you. Complete the letter with the appropriate words, and then indicate the purpose of the letter.

estudiar	casarse	hacer
ser	depender	empezar
tener	ayudar	dar

Nombre: _____   Fecha: _____

Querida nieta:

Me pregunto muchas veces cómo (1) _____ tu vida dentro de unos cuantos años.

Todo (2) _____ en gran parte de ti. Sé que (3) _____ mucho hasta

terminar tu carrera. Después de tu graduación (4) _____ a trabajar, y probablemente

(5) _____ con un hombre que tenga una educación similar a la tuya. Seguramente

(6) _____ hijos, pero ya sea con hijos o sin ellos, la vida te (7) _____

alegrías y tristezas. Te conozco bien, y estoy segura de que siempre (8) _____

a las personas que estén a tu alrededor y (9) _____ todo lo que puedas para

mejorar su vida.

Recibe un beso y un abrazo de tu abuela,

Carmen

10. Which sentence best describes the purpose of the letter?
    a. La abuela explica los planes que hizo para la vida de su nieta.
    b. La abuela le cuenta a su nieta lo que hizo con su propia vida.
    c. La abuela hace hipótesis sobre el futuro de su nieta.

12-20   En el año 2050. Do you think life in 50 years will be very different? Write five sentences explaining what you think life will be like in the year 2050. Use verbs from the list to think of your own.

| poder | hacer | tener | salir | poner |
| viajar | estar | ir | ver | vivir |

MODELO: *En el año 2050 no habrá que pagar impuestos.*

1. _____

2. _____

3. _____

4. _____

5. _____

MOSAICOS

12-21   Antes de leer. Mucho que hacer. If you need to travel across the country by plane, in what order do you need to do the following activities?

1. _____   a. Busco el asiento apropiado.

2. _____   b. Llego a la sala de espera.

3. _____   c. Llamo al aeropuerto.

4. _____   d. Hago la maleta.

5. _____   e. Tomo un taxi al aeropuerto.

6. _____   f. Compro un boleto.

7. _____   g. Le pido una revista al auxiliar de vuelo.

8. _____   h. Entro al avión.

12-22   A leer. Unas vacaciones perfectas. Read the following text in which Maite tells you about her last vacation to Costa Rica. Then answer the questions that follow.

Mis últimas vacaciones fueron maravillosas. El año pasado durante el mes de junio fui con dos amigas de vacaciones a Costa Rica por dos semanas. Pasamos las mejores vacaciones de nuestra vida.

En enero del año pasado decidí de repente (*all of a sudden*) que quería ir de vacaciones a algún lugar exótico. Llamé a mi agente de viajes y le pedí sugerencias. Mi agente de viajes me dijo que había una oferta especial para viajar a Brasil o a Costa Rica. Como no hablo portugués decidí que era mejor ir a Costa Rica; allí todo el mundo habla español, y sería más fácil. Llamé a dos de mis mejores amigas y les hablé del viaje que quería hacer. Les expliqué que era por dos semanas y que costaba 1.400 dólares, con avión y hotel de lujo incluídos. Me dijeron que sí, y entonces compramos los boletos de avión e hicimos las reservaciones de los hoteles. Luego, esperamos hasta junio.

Los meses desde enero hasta junio se hicieron muy largos; no veía la hora de ir a Costa Rica. Cada vez que mis amigas y yo nos veíamos, hablábamos sobre el viaje. Compramos varias guías de Costa Rica, y pensamos en todos los lugares maravillosos que íbamos a visitar. Por fin llegó el día del viaje. Me levanté temprano y agarré (*took*) las maletas, preparadas el día anterior, y fui al aeropuerto en taxi. Mis dos amigas llegaron unos minutos después. Fuimos a facturar el equipaje y pasamos a la sala de espera. Tuvimos que esperar casi una hora, pero por fin pudimos subir al avión. Busqué mi asiento y me senté. Estaba ilusionada y nerviosa: ¡el viaje iba a comenzar! Por fin llegamos a San José. Hacía sol y calor. Agarramos nuestras maletas y fuimos en un taxi al hotel. Fuimos a recepción, y nos dieron las llaves de las habitaciones. El hotel era maravilloso. Era muy bonito y tenía unas habitaciones grandes y limpias. El botones (*bellhop*) nos ayudó con las maletas. Todos en el hotel fueron muy amables.

En San José lo pasamos fenomenal. Todas las mañanas salíamos a visitar la ciudad y conocer los lugares históricos más interesantes. Después comíamos en los restaurantes más típicos: intentamos evitar los lugares más dedicados a los turistas para probar la comida más auténtica de Costa Rica. El conserje nos recomendó un restaurante pequeño no muy lejos del hotel. Fuimos a este restaurante muchas veces; la comida era exquisita. Por las tardes, después de comer, nos relajábamos en la piscina del hotel y tomábamos el sol. Después íbamos a la habitación y nos arreglábamos (*got ready*). Íbamos a cenar por ahí y después íbamos a los bares y discotecas. La música y el baile son muy importantes en Costa Rica. Lo pasamos genial (*great*). Conocimos a muchos "ticos". Son personas muy amables y simpáticas.

Un día fuimos al pueblo de Sarchí; alquilamos un auto y condujimos hasta allí. Este pueblo es famoso por sus hermosas carretas pintadas de brillantes colores y por sus carteras de cuero. Todas nos compramos carteras de cuero como recuerdo de Sarchí.

Otro día hicimos una excursión al volcán Irazú. El viaje en carro hasta allí fue increíble. Pudimos observar la belleza natural de Costa Rica y el volcán. Pasamos una semana en San José, y finalmente nos fuimos a Puntarenas.

En Puntarenas fuimos a otro hotel, igual de (*just as*) maravilloso que el anterior. Puntarenas está en la playa, así que aprovechamos para pasear y tomar el sol. También aprendimos a hacer windsurfing y tabla hawaiana. El profesor de tabla hawaiana era muy guapo, y fue muy divertido. Después de otra semana nuestro viaje terminó, y regresamos a casa.

Mis amigas y yo siempre hablamos mucho de Costa Rica, y miramos el álbum de fotos constantemente. Las fotos nos recuerdan de nuestro maravilloso viaje. Nunca lo olvidaremos, y algún día esperamos regresar a Costa Rica.

Indicate whether the following sentences are true (**C**) or false (**F**).

1. _____ Maite y sus amigas pasaron dos semanas en San José.

2. _____ Durante su viaje fueron a la playa y a la piscina.

3. _____ A Maite y a sus amigas no les gustó la comida costarricense.

4. _____ Las maletas de Maite se perdieron en el vuelo a San José.

5. _____ Maite y sus amigas hicieron deportes en Costa Rica.

6. _____ Maite y sus amigas van a regresar a Costa Rica dentro de un año.

7. _____ Maite no fue a Brasil porque no le gusta este país.

8. _____ Maite y sus amigas tenían pensión completa (*full board*) en sus hoteles.

12-23   Después de leer. ¿Qué opina? These are the activities that Maite and her friends did while in Costa Rica. Indicate which activities are important for you to have a wonderful vacation. Add at least three more of your own.

_____ visitar lugares históricos   _____ hacer deportes acuáticos

_____ conocer los parajes ecológicos   _____ bañarse en la piscina del hotel

_____ pasear por las calles de las ciudades _____ comprar recuerdos de la zona

_____ probar la comida típica   _____ conocer a residentes de la zona

_____ ir a los bares y las discotecas   _____ _____

_____ _____   _____ _____

12-24   Antes de escribir. Sus vacaciones favoritas. Now think of your favorite vacation and fill in the chart with the following information.

¿Adónde fue?	
¿Cómo fue (avión, coche, etc.)?	
¿Con quién fue?	
¿Cuánto tiempo?	
¿Dónde se quedó?	
¿Hace cuánto tiempo fue?	

12-25   A escribir. Mis mejores vacaciones. Your friend wants to go on a vacation, but he does not know where to go. Write a letter to your friend, describing your favorite vacation. Say where you went, with whom, what the place where you stayed was like, how the people were, the places you visited, the transportation you used, what you did, how long you were there, how long ago you took this vacation, and why it was so good. Recommend that your friend visit this place, and advise him where to stay, what places to visit, what to do or not to do, and so on.

_____

_____

_____

_____

_____

_____

_____

_____

_____

_____

_____

_____

_____

12-26   **Después de escribir. ¿Qué tal?** After reading your letter your friend decided to go to the place you recommended. He has already returned, and you want to find out how the vacation went. Write five questions you could ask your friend about his trip.

1. _____

2. _____

3. _____

4. _____

5. _____

ENFOQUE CULTURAL

12-27   **El mundo hispano. Primera fase. La música.** Read again the **Enfoque cultural** section on pages 461–466 in your textbook and indicate whether the following statements about Hispanic music are true (**C**) or false (**F**).

1. _____ La música y el baile son diversiones muy populares en los países hispanos.

2. _____ La diversidad étnica influye en la música del mundo hispano.

3. _____ La música indígena es vibrante y muy alegre.

4. _____ La cumbia es un ejemplo de la música de los indígenas de América del Sur.

5. _____ En el mundo de la música, se conoce a Gloria Estefan como la reina de la salsa.

Segunda fase. Costa Rica y Panamá. You have read that music is very popular in Costa Rica and Panama, but what else do you know about these two countries? Complete the following paragraph with the appropriate information about Costa Rica and Panama.

La ciudad de Panamá, capital del país del mismo nombre, tiene lugares muy interesantes, como por ejemplo la parte antigua de la ciudad, conocida como el (1) _____.
Muy cerca de la capital está el Canal de Panamá, que conecta el Mar Caribe con
(2) _____. Los bailes y las fiestas tradicionales son muy importantes. Al norte de Panamá, todos los años se celebra la (3) _____.

Otro país centroamericano muy interesante es Costa Rica. Su capital es (4) _____, situada cerca del volcán Irazú. A los costarricenses, que también se les llama
(5) _____, les gustan mucho el baile y la música. La guitarra y también la
(6) _____ son instrumentos importantes en la música de Costa Rica.

A PRIMERA VISTA

12-28 **¿Qué medio de transporte es?** Look at the following list of modes of transportation, and think about how you would briefly describe them. Then listen to the descriptions and identify the mode of transportation being described by writing the appropriate number in the space provided.

_____ el autobús	_____ el auto
_____ el avión	_____ el tren
_____ el barco	_____ la bicicleta

Y usted, ¿qué medio de transporte prefiere...

- en la ciudad? _____
- para viajes largos? _____
- para vacaciones? _____

12-29 **Preparando las vacaciones.** Irene and Luis want go to Costa Rica on vacation. They want to plan everything carefully so that they can enjoy themselves fully once they are there. Below is their "to do" list. Look at it and number the activities in the order in which they should be completed.

When you finish, listen to their conversation. Are they going to do everything in the order you made? If not, listen again and change your order accordingly.

_____ a. Ir al banco para comprar cheques de viajero.

_____ b. Preparar el equipaje.

_____ c. Comprar guías de viaje.

_____ d. Investigar sobre Costa Rica en Internet.

_____ e. Pedir un taxi para el aeropuerto.

_____ f. Hacer reservas de avión y hoteles.

_____ g. Preparar los documentos de viaje.

_____ h. Ir a una agencia de viajes.

12-30   Una llamada al Hotel Alameda. Luis and Irene are in the middle of preparations for the trip. Today Luis wants to book the hotel rooms, and he is calling Hotel Alameda. Before listening, try to anticipate the questions both Luis and the hotel employee might ask. Then listen to the employee's statements and questions, and identify Luis's responses by writing the appropriate letter next to each number. After you fill in all the blanks, listen to the complete dialog.

1. _____   a. Sí, vamos a tomar un taxi entonces. Muchas gracias.

2. _____   b. Perfecto. ¿Cuál es el precio, por favor?

3. _____   c. Adiós.

4. _____   d. Sí, el 12 y el 13.

5. _____   e. Buenos días. Por favor, necesito una habitación doble para el
                    lunes y martes por la noche. ¿Tienen alguna disponible (*available*)?

6. _____   f. Está bien. Pensamos llegar a eso de las cuatro. Una pregunta más, ¿tienen
                    ustedes un autobús que vaya a buscarnos al aeropuerto?

7. _____   g. Excelente, pues quiero reservar una habitación a nombre de Luis Jiménez
                    para esas dos noches.

Now listen to the complete dialog and check your answers.

12-31   En el mostrador de la aerolínea. Luis and Irene are finally starting their vacation. They just arrived at the airport, and they are checking in. Read the following statements and then listen to their conversation with the airline agent. Indicate whether each statement is **Cierto** or **Falso.** Then correct the false statements to make them true.

	CIERTO	FALSO
1. La empleada les pide sólo los boletos.		
2. Irene va a sentarse junto al pasillo.		
3. Quedan sólo algunos asientos en el avión.		
4. Les dan asientos en las primeras filas.		
5. Facturan una maleta y las mochilas.		
6. Deben embarcar (*board*) por la puerta B22 a las once menos veinte.		

12-32   En el aeropuerto. At the airport Luis and Irene hear several departure announce-ments (each announcement is repeated once). Listen to them and complete the chart with each flight number, destination, and gate number; the first one is done for you as a model. Use the following list of major airlines from Hispanic countries.

Aerolíneas Argentinas   Aeroméxico   Avianca (Colombia)   Cubana de Aviación

Iberia (España)   Lan Chile   Lan Ecuador   Lan Perú

Lloyd Aéreo Boliviano   Pluna (Uruguay)   Travelair (Costa Rica)

	VUELO	DESTINO	PUERTA DE SALIDA
1. *Aeroméxico*	*120*	*Cancún*	*10*
2.			
3.			
4.			
5.			

(remember their destination)

12-33   El automóvil. Many people rent a car when they travel. If you went to a Spanish-speaking country and something was wrong with your car, could you explain what part of the car was not working? Look at the following illustration and notice the labeled parts of the car. You will be asked to identify a car part for each lettered label. Respond by giving the name of that part both orally and in writing. Remember to include the appropriate definite article.

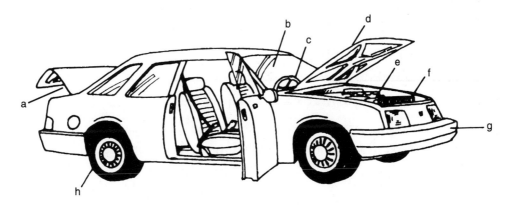

MODELO: You hear: ¿Qué es "c"?
          You say and write: *Es el volante.*

1. _____   4. _____   6. _____

2. _____   5. _____   7. _____

3. _____

EXPLICACIÓN Y EXPANSIÓN

1. Affirmative and negative expressions

12-34 **En la agencia de viajes.** Raúl has decided to spend his vacation with relatives in Panama, and he wants to get the plane ticket now. Listen to his conversation with a travel agent and to the questions that follow. Answer each question by choosing among the following options. You may listen to the conversation more than once.

1. a. Un viaje a Costa Rica.
   b. Un boleto a Panamá de ida y vuelta.
   c. Un boleto para ir a Panamá, sin vuelta.

2. a. Que viaje el jueves.
   b. Que haga una escala (*stopover*).
   c. Que busque una aerolínea más barata.

3. a. No hay vuelos a Panamá.
   b. El avión está lleno.
   c. El avión llega tarde.

4. a. Buscar una tarifa (*price*) más barata.
   b. Esperar en caso de que alguna persona cancele su viaje.
   c. Volar con Lan Chile.

5. a. Quedan muy pocos asientos.
   b. Es más caro.
   c. Hace escala en otra ciudad.

6. a. No, no hay ningún problema.
   b. Sí, no puede pagar con tarjeta de crédito.
   c. Sí, no hay ningún asiento libre para el viaje de vuelta.

12-35 **Hablando de viajes.** You have traveled more than your friend has, and she is asking you about what you have seen and done. Listen to her questions and choose the appropriate answer.

1. _____ a. No, nada.   4. _____ d. Sí, con todos.
2. _____ b. Sí, a algunos.   5. _____ e. Sí, alguna.
3. _____ c. No, nunca.

12-36   Hoy no me quiero levantar. It has been a long week, and it is finally Saturday! Your roommate is asking what you are going to do today. You do not feel like doing anything at all. Listen to her questions and answer negatively, both orally and in writing. Remember to use double negatives.

MODELO: You hear: ¿Vas a salir con alguien esta noche?
           You say and write: *No, no voy a salir con nadie esta noche.*

1. _____

2. _____

3. _____

4. _____

5. _____

6. _____

12-37   En este momento. Look around and observe the place where you are at this moment. Then listen to the questions that follow and answer them both orally and in writing.

1. _____

2. _____

3. _____

4. _____

5. _____

6. _____

2. Indicative and subjunctive in adjective clauses

12-38   El carro que tiene y el que quiere. Alberto loves cars. He is talking about the car he has and the car he would like to have. You can hear only bits and pieces of what he is saying; for each bit you hear, say whether he is referring to the car he has or the car he wants.

		TENGO...	QUIERO...
1.			
2.			
3.			
4.			
5.			
6.			

12-39   Buscando el carro perfecto. Alberto has decided to buy a new car, and now he is talking about the requirements the car should meet. Listen to him and then tell your other friends what Alberto wants, in case they know of such a car.

MODELO: You hear: Debe ser nuevo.
           You say and write: *Busca un carro que sea nuevo.*

1. _____

2. _____

3. _____

4. _____

5. _____

12-40   En su clase de español. Think about your Spanish classmates for a minute. Do any students stand out because of their performance, behavior, or anything else? Listen to the following questions and answer with complete sentences, using information that is true for you.

MODELO: You hear: ¿Hay algún estudiante que hable español muy bien?
           You say and write: *Sí, hay una estudiante que habla español muy bien: Jessica.*
                                  OR *No, no hay ningún estudiante que hable español muy bien.*

1. _____

2. _____

3. _____

4. _____

5. _____

3. Stressed possessive adjectives and 4. Possessive pronouns

12-41   Al llegar al hotel. After a long trip, your friends and you arrive at your hotel in Panama City. Bea is very tired and is getting distracted. Listen to Ángel, Ernesto, and to Bea's questions. Respond by clarifying for Bea, as in the model.

MODELO: You hear Ángel say: Bea, tus maletas están en el corredor.
                   You hear Bea ask: ¿Qué maletas?
                   You say and write: *Las maletas tuyas.*

1. _____

2. _____

3. _____

4. _____

5. _____

12-42   Un problema serio. Ernesto and Ángel finally get to their room and are looking forward to some rest. However, they soon find out they have a problem. Listen to their conversation once for the gist and select the correct answer for question 1. Then read questions 2 through 6 and try to answer them based on what you remember and what you know about agreement between pronouns and the nouns to which they refer. Finally, listen to the conversation again to check your answers.

1. ¿Qué problema tienen Ernesto y Ángel?
   a. Su habitación está en el décimo piso.
   b. Perdieron sus pasaportes.
   c. Tienen las maletas equivocadas (*wrong*).

2. Cuando Ernesto dice "trajo las tuyas pero no las mías", se refiere a:
   a. las maletas   b. las mochilas   c. el equipaje

3. Cuando Ángel pregunta "¿Y los tuyos, Ernesto?", se refiere a:
   a. las maletas   b. los cheques de viajero   c. los documentos

4. Cuando Ángel dice "la mía está en la maleta", se refiere a:
   a. la mochila   b. el pasaporte   c. la cámara

5. Cuando Ernesto dice "¡Ay, pero esta tampoco es la mía!", se refiere a:
   a. la chaqueta   b. el pasaporte   c. la mochila

12-43 **¿Dónde está?** Ernesto and Ángel found their suitcases, and you were all able to rest last night. Now you are all getting ready to drive to your next destination, and they want to make sure nobody leaves anything behind. Listen to their questions about where various objects are. Answer affirmatively and use a possessive pronoun to avoid repetition.

MODELO: You hear: ¿Tu pasaporte está en la maleta?
                  You say and write: *Sí, el mío está en la maleta.*

1. _____

2. _____

3. _____

4. _____

5. _____

12-44 **¡Qué coincidencia!** While you are traveling in Panama, you meet a young woman from Chile. You start talking and realize you have many things in common. Listen and respond to her, as in the model.

MODELO: You hear: Mi materia favorita es la historia.
                  You say and write: *¡La mía también!*

1. _____

2. _____

3. _____

4. _____

5. _____

5. The future tense

12-45   Planes para mañana. When you arrived at the hotel you fell asleep while your friends were making plans for tomorrow. Listen to Bea as she explains what you all will do, and select who will be doing each of these things.

	BEA	TÚ	ERNESTO Y ÁNGEL	TODOS (NOSOTROS)
1. levantarse temprano				
2. ir a alquilar un coche				
3. llamar a los museos				
4. bajar a la recepción para pagar				
5. salir del hotel a las 9:30				
6. poner el equipaje en el coche				
7. querer ir a un restaurante				
8. hacer una excursión				
9. manejar el coche				
10. decir (*indicate*) el camino				

12-46   Una mamá típica. You call your mother from the hotel and, as any mother would be, she is concerned about you. Listen to her and reassure her that you will do as she tells you and that you will be fine.

MODELO: You hear: Espero que no pases frío.
                   You say and write: *No, mamá, no pasaré frío.*

                   You hear: Quiero que me llames más.
                   You say and write: *Sí, mamá, te llamaré más.*

1. _____

2. _____

3. _____

4. _____

5. _____

MOSAICOS

 12-47 **En la aduana.** Whenever you travel internationally, you are required to go through customs. What questions would you expect to be asked? Upon arriving in Panama City, you overhear this exchange between a Panamanian customs official and a fellow passenger. Listen to the conversation and decide whether the following statements are true (**Cierto**) or false (**Falso**). Then correct the false statements to make them true.

	CIERTO	FALSO
1. El inspector de aduana quiere sólo la declaración de compras. _____		
2. El pasajero no trae ningún electrodoméstico. _____		
3. El pasajero trae algunas botellas de vino. _____		
4. El pasajero no declaró algunas compras en su lista. _____		
5. El inspector quiere que el pasajero abra sus maletas. _____		

Lección 13

Nombre: _____

Fecha: _____

La cultura y el arte

A PRIMERA VISTA

13-1   El arte. Do you like the arts? Read these sentences related to the arts and indicate whether they are true (**C**) or false (**F**).

1. _____ Los guitarristas son músicos.

2. _____ El flamenco es un tipo de obra de teatro popular de Andalucía.

3. _____ Los muralistas son pintores que muchas veces pintan sobre temas sociales.

4. _____ Las personas a quienes les gusta escribir se dedican a (*work in*) la danza.

5. _____ La trompeta es un tipo de instrumento musical típico en la música caribeña.

13-2   El español en el mundo. Millions of people speak Spanish. Each of these sentences has to do with something related to Spanish speakers. Indicate what is being referred to in each statement.

1. _____ idioma

2. _____ emigrante

3. _____ castellano

4. _____ hispanohablantes

5. _____ pintor

a. persona que se va a otro país a vivir y trabajar

b. es otra forma de referirse al español

c. lengua que se habla en un país

d. persona que crea cuadros

e. personas que hablan español

13-3   Los hispanos en los Estados Unidos. Read the following text and indicate whether the statements that follow are true (**C**) or false (**F**).

La población hispana en Estados Unidos ha aumentado de forma espectacular en los últimos años. Ya hay 33 millones de hispanos, es decir, el 12 por ciento de la población. Dentro de diez años se espera que sean 42 millones, y el doble en el año 2050. Obviamente los hispanos representan una fuerza económica importante: su capacidad de consumo (*purchasing power*) supera (*exceeds*) los 350.000 dólares al año, y ya hay un millón y medio de empresas que son propiedad de hispanos.

Los hispanos se concentran principalmente en las áreas metropolitanas y en los estados del oeste y del sur. Su influencia no se limita a la economía sino que (*but also*) cada vez más, se oye la voz de los hispanos en la política. De hecho (*As a matter of fact*), el voto hispano puede ser determinante para los candidatos presidenciales.

Los hispanos van imponiendo (*establishing*) poco a poco su cultura: actores, músicos, escritores reclaman (*claim*) su doble identidad de americanos que hablan español, bailan salsa, etcétera. Incluso (*Even*) en algo tan esencialmente americano como el béisbol, han conseguido imponerse (*establish themselves*) los hispanos, que se cuentan entre (*are numbered among*) los mejores jugadores del país.

---

1. _____ En Estados Unidos en el año 2050, habrá 84 millones de hispanos.

2. _____ Los hispanos viven en las ciudades y en los estados del oeste y del sur.

3. _____ Los hispanos no pueden votar en las elecciones.

4. _____ Los jugadores de béisbol hispanos son excelentes.

5. _____ Todos los hispanos son trabajadores del campo.

13-4   El ballet. Read the following article about a famous Hispanic ballet dancer and answer the questions that follow.

Fernando Bujones: El ballet es su vida

Fernando Bujones es un artista de fama internacional. Ha sido aclamado como el mejor bailarín americano de su generación. De origen hispano, nació en 1955 en los Estados Unidos en Miami, Florida. Cuando tenía ocho años fue a estudiar a La Habana, Cuba, y cuatro años después recibió una beca completa de la fundación Ford para estudiar en la Escuela Americana de Ballet en Nueva York.

En 1972 se unió a la Compañía Americana de Teatro Ballet y demostró un talento tan asombroso (*amazing*) que en dos años ya había alcanzado el puesto (*position*) de bailarín principal. Este puesto lo convirtió en uno de los bailarines principales más jóvenes del mundo. En 1974 se convirtió en el primer bailarín americano en ganar la medalla de oro y el premio especial por la calidad técnica en una competencia internacional en Varna, Bulgaria. Desde entonces ha trabajado con numerosas compañías de renombre mundial, como el Ballet Real, el Ballet Real Danés, el Ballet Opera de París, el Ballet de Stuttgart, el Ballet Opera de Berlín, La Scala en Milán, el Maurice Béjart Ballet XX Century y muchos otros. El éxito de Fernando Bujones en su carrera artística ha sido innegable (*indisputable*). No sólo ha colaborado con muchas de las mejores compañías de ballet del mundo sino que ha recibido numerosos premios. Entre (*Among*) ellos destacan (*stand out*) el premio al "Outstanding Young Man of America", el premio del "New York Times" y el premio de la "Dance Magazine".

Bujones no es sólo bailarín sino coreógrafo y profesor. Como coreógrafo ha producido obras que las compañías de ballet más prestigiosas del mundo han interpretado. Como profesor Bujones ha inspirado a generaciones de jóvenes bailarines. Asimismo (*Likewise*) ha contribuido a muchas de las organizaciones de ballet de Florida. Hoy en día Bujones es el director artístico del Ballet Orlando.

1. ¿Quién es Fernando Bujones?

   _____

2. ¿De dónde es?

   _____

3. ¿Cuándo empezó a bailar profesionalmente?

   _____

4. ¿Qué hizo Fernando Bujones que ningún bailarín americano había hecho (*had done*) antes?

_____

5. ¿Cuáles son las profesiones de Bujones?

_____

6. ¿Cuáles son tres actividades en la carrera de Bujones que lo hacen especial?

_____

7. ¿A qué se dedica Bujones en el presente?

_____

EXPLICACIÓN Y EXPANSIÓN

Síntesis gramatical

1. The conditional

	HABLAR	COMER	VIVIR
yo	hablaría	comería	viviría
tú	hablarías	comerías	vivirías
Ud., él, ella	hablaría	comería	viviría
nosotros/as	hablaríamos	comeríamos	viviríamos
vosotros/as	hablaríais	comeríais	viviríais
Uds., ellos/as	hablarían	comerían	vivirían

2. The past participle and the present perfect

hablar	**hablado**		
comer	**comido**		
vivir	**vivido**		

yo	he		
tú	has		
Ud., él, ella	ha		hablado
nosotros/s	hemos	+	comido
vosotros/as	habéis		vivido
Uds., ellos/as	han		

3. Past participles used as adjectives

un apartamento alquilad**o**	unos apartamentos alquilad**os**
una puerta cerrad**a**	unas puertas cerrad**as**

4. Reciprocal verbs and pronouns

Nosotros/as nos comprendemos. *We understand each other.*

Vosotros/as os comprendéis. *You understand each other.*

Uds., ellos/as se comprenden. *You/They understand each other.*

1. The conditional

13-5   ¿Qué pasaría? Are you one of those people who find themselves in a situation and act right away, or do you need time to think about how to respond? Read the following situations and indicate the best action to take.

1. _____ Estás solo en casa, oyes un ruido y ves a alguien que está tratando de abrir una ventana.

2. _____ Mañana es el día del santo de tu novio/a.

3. _____ Quieres pasar el fin de semana en un pequeño hotel de las montañas.

4. _____ Te sientes mal, tienes fiebre y te duele todo el cuerpo.

5. _____ Necesitas 100 dólares para arreglar tu auto, pero no los tienes.

a. Haría una reservación.

b. Llamaría a la policía.

c. Iría a ver al médico.

d. Lo llevaría al aeropuerto.

e. Le compraría un regalo.

f. Le pediría dinero a un amigo.

13-6   ¿Qué harías? Patricia tells you what she would do in various situations. Unscramble the sentences and conjugate the verb to learn what she would do. Then indicate whether you would do the same as Patricia.

1. Vas caminando por la calle, y a la chica que camina delante de ti se le cae un billete de cien dólares. ¿Qué harías?

   a la chica/el dinero/Devolverle   **¿Y usted?**

   _____   sí   no

2. Tienes un problema con tu novio. ¿Qué harías?
   por teléfono/Llamar/a mi novio/con él/y/hablar

   _____   sí   no

3. No estás de acuerdo con la nota de tu examen. ¿Qué harías?
   sobre la nota/con el profesor/Hablar

   _____   sí   no

4. Hay un fuego en tu casa. ¿Qué harías?
   a los bomberos/Llamar/de casa/y/salir rápido

   _____   sí   no

5. Ves un accidente automovilístico. ¿Qué harías?
   mi teléfono móvil (*mobile*)/llamar/a la policía/y/Usar

   _____   sí   no

13-7   El cumpleaños. Eva had a birthday celebration last weekend. She invited Miguel, but he could not go because he had to work. Now Miguel wants to find out all about the celebration. Read the conversation between Eva and Miguel and complete Eva's answers by using the conditional to express probability.

EVA: Hola, Miguel. Te eché de menos (*missed*) en mi fiesta.

MIGUEL: No pude ir; tenía que trabajar.

EVA: Fuimos al restaurante *Los Amigos*.

MIGUEL: Anda (*Hey*), cuéntame todo. ¿Cuánto tiempo estuvieron ustedes allí?

EVA: (1) _____ más o menos dos horas.

MIGUEL: ¿Cuántas personas había en la fiesta?

EVA: El restaurante estaba lleno, pero en mi fiesta (2) _____ unas veinte personas.

MIGUEL: Parece divertido. ¿Cuánto fue la cuenta?

EVA: No sé. Mi padre pagó, pero yo creo que (3) _____ unos 500 dólares.

MIGUEL: ¿Adónde fueron después de la fiesta?

EVA: Algunos fuimos a la discoteca *El bailarín*.

MIGUEL: ¿Cuántos fueron a la discoteca?

EVA: No sé. La discoteca estaba llena, y no pude hablar con todo el mundo, pero yo creo que unas ocho personas (4) _____ a la discoteca.

MIGUEL: ¿A qué hora terminó la fiesta?

EVA: Era muy tarde. Yo no tenía reloj, pero creo que (5) _____ las 6:30 de la mañana.

MIGUEL: Parece que se divirtieron mucho.

EVA: Fue una fiesta excelente. Espero que el año que viene puedas ir.

2. The past participle and the present perfect

13-8 **¿Quién lo ha dicho?** Read the following statements and indicate the people from the list who might have said them.

    a. Britney Spears   d. Jennifer Aniston

    b. el presidente Bush   e. Mel Gibson

    c. Sammy Sosa

1. _____ He tenido muchos problemas con mi codo, y no he podido jugar los últimos dos meses.

2. _____ He visitado varios países para hablar con los representantes de estos países.

3. _____ He tenido una gira (*tour*) de conciertos, y estoy muy cansada. Han sido dos meses muy difíciles.

4. _____ He viajado a Escocia para terminar de rodar (*to film*) una película.

5. _____ Me he separado de mi esposo. Tenemos problemas en nuestra relación.

13-9 **¿Eres una persona activa?** Think of the things you have done this semester, and take the following survey to find out if you are an active or a passive person.

1. ¿Has ido a muchas fiestas?   sí   no

2. ¿Has practicado deportes frecuentemente?   sí   no

3. ¿Has comido en restaurantes diferentes?   sí   no

4. ¿Has ido a algún concierto?   sí   no

5. ¿Has conocido a mucha gente recientemente?   sí   no

6. ¿Has participado en un grupo de estudio?   sí   no

7. ¿Has viajado a algún lugar?   sí   no

8. ¿Has salido con los amigos frecuentemente?   sí   no

Now count the answers for which you answered **sí**, and read the category where you belong:

    a. If you answered six or more questions **sí**: ¡Felicidades! Eres una persona muy activa.

    b. If you answered three to five questions **sí**: Eres una persona un poco activa, pero también te gusta tener tiempo para relajarte.

    c. If you answered zero to two questions **sí**: Eres una persona poco activa. Probablemente llevas una vida tranquila. Para ti es esencial el tiempo para relajarte. Muchas veces te gusta quedarte en casa y no hacer nada.

13-10   Los hispanos en el béisbol. As you have read, some of the best baseball players are Hispanic. Complete this paragraph with the correct form of the verbs in present perfect to learn about the contributions and accomplishments of Hispanics.

hacer   desear   tener   ser   participar   sufrir

Los hispanos (1) _____ en las Grandes Ligas (*Leagues*) por muchos años. Varios hispanos (2) _____ mucho éxito en el béisbol. Por ejemplo, Sammy Sosa (3) _____ más de 300 cuadrangulares (*homeruns*). El cubano Orlando Hernández es un jugador excelente, aunque (4) _____ mucho debido a los problemas con su codo. Roberto Alomar siempre (5) _____ ser tan famoso como su padre y su hermano. Los tres (6) _____ muy buenos jugadores de las Grandes Ligas.

13-11   Justo ahora. Read where the following people are and indicate what they have just done.

MODELO: Ana sale del restaurante con sus amigos: *Acaba de cenar con unos amigos.*

1. Rolando sale del supermercado con el carro lleno.

    _____

2. María y Cristina salen del hospital donde está su amiga.

    _____

4. Un hombre sale corriendo de una casa cuando suena la alarma.

    _____

5. Miranda y Lucas devuelven los menús al camarero y esperan.

    _____

6. Esther cuelga (*hangs*) el teléfono.

    _____

3. Past participles used as adjectives

13-12   Después de la fiesta. Mark and his friends had a wild party last night. Complete the sentences with the appropriate words to describe the condition of the apartment after the party. You will need to change the word form to make it fit the context.

roto   abierto   desordenado   encendido

MODELO: La puerta *está abierta*. Nos olvidamos de cerrarla.

1. Las cortinas _____. Tenemos que repararlas.

2. Las ventanas _____. Por favor, ¡ciérralas!

3. El apartamento _____. Vamos a repartirnos el trabajo para ordenarlo.

4. El televisor _____. Tenemos que apagarlo.

13-13   En busca de un apartamento. Mariana and her best friend have decided to share an apartment and are looking for one. Complete Mariana's description about their search and answer the questions that follow.

cortar   anunciar   alquilar   interesar

recoger   sentar   abrir   cerrar

Nosotras estamos buscando un apartamento, y ayer fuimos a ver uno que estaba (1) _____ en el periódico. Nos gustó mucho el edificio por fuera. La hierba del pequeño jardín detrás del edificio estaba (2) _____, y las hojas (3) _____. Fuimos al tercer piso y vimos que la puerta del apartamento estaba (4) _____. Tocamos a la puerta, y el agente de bienes raíces nos abrió. En la sala había unos señores (5) _____ en un pequeño sofá al lado de una ventana que estaba (6)_____. Cuando le expliqué al agente que nosotras estábamos (7) _____ en ver el apartamento, él nos dijo que lo sentía mucho, pero que ya estaba (8) _____, y nos presentó a los señores que acababan de alquilarlo.

9. ¿Han alquilado Mariana y su amiga un apartamento?   a. sí   b. no

10. ¿Qué pasó con el apartamento que fueron a ver?
    a. No pueden verlo porque el agente de bienes raíces no tiene tiempo.
    b. No les gusta el apartamento, y deciden no alquilarlo.
    c. No pueden alquilarlo porque otras personas ya lo han alquilado.

13-14   El huracán La tormenta. You are on vacation in Cancún when the coast is hit by a major storm. You call your mother to reassure her that you are fine, and you describe the damage caused by the storm. Write descriptions using the correct form of estar and the past participle. You can use words from the list or any others you need.

los árboles	los tejados de las casas	los autos	los ríos
las playas	las casas	las personas	los supermercados
abierto	cerrado	asustado	desaparecido
roto	destrozado	caído	desbordado

MODELO: *Los hoteles están cerrados.*

1. _____

2. _____

3. _____

4. _____

5. _____

4. Reciprocal verbs and pronouns

13-15   Relaciones personales. How do these people feel for each other? Based on how they relate to each other, indicate how they feel about one another.

1. Carmen y Mauro van a casarse. Están muy enamorados.
   a. se quieren   b. se odian   c. se admiran

2. Fernando respeta mucho a su compañero de trabajo Federico, y Federico respeta mucho a Fernando. Cada uno piensa que el otro es un gran profesional y una buena persona.
   a. se ven   b. se admiran   c. se pelean

3. Bárbara y Ángel saben todo el uno sobre el otro. Cuando quieren algo no tienen que decir nada, ya que el otro sabe bien lo que está pensando.
   a. se toleran   b. se odian   c. se conocen

4. Carmen y Asunción no se hablan. Carmen no quiere ni ver a Asunción, y Asunción no soporta a (*can not stand*) Carmen.
   a. se odian   b. se quieren   c. se llevan bien

5. Carolina y Santiago hablan por teléfono todos los días.
   a. se llaman   b. se miran   c. se abrazan

13-16 **Historia de amor.** Think about your relationship with a loved one. Describe at least five things that happened between you. You may use verbs from the list or any other reciprocal verb of your choice.

conocerse	hablarse	pelearse	besarse
quererse/amarse	verse	comunicarse	abrazarse

MODELO: *José y yo nos conocimos cuando estábamos de vacaciones en Miami.*

1. _____

2. _____

3. _____

4. _____

5. _____

MOSAICOS

13-17 **Antes de leer. Los filántropos.** Do you know of any philanthropists? Write the names of philanthropists you know of and explain what they do to deserve the description.

Filántropo   *¿Por qué?*

1. _____   _____

2. _____   _____

3. _____   _____

13-18   A leer. Un filántropo fuera de serie. Read the following article about a Cuban philanthropist and indicate whether the sentences that follow are true (**C**) or false (**F**).

Filántropo cubano enamorado de las artes

El multimillonario cubano Alberto Vilar, amante (*lover*) declarado de las artes, se ha convertido en el filántropo hispano más conocido en el mundo artístico norteamericano y europeo. Economista de profesión y literato aficionado, Vilar ha donado la cifra astronómica de más de unos 300 millones de dólares a través de sus años de apasionado amor por el arte. Entre algunas de las instituciones que se han beneficiado significativamente de la generosidad de Vilar se encuentran Carnegie Hall (3.6 millones donados para ser usados en restauración), la Universidad de Nueva York (20 millones, creación de una beca [*scholarship*] para que los alumnos internacionales estudien artes); la Universidad Washington y Jefferson (15 millones para el Centro de Tecnología Vilar, además de la creación de un fondo para que los alumnos con limitaciones económicas disfruten de la ópera, el ballet y la música clásica); el Centro de Artes Vilar en Beaver Creek, Colorado (10 millones); la compañía Kirov de Ópera y Ballet en San Petersburgo, Rusia (auspicio de nuevas producciones de *La guerra y la paz* y *El cascanueces* presentadas en Nueva York y Londres); etcétera.

A pesar de formar parte de una élite financiera internacional, Vilar —de 60 años— es reconocido por su sencillez (*humbleness*) y sensibilidad. Viajero incansable (*tireless*), especialmente si se trata de (*it has to do with*) un espectáculo de primera calidad. Es así como cada dos o tres días, Vilar rompe el ritmo acelerado (*fast-paced*) de su trabajo en Wall Street para viajar a Europa, en particular a París y Viena, y disfrutar de un concierto de música clásica o de una buena ópera.

Pero es su generosidad lo que lo ha convertido en una leyenda en vida. Los amigos del multimillonario hablan maravillas de su generosidad; tal es el caso del tenor español Plácido Domingo. Según este, se llaman por teléfono dos o tres veces por semana para compartir (*share*) las muchas cosas en común que ambos (*both*) tienen. Las personas que lo conocen de cerca (*closely*) describen a Vilar como un hombre generoso y lleno de amor, atributos extremadamente raros. Según sus amigos Alberto Vilar es único.

Indicate whether the following sentences are true (**C**) or false (**F**).

1. _____ Al multimillonario cubano Alberto Vilar le encanta la música folclórica rusa.

2. _____ La riqueza (*wealth*) de Vilar ha beneficiado a varias instituciones artísticas.

3. _____ Vilar ha participado en varias producciones de ópera, entre otras *La guerra y la paz* y *El cascanueces*.

4. _____ Aunque (*Although*) tiene una profesión relacionada con los números, Vilar disfruta del arte.

5. _____ La familia de Vilar opina que es una persona única porque viaja mucho.

6. _____ Las personas que conocen al millonario piensan que una extraña combinación de amor y generosidad hacen de Alberto Vilar un individuo especial.

13-19   Después de leer. Entrevista. You are a reporter for your city's newspaper, and you have been assigned a series of columns titled "Los hispanos en Estados Unidos." For your first column, you need to interview Alberto Vilar, the Cuban philanthropist who wants to help the arts. What questions would you ask him?

1. _____

2. _____

3. _____

4. _____

5. _____

13-20   Antes de escribir. Personas importantes. Think of the personality traits and virtues that an important figure like Vilar has. List his personality traits and virtues as described in the article in exercise 13-18. Then think of a famous Hispanic citizen of the United States. This person can be a public figure or a member of your community or university. Does he or she share these traits? Indicate the ones he or she shares and add any others that make him or her special.

Vilar   *Nombre:* _____

1. _____   1. _____

2. _____   2. _____

3. _____   3. _____

4. _____   4. _____

5. _____   5. _____

6. _____   6. _____

7. _____   7. _____

13-21   A escribir. El artículo. As part of your series of columns on Hispanics in the United States, you are going to write a short profile of the Hispanic citizen of the United States you thought about in exercise 13-20. Describe this person in terms of:

- His/her special personality traits/skills/virtues
- His/her personal accomplishments in detail (**¿Qué ha hecho esta persona?**)
- Explain why he/she has become an important public figure or member of your community or university

_____

_____

_____

_____

_____

_____

_____

_____

_____

_____

_____

_____

_____

_____

_____

_____

_____

_____

13-22   Después de escribir. ¿Y usted? If you were a millionaire, would you become a philanthropist? What causes would you help? Write a brief paragraph explaining what you would do with your money.

_____

_____

_____

_____

ENFOQUE CULTURAL

13-23   Cultura y arte. Read again the **Enfoque cultural** section on pages 495–498 in your textbook and indicate whether the following statements about the arts in the Hispanic world are true (**C**) or false (**F**).

1. _____ Frida Kahlo fue una famosa pintora mexicana cuya obra fue influenciada por la teoría freudiana.

2. _____ Pedro Almodóvar es un director de cine español. Dos de sus películas han recibido Óscars.

3. _____ *Don Quijote de la Mancha* es una novela española muy famosa.

4. _____ Gabriela Mistral es una poeta cubana que ganó el Premio Nobel de Literatura.

5. _____ Picasso es uno de los artistas hispanoamericanos más famosos en el mundo.

A PRIMERA VISTA

13-24   Profesiones del arte y la cultura. Look at the following professions, all related to the world of art and culture, and think about what they involve (subject matter, activities, skills, and so on). Then listen to the people talk about their occupations and indicate the name of their profession.

1. _____   a. pintor/a

2. _____   b. escritor/a

3. _____   c. periodista

4. _____   d. guitarrista

5. _____   e. cantante y bailarín/ina

6. _____   f. director/a de cine

Do you know any Hispanic people with these professions? Write three names and their professions below. If you know where they are (or were) from, write that as well.

MODELO: *Pablo Picasso era un pintor español.*

7. _____

8. _____

9. _____

13-25   Más que actriz. Salma Hayek has become a familiar face on movie theatre screens, and lately she has been making a place for herself behind the cameras as well. Listen to a brief biography of this actress. Then select whether the following statements are true (**Cierto**) or false (**Falso**).

	CIERTO	FALSO
1. Ya vivía en los Estados Unidos antes de los diecisiete años.		
2. Tiene un diploma universitario de relaciones internacionales.		
3. Era una famosa actriz de telenovelas (*soap operas*) en México.		
4. Su primera película importante en los Estados Unidos fue *Desperado*.		
5. Ha ganado un premio Óscar como mejor actriz, por *Frida*.		
6. Salma Hayek ha producido y ha sido directora de películas.		

Have you learned anything new about this actress?

 13-26   Los muralistas mexicanos en los Estados Unidos. Look at the chart below before listening to an art lecture about Mexican mural painters in the United States. Then select the painter or painters for whom each statement is true.

	OROZCO	SIQUEIROS	RIVERA
1. Estaba en los Estados Unidos en 1933.			
2. Trabajó en California.			
3. Su trabajo influyó a Jackson Pollock.			
4. Podemos encontrar sus murales en Nueva York.			
5. Lenin aparece en un mural suyo que pintó en Estados Unidos.			

If you want to know more about Diego Rivera and his wife Frida Kahlo, watch *Frida*, the film mentioned in exercise 13-25.

13-27   El español en el mundo. In Lección 1 you heard about Daniel, an American student in a study abroad program in Spain, and his Spanish friend Andrea. Now Daniel is back home, and Andrea is visiting him. Daniel is wondering whether he should continue studying Spanish. What would you tell him? Why would speaking Spanish well be beneficial?

Listen to their conversation once to get the gist and answer the question. Then read the other questions and listen to the conversation again, this time paying attention to the specific information you need.

1. a. Debe aprender más español.
   b. Debe aprender otra lengua.
   c. No debe aprender español; ya lo hablan muchas personas.

2. a. Más de 400 millones de personas.
   b. Aproximadamente 400 millones de personas.
   c. Más o menos 40 millones de personas.

3. a. En España e Hispanoamérica.
   b. En casi todos los continentes.
   c. En España, Hispanoamérica y los Estados Unidos.

4. a. Hay muchos, pero son una pequeña minoría.
   b. Hay 40 millones de inmigrantes y otros que no son inmigrantes.
   c. Hay unos 40 millones en total.

5. a. Para el trabajo y los negocios, para hacer amigos y para el político.
   b. Para hablar español con los amigos, para entender a los políticos y para ver las películas en español.
   c. Para el trabajo y los negocios, para leer y ver cine en español y para hacer amigos hispanos.

EXPLICACIÓN Y EXPANSIÓN

1. The conditional

 13-28   Con 20 millones. Cecilia and Raúl are talking about what they would do if they had a lot of money, and they have many ideas. Think about what you would do. Then listen to their conversation and indicate whether the statements that follow are part of Cecilia or Raúl's ideas by checking the appropriate column.

	CECILIA	RAÚL
1. Compraría un coche muy bueno.		
2. Tendría una casa grandísima.		
3. Viviría en los Estados Unidos y España.		
4. Compraría un apartamento frente a la playa.		
5. Viajaría a muchos lugares y países.		
6. Ayudaría a muchos niños pobres.		
7. Les pagaría los estudios a algunos estudiantes universitarios.		

What do you think about their ideas? Is there anything Cecilia or Raúl said that you would do too?

13-29   Situaciones hipotéticas. Look at the following list of hypothetical situations. The audio will indicate six people or groups of people. For every person or group, choose a situation from the box and say what that person (or people) would do in such a situation. Use your imagination! The only rules are that you *cannot repeat the same situation more than twice,* and you *cannot repeat any verbs.*

con mil millones de dólares   con tres meses de vacaciones

con el trabajo de presidente del país   con los tres deseos de la lámpara mágica

con un Porsche nuevo

MODELO: You hear: tu mamá
           You choose: con tres meses de vacaciones
           You say and write: *Con tres meses de vacaciones mi mamá visitaría a
                                toda su familia.*

1. _____

   _____

2. _____

   _____

3. _____

   _____

4. _____

   _____

5. _____

   _____

6. _____

   _____

2. The past participle and the present perfect

 13-30   **El día de Silvia.** Today you have not seen your friend Silvia in class. This evening you call her apartment, and her roommate Marina tells you what happened and what Silvia has done all day. Listen to her once to find out what happened. Then look at the activities below and number them in the order Silvia completed them. You may listen to her roommate again to check or complete your answers.

1. _____   a. comer

2. _____   b. ver su programa favorito en la televisión

3. _____   c. desayunar

4. _____   d. hablar por teléfono con su novio

5. _____   e. escribir una carta

6. _____   f. decidir quedarse en casa

7. _____   g. llamar a su madre

8. _____   h. acostarse para dormir

9. _____   i. acostarse para leer y descansar

10. _____   j. lavar los platos

13-31   **¡No te preocupes, Mamá!** Silvia's mother calls the next day. She is worried about her daughter and tells Silvia what she and her roommate Marina should do, but everything has been done already. Tell her so, as if you were Silvia, using direct object pronouns to avoid repetition.

MODELO: You hear: Bebe muchos líquidos.
           You say and write: *Ya los he bebido.*

1. _____

2. _____

3. _____

4. _____

5. _____

13-32   **¿Qué ha pasado?** Look at the following list of situations. What might be the consequence of such events? Listen to each question and respond with the most logical explanation, using the expression **acabar de**, as in the model.

las rebajas: acabar de empezar   yo: ver a un ladrón en la casa

tú: decirme algo muy feo   ese perro: llevarse su pelota

él: correr una carrera   yo: abrir las ventanas

yo: romper una botella

MODELO: You hear: ¿Por qué estás gritando?
           You see: yo: ver un ladrón en la casa
           You say and write: *Porque yo acabo de ver a un ladrón en la casa.*

1. _____

2. _____

3. _____

4. _____

5. _____

6. _____

3. Past participles used as adjectives

13-33   ¿De qué estás hablando? Your friend and you have been talking about art, films, and literature by Hispanic authors. Now your friend is making some more remarks about those works and artists. Can you identify what he is discussing? Remember that verb and number agreement will help you even if you do not understand every word.

1. _____   a. las películas de Pedro Almodóvar

2. _____   b. el nuevo disco de Shakira

3. _____   c. la escultura de Botero

4. _____   d. los libros de Gabriel García Márquez

5. _____   e. el cuadro *Guernica* de Picasso

13-34   La obra de teatro. You are putting on a Spanish play at your school. Today is your premier performance, and you want to double-check what other students have told you about the preparations. Listen to their reports and then check for confirmation by using **estar** and the past participle, as in the model.

MODELO: You hear: Distribuyeron la ropa de los actores.
            You say and write: *¿Entonces la ropa ya está distribuida?*

1. _____

2. _____

3. _____

4. _____

5. _____

4. Reciprocal verbs and pronouns

13-35   Una pareja de enamorados. Listen as Gloria talks about Eduardo, how they met, and their relationship. Then complete the following sentences with reciprocal verbs, based on what you heard. You may listen to Gloria again to check or complete your answers.

1. Gloria y Eduardo _____ hace tres años.

2. Durante esas vacaciones ellos _____ todos los días.

3. Mientras Gloria estaba en la universidad, _____ frecuentemente y también _____ por teléfono.

4. Cuando Eduardo fue a la graduación de Gloria, ella supo que Eduardo y ella _____.

5. En ese momento tan feliz Gloria y Eduardo _____ y _____.

13-36   Sentimientos mutuos. Many feelings and actions can be mutual. Listen to what these people feel for or do with each other, and then explain what that feeling or action is, as in the model.

MODELO: You hear: Gregorio y su padre no tienen problemas en su relación. Normalmente están de acuerdo, y siempre resuelven sus diferencias rápidamente.
            You say and write: *Gregorio y su padre se llevan bien.*

1. _____

2. _____

3. _____

4. _____

5. _____

MOSAICOS

 13-37   Una visita a la capital, con sabor latino. Your friend Alejandro is telling you about the vacation he just enjoyed with his family. Listen to him once for the gist and indicate whether each of the statements that follow is true (**Cierto**) or false (**Falso**). Then correct the false statements to make them true. You may want to listen to Alejandro more than once to check or complete your answers.

	CIERTO	FALSO
1. Alejandro fue a la capital de Estados Unidos con sus padres y hermanos. _____		
2. No visitaron la Casa Blanca, el Capitolio ni el monumento a Lincoln. _____		
3. Antes de llegar a la ciudad, ya planeaban visitar el barrio hispano. _____		
4. Compraron vino de Chile y productos de otros países en un mercado. _____		
5. Cenaron en un restaurante cubano que también sirve platos peruanos. _____		
6. Los periódicos hispanos eran difíciles de encontrar y un poco caros. _____		

Do you know of any Hispanic neighborhoods? Have you visited any?

Lección 14

Cambios de la sociedad

A PRIMERA VISTA

14-1   La sociedad. Indicate the appropriate description for each society-related word.

1. confianza _____   a. conexión de una cosa con otra

2. edad _____   b. sentimiento de poder comunicarte íntimamente con una
                               persona

3. hogar _____   c. persona que vive en un país

4. enlace _____   d. la casa

5. habitante _____   e. número de años

14-2   Asuntos sociales. Many issues affect our society. For each social problem indicate which concept does not belong.

1. la estadística
   a. los datos   b. el promedio   c. la mayoría   d. la aduana

2. el divorcio
   a. la familia   b. la tensión   c. el porcentaje   d. los problemas económicos

3. la política
   a. el promedio   b. las elecciones   c. el gobierno   d. el presidente

4. el analfabetismo
   a. la escuela   b. la eficiencia   c. la educación   d. los libros

5. el tráfico
   a. los coches   b. el hogar   c. el autobús   d. la contaminación del aire

6. la confianza
   a. el amor   b. la honestidad   c. la ventaja   d. la amistad

14-3   **Contra el sexismo en el lenguaje.** The Institute of Women's Affairs (**Instituto de la Mujer**) in Spain has addressed the issue of sexism in the Spanish language. Read the resulting proposal and indicate whether the statements that follow are true (**C**) or false (**F**).

Reflexiones sobre formas lingüísticas sexistas que se deben evitar y ejemplos de propuestas alternativas: El género masculino utilizado como genérico

Tradicionalmente se han utilizado las palabras *hombre* y *hombres* con un sentido universal, ocultando o desdibujando la presencia, las aportaciones y el protagonismo de las mujeres.

Se propone la sustitución de *hombres y mujeres* en estos casos por *persona* o *personas, ser humano* o *seres humanos, humanidad, hombres y mujeres* o *mujeres y hombres,* sin dar preferencia en el orden al masculino o femenino.

NO	SÍ
El hombre	Los hombres y las mujeres / La humanidad
Los derechos del hombre	Los derechos de la mujer / Los derechos de las personas
El cuerpo del hombre	El cuerpo humano
La inteligencia del hombre	La inteligencia humana
El trabajo del hombre	El trabajo humano / El trabajo de mujeres y hombres
El hombre de la calle	La gente de la calle
A la medida del hombre	A la medida humana/de la humanidad/del ser humano

---

1. _____ La palabra "hombre" se ha usado con un sentido general que hace referencia a hombres y mujeres.

2. _____ El Instituto de la Mujer considera que el español es un idioma sexista.

3. _____ Según el Instituto de la Mujer, decir "el trabajo de los hombres y las mujeres" es sexista porque "los hombres" aparece antes que "las mujeres" en la frase.

4. _____ El Instituto de la Mujer propone sustituir "hombre" por "humano".

5. _____ Utilizar la palabra "hombre" en estas expresiones niega la contribución de la mujer a la sociedad.

14-4   El papel de la mujer. The role of women in society has changed over the years. You can probably see the change in your own family. Think of the domestic responsibilities and career of an older married family member (grandmother, mother, aunt, etc.) and the domestic responsibilities and career of a younger one (sister, cousin, etc.). Write a paragraph contrasting their domestic responsibilities and professional careers.

_____

_____

_____

_____

_____

_____

_____

_____

_____

_____

EXPLICACIÓN Y EXPANSIÓN

Síntesis gramatical

1. Adverbial conjunctions that always require the subjunctive

a menos que	para que
antes (de) que	sin que
con tal (de) que	

2. Adverbial conjunctions: Subjunctive or indicative

aunque	hasta que
cuando	mientras
después (de) que	según
donde	tan pronto como
en cuanto	

3. The past perfect

yo	había		
tú	habías		
Ud., él, ella	había	+	hablado
nosotros/as	habíamos		comido
vosotros/as	habíais		vivido
Uds., ellos/as	habían		

4. Infinitive as subject of a sentence and as object of a preposition

Caminar es buen ejercicio. *Walking is good exercise.*

Llama antes de **ir**. *Call before going.*

1. Adverbial conjunctions that always require the subjunctive

14-5   Los problemas de la sociedad. Society has many problems. For each of the following sentences, indicate which ending is better. Then indicate whether you agree with the statements.

	Estoy de acuerdo	*No estoy de acuerdo*
1. Muchas personas piensan que se dará el primer paso para terminar el racismo cuando... a. la sociedad admita que todavía existe el racismo. b. la sociedad admite que todavía existe el racismo. c. la sociedad ha admitido que todavía existe el racismo.	_____	_____
2. El problema de las drogas va a continuar hasta que... a. los padres y las escuelas se unen para combatir el problema. b. los padres y las escuelas se han unido para combatir el problema. c. los padres y las escuelas se unan para combatir el problema.	_____	_____
3. El desprecio (*disdain*) a las personas con SIDA va a desaparecer cuando... a. la gente comprende mejor la enfermedad y las formas de contagio. b. la gente comprenda mejor la enfermedad y las formas de contagio. c. la gente ha comprendido mejor la enfermedad y las formas de contagio.	_____	_____

4. Una mujer nunca va a ser presidenta de Estados   _____   _____
   Unidos a menos que...
   a. la sociedad sea menos sexista.
   b. la sociedad era menos sexista.
   c. la sociedad es menos sexista.

5. Los problemas en la educación no van a mejorar sin   _____   _____
   que el gobierno...
   a. dedica más dinero a la educación.
   b. dedique más dinero a la educación.
   c. dedicaba más dinero a la educación.

14-6   Del campo a la ciudad. Many people have emigrated from the country to the cities in search of a job and a better life. Mario's wife wants to move to Caracas from their small town, but her husband is reluctant. Complete the following sentences to find out Mario's concerns.

poder	encontrar	estudiar	vender	tener

1. No voy a la ciudad a menos que yo _____ un buen trabajo.

2. Voy a la ciudad con tal que nosotros _____ regresar a visitar a la familia frecuentemente.

3. No podemos ir a la ciudad antes de que _____ nuestra casa en el campo.

4. Iremos a la ciudad para que mi hija _____ en una buena escuela.

5. No iremos a la ciudad sin que _____ un apartamento que nos guste.

14-7   Las responsabilidades. Alicia and Jorge plan to get married, and Alicia is giving her expectations about the roles and responsibilities of their future home. Complete the sentences with the appropriate form of the verbs to find out how Alicia thinks responsibilities should be divided in their household. Then answer the questions that follow.

| sacar | lavar | trabajar | casarse | hacer |

Antes de que nosotros (1) _____, tenemos que ponernos de acuerdo sobre

las responsabilidades de cada uno. Yo puedo preparar el desayuno con tal que tú

(2) _____ las camas. Yo no voy a cocinar a menos que tú (3) _____

los platos. Yo estoy dispuesta a limpiar la casa para que tú (4) _____ algunas

horas extras si quieres. Yo no limpio la barbacoa a menos que tú (5) _____ al

perro a pasear.

6. ¿Quién sacará el perro a pasear?   a. Alicia   b. Jorge

7. ¿Quién hará las camas?   a. Alicia   b. Jorge

8. ¿Quién cocinará?   a. Alicia   b. Jorge

2. Adverbial conjunctions: Subjunctive or indicative

14-8   La rutina diaria. Cristina tells you about her daily activities as a working student. Complete the sentences with the correct form of the verbs to find out what her routine is like.

Me levanto a las seis, aunque (1) _____ (preferir) dormir hasta las siete. Me baño

tan pronto como (2) _____ (levantarse). Mientras (3) _____ (desayunar)

me gusta leer el periódico. En cuanto (4) _____ (llegar) a la oficina me pongo a

trabajar. Allí hago mis tareas según me (5) _____ (decir) el jefe. Trabajo hasta que

la oficina (6) _____ (cerrar) a la una. Almuerzo algo muy ligero, y salgo para la

universidad. Tan pronto como (7) _____ (llegar) a la universidad, voy a la

biblioteca. Me gusta estudiar donde no (8) _____ (haber) ruido. Cuando las clases

(9) _____ (terminar) a veces voy a la cafetería a tomar un café con mis amigos.

Después de que nosotros (10) _____ (hablar) un rato (*a while*), nos gusta salir a

caminar.

11. ¿Es la rutina de Cristina típica de un estudiante que trabaja? ¿Por qué? ¿Por qué no?

_____

_____

_____

14-9   Los planes futuros. Virginia tells you of her future plans. Complete the paragraph with the correct form of the verbs to discover what Virginia plans on doing in the future.

poder   recibir   existir   llegar   terminar

Cuando empecé a estudiar aquí en la universidad, nunca pensé que iba a terminar, pero eso ya es casi una realidad. El año próximo cuando (1) _____ mis estudios, pienso practicar mi profesión en otro país, pero todavía no sé en cuál. Mis padres no quieren que me vaya, pero vivimos en una ciudad pequeña donde no hay muchas oportunidades para una persona con mi especialidad. Me voy a quedar aquí hasta que (2) _____ ahorrar (*save*) bastante dinero para el viaje. Después de que (3) _____ la información acerca de las posibilidades de trabajo en otros países, decidiré adónde voy a ir, y haré los preparativos necesarios. Mis padres dicen que hay una posibilidad de que la fábrica de plásticos de nuestra ciudad me ofrezca un empleo, y ellos quieren que lo acepte cuando (4) _____ ese momento si es que llega. Aunque (5) _____ esa posibilidad no creo que cambie de parecer. Quiero una oportunidad para avanzar, pero también quiero conocer otros lugares, culturas y costumbres.

14-10   Condiciones para el matrimonio. Think about what kind of person you would marry. Complete each of the following sentences with the correct form of the verb and then indicate whether this applies to you (**sí**) or not (**no**).

	Sí	*No*

1. Me voy a casar cuando _____ (conocer) a una persona que sea comprensiva.   _____ _____

2. Me voy a casar aunque no _____ (encontrar) a una persona con buen sentido del humor.   _____ _____

3. Me voy a casar tan pronto como mi novio/a y yo _____ (ganar) suficiente dinero para comprar una casa.   _____ _____

4. Me voy a casar en cuanto yo _____ (graduarse).   _____ _____

5. Me voy a casar aunque mi pareja no _____ (querer) tener hijos.   _____ _____

6. Me voy a casar después de que yo _____ (establecerse) como profesional.   _____ _____

3. The past perfect

14-11   La clase de sociología. María's sociology instructor asked members of her class to pair up and do some research on women's roles in society during the last 30 years. María had an appointment in the library with her partner, Sofía, to do the research. Sofía was late, and María had done many things before Sofía arrived. Complete the following paragraph in which María tells you what she did before Sofía arrived.

Para cuando llegó Sofía yo ya (1) _____ (buscar) información sobre el tema en

Internet. También (2) _____ (leer) varios artículos sobre mujeres ejecutivas.

Asimismo (3) _____ (entrevistar) a la directora de un banco sobre su carrera

profesional y su vida en la casa. Además (4) _____ (consultar) varios libros en la

biblioteca y (5) _____ (encontrar) datos interesantes en algunas encuestas

realizadas.

14-12   ¿Qué había hecho? Have you done many different things in your life? Complete the following sentences about life events and then indicate whether they apply to you by writing **sí** or **no** at the end of each sentence.

manejar   recibir   viajar   hacer   participar

1. Para cuando tenía diez años, _____ en avión muchas veces. _____

2. Para cuando tenía cuatro años, _____ en varias obras de teatro de la

   escuela. _____

3. Para los diecisiete años _____ un coche deportivo. _____

4. Para cuando terminé la escuela secundaria, ya _____ muchas cartas de

   aceptación a diferentes universidades. _____

5. Para cuando terminó el primer semestre en la universidad, ya _____ muchos

   amigos. _____

14-13   La fiesta. You were supposed to help a friend get ready for a dinner party, but you got caught in traffic. When you finally arrived everything was ready. Write five sentences describing what your friend had done before you arrived.

MODELO: Mi amiga *había preparado un pastel.*

Para cuando llegué a su casa, mi amiga ya...

1. _____

2. _____

3. _____

4. _____

5. _____

4. Infinitive as subject of a sentence and as object of a preposition
_____

14-14   No puedo. Your little sister wants to know why you are not able to do certain things. Indicate the things without which you cannot perform the following actions.

1. No puedo manejar un auto sin tener _____.   a. un pasaporte

2. No puedo escribir una carta sin tener _____.   b. bolígrafo

3. No puedo comer pollo frito sin tener _____.   c. un sello

4. No puedo viajar a otro país sin tener _____.   d. licencia

5. No puedo mandar una tarjeta postal sin tener _____. e. aire

6. No puedo respirar sin tener _____.   f. tenedor y cuchillo

14-15   Reglas a seguir. Every day we see signs indicating what can or cannot be done at certain places. Write down the signs you might find in the following places.

MODELO: en una puerta de salida: *No entrar*

           estacionar   fumar   tocar   nadar   hablar

1. en las clases de la universidad: _____

2. en una playa donde el agua es profunda y las olas son muy altas: _____

3. enfrente de la entrada de un hospital: _____

4. en el cine cuando todos están viendo la película: _____

5. en una tienda donde se venden objetos de cristal: _____

14-16   ¿Qué hiciste? You have just returned home from your vacation, and your mother wants to know everything about it. Answer your mother's questions.

MODELO: ¿Qué hiciste al comprar el boleto?
Dar las gracias al agente.

1. ¿Qué hiciste antes de hacer la maleta? ¿Y antes de salir de casa?

_____

2. ¿Qué hiciste al llegar al aeropuerto?

_____

3. ¿Qué no pudiste hacer al acomodarte (*get settled*) en tu asiento de avión?

_____

4. ¿Qué hacías después de llegar a los hoteles? ¿Y después de cenar?

_____

MOSAICOS

14-17   Antes de leer. Roles distintos. Write a statement refuting or defending the following assertions.

1. Todos los miércoles las mujeres deben tener el derecho a entrar gratis a la discoteca.

_____

2. Un hombre siempre debe abrirle la puerta a una mujer.

_____

3. La mujer norteamericana se debe cambiar de apellido cuando se casa.

_____

4. El servicio militar debe ser obligatorio para los hombres y no para las mujeres.

_____

14-18   A leer. Roles compartidos. Read this article about roles shared by men and women, and then answer the questions that follow.

ESPECIAL: *VIDA EN PAREJA*

Roles compartidos

Desde hace varias décadas, la mujer ha abandonado su papel tradicional de ama de casa, de madre, de esposa, para incursionar en (*enter*) áreas que por siglos (*centuries*) han sido casi exclusivas del quehacer (*sphere of action*) masculino: ir a la universidad, prepararse y entrar a competir en el campo profesional. Asimismo (*Likewise*) los hombres también han demostrado una tendencia al cambio. Según algunos expertos en el campo de las relaciones de pareja, hoy en día, "los hombres se interesan cada vez más en que su matrimonio o relación de pareja funcione y se mantenga de por vida". En el aspecto sentimental, antes el hombre casi no se expresaba; generalmente optaba por guardarse (*keep to himself*) sus sentimientos, frustraciones, alegrías, desesperanzas, etcétera. Por ser una experiencia relativamente desconocida para la mujer, ésta se desconcierta, se sorprende, se confunde cuando el hombre se expresa, cuando llora en un intento de exteriorizar (*express*) sus emociones más íntimas.

De la misma manera (*Similarly*), en lo que respecta a (*concerning*) la vida del hogar, los hombres quieren participar activamente en más aspectos de la vida familiar, como en la educación de los hijos y en los asuntos (*matters*) del hogar y la familia: la limpieza de la casa, la preparación de la comida, el ciudado de los hijos, el lavado de la ropa, etcétera.

Lo positivo de todo esto es que ahora, más que antes, el hombre ha entendido que sus contribuciones al hogar no son exclusivamente económicas. Y ha sido la mujer quien ha sido responsable, tal vez sin quererlo, de incentivar este cambio de roles.

Indicate whether the following sentences are true (**C**) or false (**F**).

1. _____ Los hombres ya no contribuyen económicamente al hogar.

2. _____ Cada vez hay más mujeres que van a la universidad.

3. _____ Las mujeres muchas veces no comprenden bien cuando los hombres expresan sus sentimientos.

4. _____ Los hombres de hoy en día colaboran más en las tareas domésticas.

5. _____ Estos cambios de roles han sido causados por las mujeres.

6. _____ Los hombres antes estaban más preocupados por mantener relaciones estables.

14-19   Después de leer. Su opinión. Think about your opinions about the roles of women and men in society. Do you agree with the article? Explain why.

_____

_____

_____

_____

_____

14-20   Antes de escribir. Hombres y mujeres. List the various issues affecting men and women and indicate whether the status of the issue has changed in the last century and if it is likely to change in the future (improve or worsen).

	¿HA CAMBIADO?	**¿VA A CAMBIAR?**
MODELO: *el hombre y las tareas domésticas*	*Ha mejorado.*	*Va a mejorar aún más.*
1. _____	_____	_____
2. _____	_____	_____
3. _____	_____	_____
4. _____	_____	_____
5. _____	_____	_____
6. _____	_____	_____

14-21   A escribir. Conjeturas sobre el año 2050. In your view how will women and men's roles change by the mid–twenty-first century? Write a **pronóstico** for the year 2050. Think about the issues you mentioned in exercise 14-20. Think about other issues you might not have mentioned in exercise 14-20. Consider the following topics in your **pronóstico:**

- rol de ambos en el hogar: *Will they continue to share responsibilities? Will there be a reversal in parents' roles? Will men and women both receive time off to care for children? If not by 2050, when will they? Will they receive paid leave? If not by 2050, when?*

- acceso de la mujer al poder: *Will a woman become president of the United States? Why? If not, by when will a woman become president? What changes will need to occur?*

- igualdad en el trabajo: *Will an equal number of men and women hold positions as top executives? If not, when will this be a reality?*

_____

_____

_____

_____

_____

_____

_____

_____

_____

_____

_____

_____

_____

_____

_____

_____

14-22   **Después de escribir. ¿Y usted?** Think about your own life. Are you planning to have a career? And children? How will you manage both (e.g. will you take the children to day care? Will your husband/wife take care of them?)? Would you like your partner to have a career? Write a brief paragraph to describe how you see the female and male roles in your own life.

_____

_____

_____

_____

_____

_____

ENFOQUE CULTURAL

14-23   **La política en los países hispanos.** Read again the **Enfoque cultural** section on pages 527–530 in your textbook and indicate whether the following statements about the political situation in Hispanic countries are true (**C**) or false (**F**).

1. _____ Todos los países hispanoamericanos tienen democracia.

2. _____ Los guerrilleros son traficantes de drogas que luchan por proteger su negocio y sus intereses económicos.

3. _____ Los guerrilleros y el narcotráfico son problemas que afectan a algunos países hispanoamericanos.

4. _____ La desigualdad social y los problemas económicos se encuentran entre las causas de la existencia de las guerrillas.

5. _____ La transición política de España después de la muerte de Franco fue muy violenta.

6. _____ La mayoría de los jóvenes hispanos están muy interesados en política.

A PRIMERA VISTA

 14-24 **Actitudes diferentes.** Our society has undergone major changes in the last few decades; the beliefs and attitudes of our grandparents differ greatly from our own. Think about women in your grandmother's generation, how they lived and what their values were.

Now you are going to listen to a conversation between a young Hispanic woman and her grandmother. Listen once for the gist and select the answer for item 1 below. Then look at the rest of the items and listen again, this time focusing on the specific information you need.

1. La abuela de Elena tiene actitudes...
   a. modernas.
   b. tradicionales.
   c. a veces modernas y a veces tradicionales.

2. La abuela de Elena no quiere que...
   a. Elena invite a un chico a salir.
   b. Elena salga con un chico.
   c. Elena espere la llamada de un chico.

3. Elena piensa que ella...
   a. quiere estudiar, pero no quiere casarse.
   b. quiere casarse, pero no puede.
   c. puede hacer cualquier cosa que quiera.

4. La abuela teme que Elena...
   a. no quiera casarse nunca.
   b. no encuentre un chico que quiera casarse con ella.
   c. no se case si trabaja.

5. La abuela piensa que...
   a. las ideas de Elena son buenas en teoría, pero que la realidad es diferente.
   b. las ideas de Elena son muy malas: la mujer debe ser responsable del hogar y de la familia.
   c. las ideas de Elena son injustas para los hombres.

14-25   La mujer en la sociedad hispánica. You will now hear someone briefly describing the current situation of women in the Hispanic world, followed by several statements. Listen to both the description and the statements and indicate whether each of the following statements is true (**C**) or false (**F**).

1. _____ En los países hispanos todas las mujeres tienen una situación similar.

2. _____ La situación de la mujer ha mejorado más en la ciudad que en el campo.

3. _____ Los países hispanos están cerca de llegar a la igualdad entre hombres y mujeres.

4. _____ Casi todas las mujeres hispanas que trabajan fuera de casa comparten el trabajo doméstico con sus esposos.

5. _____ Las mujeres siempre ganan el mismo sueldo que ganan los hombres cuando hacen el mismo trabajo.

6. _____ Actualmente hay mujeres en grupos feministas y en algunos gobiernos, que trabajan por la igualdad en el trabajo y la sociedad.

14-26   La universidad virtual. With the development of the Internet, a multitude of services and information are available to people who had no access to them before. One area that is benefiting greatly from these technologies is education. Before listening to the presentation, think about how you use the Internet for your courses and academic work.

The **Universidad Abierta de Cataluña** in Spain has started a new program wherein the Internet plays a major role. Listen to the university's brief press presentation. Then look at the following incomplete summary and listen again, this time focusing on the specific information you need to complete the summary.

1. Algunos estudiantes no podían asistir a clase porque _____ o porque

   _____.

2. La educación a distancia ofrecía dos tipos de cursos: _____ y _____.

3. La nueva opción es un campus _____.

4. Dos ejemplos de actividades que los estudiantes pueden hacer desde sus casas:

   _____ y _____.

5. Hay sólo dos actividades que no pueden hacer en casa: _____ y

   _____.

14-27   Los alumnos de la universidad virtual. The presentation of the new program at the **Universidad Abierta de Cataluña** reports data on the student body of the program's inaugural class. You are writing a paper on the evolution of education, so you are interested in recording these data. Listen and complete the following table with the numerical figures mentioned. Write "%" after the figure if it is a percentage (for instance, "12%"). You may need to listen to the passage more than once.

1. número de solicitudes:	
2. número de alumnos aceptados:	
3. porcentaje que viven en el área de Barcelona:	
4. porcentaje que trabajan:	
5. porcentaje entre 25 y 40 años:	
6. porcentaje de hombres en ciencias empresariales:	
7. porcentaje de mujeres en psicopedagogía:	

EXPLICACIÓN Y EXPANSIÓN

1. Adverbial conjunctions that always require the subjunctive

14-28   Pensamos igual. Rebeca and you have been very good friends for a long time. You know each other so well that you sometimes finish each other's sentences. Listen to Rebeca and finish her sentences by selecting one of the following options and by responding orally, as in a real conversation.

1. _____   a. con tal de que mi esposo haga la mitad del trabajo.

2. _____   b. a menos que el gobierno actúe con severidad.

3. _____   c. para que las mujeres puedan descansar un poco.

4. _____   d. antes de que nosotras empecemos a trabajar.

5. _____   e. sin que nadie las ayude.

14-29   ¿Y usted, qué piensa? Rebeca and you are now talking about family life in Spain today. Listen to the sentences she starts and complete them with the conjunction given and with one of the phrases below. Remember to write the verb in the correct form.

tener buena salud y muchas visitas de parientes y amigos

casarse y vivir con su propia familia   los jóvenes poder independizarse antes

saber leer y escribir   las parejas tener más hijos

1. ...a menos que _____

2. ...antes de que _____

3. ...para que _____

4. ...con tal que _____

5. ...sin que _____

2. Adverbial conjunctions: Subjunctive or indicative

14-30   En casa de los padres. Fernando has finished college but, as many young adults in Spain, he still lives with his parents. Listen to him talk about his situation, and complete his sentences by selecting the appropriate option.

1. a. cuando empecé a trabajar.
   b. cuando empiece a trabajar.

2. a. en cuanto vi los precios del alquiler.
   b. en cuanto vea los precios del alquiler.

3. a. hasta que yo quiero.
   b. hasta que yo quiera.

4. a. cuando me casé.
   b. cuando me case.

5. a. mientras vivo con mis padres.
   b. mientras viva con mis padres.

14-31   En la sala de computadoras. You and your classmates are excited because today you are going to learn how to make a webpage. You are going to work in pairs. Listen to your teacher and then select the appropriate comment you make to your partner.

1. a. Nos podemos sentar donde queremos.
   b. Nos podemos sentar donde queramos.

2. a. Debemos hacer todo como él dice.
   b. Debemos hacer todo como él diga.

3. a. Aunque es fácil, necesito practicar.
   b. Aunque sea fácil, necesito practicar.

4. a. Según dice el profesor, todos vamos a crear una página web.
   b. Según diga el profesor, todos vamos a crear una página web.

3. The past perfect

14-32   Una vida diferente. Listen to Laura talk about her first semester and all the new things she experienced. Then indicate whether she had done the following things before coming to college or she did them for the first time in college.

	ANTES DE LA UNIVERSIDAD	EN LA UNIVERSIDAD
1. Tomar una siesta en la biblioteca.		
2. Llevar sandalias en la ducha.		
3. Compartir su cuarto con otra persona.		
4. Lavar su propia ropa.		
5. Ir de vacaciones sin su familia.		

Is your experience similar to Laura's?

14-33   Mi primer año en la universidad. Now it is your turn! Tell whether you had done each of the following activities by the time you started studying at the university.

MODELO: You hear: ir al doctor sin tus padres
           You say and write: *Cuando empecé la universidad, nunca había ido al doctor solo/a.* OR *Cuando empecé la universidad, yo ya había ido al doctor solo/a.*

1. _____

2. _____

3. _____

4. _____

5. _____

6. _____

4. Infinitive as subject of a sentence and as object of a preposition

14-34   Cuestión de salud. Many college students find it hard to maintain a healthy lifestyle during their first year in college. Laura wants to get back in shape, but she needs some friendly advice. Listen to her talk about some of her habits and tell her what you think, as in the model.

Modelo: You hear: Bebo muchas cervezas los fines de semana.
           You say: *Laura, beber cervezas no es bueno.*

           You hear: Bebo mucha agua todos los días.
           You say: *Muy bien, beber agua es bueno.*

1. _____

2. _____

3. _____

4. _____

5. _____

14-35   **¡Adivina!** Look at the following chart. By combining the prepositions and verbs, you will come up with different times and situations (e.g., **para dormir, antes de dormir**). Listen to the clues and guess the time or situation to which they refer. Then write the number of that clue in the appropriate cell in the chart, as in the model. In some cases, more than one answer may be possible.

Modelo: You hear: Uno. En España algunas personas toman una siesta en este momento.
           You guess and say: *después de comer*
           You write: (see chart)

	DORMIR	COMER	TENER BUENA SALUD
para			
antes de			
después de		1	
sin			

MOSAICOS

14-36   El futuro de la población española. In this lesson you have learned about the demographics of many Hispanic countries, including Spain. In the last decade there has been a dramatic change in the projections regarding population (**la población**) in Spain. Listen to the following report on the topic and then complete the chart.

	INFORME DE J. A. FERNÁNDEZ CORDÓN	**INFORME DEL INSTITUTO NACIONAL DE ESTADÍSTICA**
Año del informe		
Población en ese momento		
Tendencia demográfica		
Causas de esa tendencia		
Población estimada para 2020		

Lección 15

Nombre: _____

Fecha: _____

La ciencia y la tecnología

A PRIMERA VISTA

15-1   Las clases. Think about the following topics and decide in which class they are most likely to be discussed.

_____ 1. ser humano

_____ 2. computadora

_____ 3. deforestación

_____ 4. planeta

_____ 5. el río Amazonas

a. informática

b. astronomía

c. geografía

d. biología

e. ecología

15-2   El mundo de mañana. Primera fase. Do you think the world will be very different in the future? Complete the following predictions about the world of tomorrow. There are more choices than words needed.

| ciudades | basura | agujero (en la capa de ozono) | energía eléctrica y solar |
| Internet | satélite | contaminación | robots |

1. Dentro de unos años los coches funcionarán con _____.

2. Todos los hogares estarán conectados a la _____.

3. La _____ de los mares provocará la extinción de los peces.

4. Compañías públicas y privadas reciclarán la _____ urbana.

5. El tráfico aéreo será controlado por _____.

6. Las personas no tendrán que preocuparse por la limpieza porque ese trabajo lo harán

   los_____.

Segunda fase. Indicate whether you agree (**sí**) or disagree (**no**) with each of the statements above.

1. _____   4. _____

2. _____   5. _____

3. _____   6. _____

15-3   El mundo hoy. Look at the following topics related to our society and indicate which word does not refer to the topic.

1. atmósfera:
   - a. contaminación
   - b. aire
   - c. ozono
   - d. el correo electrónico

2. transporte:
   - a. tren
   - b. puerta
   - c. coche
   - d. cápsula voladora (*flying*)

3. tecnología:
   - a. teléfonos móviles
   - b. robots
   - c. medio ambiente
   - d. buscapersonas (*pagers*)

4. ciudades:
   - a. edificio
   - b. selva
   - c. basura urbana
   - d. transporte público

5. criminalidad:
   - a. inundación (*flooding*)
   - b. delincuente
   - c. policía
   - d. arma de fuego

15-4   Temas controvertidos. Think of two consequences that the following issues will have on the human race and human life in general.

1. la ingeniería genética:

   _____

   _____

2. la tercera guerra mundial:

   _____

   _____

3. el uso generalizado/absoluto de la tecnología:

   _____

   _____

4. la clonación:

   _____

   _____

EXPLICACIÓN Y EXPANSIÓN

Síntesis gramatical

1. The imperfect subjunctive

	HABLAR	COMER	VIVIR	ESTAR
yo	hablara	comiera	viviera	estuviera
tú	hablaras	comieras	vivieras	estuvieras
Ud., él, ella	hablara	comiera	viviera	estuviera
nosotros/as	habláramos	comiéramos	viviéramos	estuviéramos
vosotros/as	hablarais	comierais	vivierais	estuvierais
Uds., ellos/as	hablaran	comieran	vivieran	estuvieran

2. If *clauses*

condition (*if* clause)	result
present indicative	present/**ir a** + infinitive/future
Si yo consigo el dinero,	*pago/voy a pagar/pagaré la cuenta.*
imperfect subjunctive	conditional
Si yo consiguiera el dinero,	*pagaría la cuenta.*

3. **Se** *for unplanned occurrences*

SE + INDIRECT OBJECT PRONOUN + VERB

Se nos terminó la gasolina. *We ran out of gas.*

Se nos terminaron los refrescos. *We ran out of sodas.*

1. The imperfect subjunctive

15-5   El agente de viajes. Marta went on a trip to Chile last year. Complete Marta's story with the appropriate form of the verbs to find out how the trip went. Then indicate if the statements that follow are true (**C**) or false (**F**).

> ir   cancelar   sentar   visitar   pasar   cambiar   pagar

El año pasado llamé a una agencia de viajes para planear una excusión a Chile. Después de hablar con el agente, fui a la agencia a recoger (*pick up*) mi boleto. Pero cuando revisé el itinerario me di cuenta de algunos cambios. Había pedido un asiento de ventanilla, pero el agente me recomendó que me (1) _____ en un asiento de pasillo en las últimas filas (*rows*) del avión porque había menos pasajeros, y me asignó un asiento allí. Pedí que me (2) _____ de asiento, y lo hizo de muy pocas ganas. Después noté que el agente quería que (3) _____ a Iquique. Yo le dije que quería ir a Temuco. Entonces me sugirió que (4) _____ unos días en Puerto Varas. También me recomendó que (5) _____ Viña del Mar. Cuando me dijo el precio del billete y me pidió que (6) _____ en efectivo, me pareció sospechoso. En ese momento le dije que (7) _____ la reservación y decidí ir a otra agencia de viajes.

¿Cierto (**C**) o falso (**F**)?

8. _____ Marta estaba muy contenta con su agente de viajes.

9. _____ A Marta le gustó la recomendación del agente de viajes de ir a Iquique.

10. _____ A Marta le pareció barato el viaje, y lo compró inmediatamente.

15-6   De niño. What was your life like as a child? Complete the following statements in which Ramón tells you about his childhood. Then indicate whether they apply to you (**sí**) or (**no**).

jugar	comer	ser	visitar	hacer	ver

Cuando tenía 10 años,...   *Sí*   *No*

1. mi mamá quería que _____ toda mi comida.   _____ _____

2. mi mamá quería que _____ toda la tarea.   _____ _____

3. mi hermano quería que yo _____ a los videojuegos con él.   _____ _____

4. mi papá no me dejaba que _____ películas para adultos.   _____ _____

5. mis abuelos querían que los _____ todos los veranos.   _____ _____

6. mi papá quería que yo _____ abogado cuando creciera.   _____ _____

15-7   El viaje a España. Linda went with a group of friends to Spain last summer, but Cristina could not go because she had to work. Linda is telling Cristina all about the trip. Complete the dialog to find out how the vacation went and how Cristina reacted to the account.

LINDA: El viaje fue muy divertido. Primero fuimos a Torremolinos, pero nadie quiso hacer windsurfing.

CRISTINA: ¡Oh! Qué pena que nadie (1) _____ hacer windsurfing. He oído que es muy divertido.

LINDA: Diego conoció a una chica española y pasó dos días en la casa de campo de ella.

CRISTINA: ¡Qué bien! Me alegro que Diego (2) _____ a una chica española.

LINDA: Ese fin de semana que Diego no estaba, fuimos a visitar Sevilla. Nos encantó.

CRISTINA: Me alegro que (3) _____ a Sevilla y les gustara.

LINDA: Después nos fuimos a Santander. Lo pasamos genial, pero Pilar perdió su billetera.

CRISTINA: Siento que Pilar (4) _____ su billetera. ¿La encontró?

LINDA: No, pero no tenía muchas cosas dentro —sólo un poco de dinero. Las tarjetas de crédito y el pasaporte los tenía en un bolsillo del pantalón. En Santander lo pasamos muy bien. Fuimos a la playa y tomamos el sol.

CRISTINA: ¡Qué bien que (5) _____ a la playa!

LINDA: Finalmente fuimos a Bilbao, y nos perdimos cuando caminábamos por las calles para ver el museo Guggenheim.

CRISTINA: ¡Qué pena que (6) _____ en las calles de Bilbao!

LINDA: No nos importó: así conocimos Bilbao mejor y además encontramos un restaurante pequeño donde comimos platos deliciosos.

CRISTINA: Me alegro que (7) _____ platos deliciosos.

LINDA: El viaje fue maravilloso.

CRISTINA: Me alegro que el viaje (8) _____ un éxito. Siento no haber ido.

2. *If* clauses

15-8 Si yo fuera... If you were these people what would you do?

1. una actriz famosa _____
2. el presidente _____
3. profesor/a _____
4. un joven con problemas _____
5. astronauta _____
6. viudo/a _____

a. eliminaría los impuestos
b. me casaría otra vez
c. buscaría ayuda
d. viajaría por el espacio
e. viviría en Hollywood
f. no daría exámenes difíciles

15-9   El premio gordo. Valerie is thinking about what she would do if she won the lottery. Complete the following sentences to find out what Valerie would do with the money.

1. Si ganara la lotería...
   a. he dado dinero a la investigación contra el cáncer.
   b. donaría dinero a la Cruz Roja.
   c. ayudé a los desamparados.

2. Si recibiera suficiente dinero,...
   a. compraría una casa nueva.
   b. compré un carro nuevo.
   c. he regalado una casa a mis padres.

3. Si tuviera tiempo,...
   a. he hecho un safari fotográfico en Kenia.
   b. haría un viaje por el mundo.
   c. fui a un crucero por el caribe.

4. Si mi alma mater necesitara,...
   a. contribuiría con dinero.
   b. di dinero para ayudar a desarrollar las artes.
   c. he ayudado a las investigaciones científicas.

5. Si mis hermanos aún estuvieran estudiando,...
   a. he dado dinero a mis primos favoritos.
   b. abrí guarderías para personas de bajos recursos.
   c. les pagaría la universidad.

15-10   Si nosotros... Complete the sentences, expressing what you and your friends would do in the following circumstances.

1. Si viviéramos en una ciudad del futuro,

_____

2. Si visitáramos México,

_____

3. Si practicáramos español todos los días,

_____

4. Si hiciéramos más ejercicio,

_____

5. Si comiéramos alimentos más sanos,

_____

3. *Se* for unplanned occurrences

15-11   ¡Qué mala suerte! Read the following sentences in which Saulo tells you what happened to him and his friends before they got to school. Organize the events chronologically by writing the appropriate number next to each statement.

_____ Se nos perdieron las llaves, pero no nos dimos cuenta hasta el momento de salir de casa.

_____ Quisimos entrar en la casa de nuevo, pero se nos cerró la puerta.

_____ Ayer tuvimos mala suerte.

_____ Íbamos a tomar un autobús a la universidad, pero se nos acabó el dinero.

_____ Nos salió mal todo lo que hicimos

_____ Al fin un amigo nos llevó en su auto, y al llegar a la clase de español se nos cayeron los libros.

15-12 Problemas, problemas. Andrea and her friend Allyson have had a terrible day today. Complete the following sentences with the appropriate words to find out what happened.

a. el horno
b. la leche
c. el reloj
d. el libro de francés
e. las llaves

1. Esta mañana se nos acabó _____, y no pudimos desayunar.

2. Después fuimos a clase, y se nos olvidó _____.

3. A Andrea se le cayó _____ en la ducha. Se mojó, y ahora no funciona.

4. Se nos perdieron _____ del carro, y tuvimos que ir caminando a clase.

5. Lo peor de todo es que cuando salimos de casa se nos olvidó apagar _____, y hubo un incendio en nuestro apartamento.

15-13 ¿Qué pasó? Complete the following sentences to find out what happened to Laura during her mathematics exam yesterday. Then answer the question that follows.

perderse   olvidarse   quedarse   caerse   acabarse

1. Primero _____ el lápiz cinco veces.

2. Después _____ las fórmulas más importantes.

3. También _____ el bolígrafo y no lo podía encontrar.

4. _____ el papel y tuvo que pedirle más papel al profesor.

5. Por fin se había puesto tan nerviosa que _____ la mente en blanco.

6. ¿Cómo le fue en el examen a Laura?
   a. Bien. Tuvo problemas con los lápices y el bolígrafo, pero hizo un buen examen.
   b. Muy mal. No pudo recordar las cosas que le preguntaban. Seguramente suspendió.

15-14   **¿Qué pasó?** Explain the causes of the following situations. Use **se** to refer to unplanned events.

MODELO: Juan no puede leer el periódico. *Se le rompieron las gafas.*

1. Ángela no puede ir al concierto esta noche. _____

2. María tuvo que lavar los platos en el restaurante. _____

3. Carlos y Pedro no pueden entrar en casa. _____

4. Mario dejó su carro en el taller (*shop*). _____

5. Valentina se levantó tarde. _____

MOSAICOS

15-15   **Antes de leer. La tecnología.** It is clear that we are surrounded by technology, and we use it every day. There are many advantages to new technologies, but there are also some disadvantages. List at least four advantages and four disadvantages of the use of technology in our society.

Ventajas

1. _____

2. _____

3. _____

4. _____

5. _____

Desventajas

1. _____

2. _____

3. _____

4. _____

5. _____

15-16   A leer. Las redes computadorizadas. Read this article and answer the questions that follow.

Inminente amenaza de terrorismo cibernético

No hay duda de que la vida en nuestro planeta ha mejorado considerablemente con los avances tecnológicos de los últimos años. Indiscutiblemente, las tareas y rutinas diarias resultan más fáciles. Los medios de transporte por tierra, aire y mar son más rápidos y seguros, las comunicaciones y el correo electrónico nos ofrecen gran cantidad de información en nuestra propia casa, y los avances en el cuidado de la salud han prolongado la vida y la actividad de los seres humanos de una manera extraordinaria.

De esta manera (*Thus*) el ser humano depende cada vez más de la tecnología, y en particular de la informática. Esta realidad indiscutible se aplica con mayor fuerza a las naciones más industrializadas del mundo, donde tanto (*both . . .*) las ventajas como (*. . . and*) las desventajas de la tecnología se ven a diario. Estas últimas preocupan enormemente a las autoridades de las grandes potencias (*powers*), quienes temen desastres de consecuencias impredecibles (*unpredictable*). ¿Podría usted imaginar los efectos de un ataque a la estructura cibernética de su país? ¿Qué ocurriría si un genio de la informática infiltrara las redes de comunicación de su país y las paralizara? ¿Estaría el gobierno de su país preparado para enfrentar (*to face*) el terrorismo cibernético? Ataques de este tipo no sólo (*not only*) afectarían a la infraestructura de las comunicaciones sino también (*but also*) a la seguridad del país. Esta preocupación ha llevado a los Estados Unidos a crear comisiones de expertos que estudien estos problemas y propongan recomendaciones que ayuden a prevenir y, en el peor de los casos, a hacerles frente a ataques terroristas realizados a través de la cibernética.

Los avances tecnológicos sin duda han cambiado el rostro (*face*) de la guerra (*war*) y las estrategias que usaremos para enfrentarla. Según los expertos el terrorismo cibernético es un peligro cada día más real e inmediato para los Estados Unidos. Algunos centros de investigación han descrito el resultado de ataques potenciales sobre estructuras privadas o públicas: se paralizarían los centros de llamadas de urgencia, se utilizarían los canales de televisión para amenazar, se modificarían las trayectorias de los trenes y aviones para provocar choques, se falsificarían cuentas bancarias y se producirían gigantescas fallas (*breakdowns*) en el sistema eléctrico.

Los expertos afirman con bastante seguridad (*certainty*) que la próxima guerra no se hará con balas (*bullets*) sino con la información. Lo peor es que la guerra cibernética está al alcance (*within the reach*) de todos. Los guerreros del espacio cibernético son anónimos y sólo requieren (*need*) un teléfono móvil, un módem y una microcomputadora (*laptop computer*).

De esto ya existen antecedentes: hace algunos años la bolsa (*stock market*) de Nueva York recibió una advertencia (*warning*) de un pirata cibernético alemán, quien les aseguró a los encargados (*clerks*) de seguridad que ya había logrado controlar los sistemas informatizados de la climatización en las salas donde están las supercomputadoras.

Indicate whether the following sentences are true (**C**) or false (**F**) according to the article.

1. _____ No hay ventajas del uso de la tecnología en nuestra sociedad.

2. _____ Un ataque cibernético tendría efectos muy negativos en la seguridad de un país.

3. _____ Los Estados Unidos es el único país que tiene riesgo (*risk*) de un ataque cibernético.

4. _____ Los Estados Unidos está preparándose por si sufre un ataque cibernético.

5. _____ Para ser un terrorista cibernético, se necesitan supercomputadoras.

6. _____ Un pirata cibernético alemán llegó a controlar las supercomputadoras de la bolsa de Nueva York.

7. _____ Un ataque cibernético podría causar accidentes aéreos.

15-17   Después de leer. Decisiones. Do you agree or disagree with the following statement related to cyberterrorism? Why?

El presidente de los Estados Unidos debería dedicar más dinero para proteger a los Estados Unidos de un ataque cibernético.

_____

_____

_____

_____

15-18 **Antes de escribir. Un ataque cibernético.** After reading the previous article, you, a common citizen, feel extremely concerned about the effects a cyberattack would have on your country, and particularly on your local community and family. Think about a possible a cyberattack and list the consequences that common citizens would face at work, home, school, and so on. Also list the problems that service institutions (hospitals, police, stores, etc.) would encounter.

CONSECUENCIAS PARA LOS CIUDADANOS	CONSECUENCIAS PARA LOS HOSPITALES, LA POLICÍA, LAS TIENDAS, ETCÉTERA

15-19   **A escribir. El terrorismo cibernético.** Having in mind all the concerns you listed in exercise 15-18, write a letter to the editor of your local newspaper, expressing your concern about a cyberattack. Make sure you explain all the concerns you mentioned and propose some realistic recommendations to the local and federal government to prevent a cyberdisaster.

_____

_____

_____

_____

_____

_____

_____

_____

_____

_____

_____

_____

_____

15-20   Después de escribir. Su opinión. A neighbor from your town has read your editorial and has become concerned about a cyberattack. He calls you to find out more about the topic.

1. ¿Crees que hay muchas posibilidades de que ocurra un ataque cibernético?

   _____

2. ¿Hay algo que los ciudadanos comunes podamos hacer para protegernos?

   _____

3. ¿Qué es, en tu opinión, lo peor que podría pasar?

   _____

4. ¿Cuándo es posible un ataque cibernético?

   _____

5. ¿Crees que los Estados Unidos está suficientemente protegido contra un ataque cibernético?

   _____

ENFOQUE CULTURAL

15-21   La economía, la industria y la tecnología en los países hispanos. Read again the **Enfoque cultural** section on pages 553–556 in your textbook and indicate whether the following statements about the economy of Hispanic countries are true (**C**) or false (**F**).

1. _____ En general en todos los países hispanos hay avances industriales y tecnológicos.

2. _____ Existen acuerdos entre algunos países hispanos para poder mejorar el comercio entre ellos.

3. _____ Colombia y Argentina son miembros del Grupo de los Tres.

4. _____ La producción de ropa y zapatos es muy importante en la economía española.

5. _____ La base de la economía de los países de América Central ha sido hasta ahora la agricultura.

6. _____ La industria ganadera es muy importante en Bolivia.

7. _____ El país que produce más aluminio del mundo es Argentina.

8. _____ El vino es una parte importante de la economía chilena.

A PRIMERA VISTA

15-22   Los cambios climáticos. Many young people are concerned about environmental issues. This concern is reflected in the growing number of college courses related to the topic. Before listening, think about courses you have taken wherein environmental issues were discussed. What did you talk about? Was there a common attitude?

Now listen to the conversation between Mario and Felipe and the questions that follow. Then select the appropriate answers from the following choices. You may listen to the conversation again to check and complete your answers.

1. a. la contaminación   b. el cambio climático   c. el pronóstico del tiempo

2. a. en Colombia   b. en España   c. en Argentina

3. a. los cambios en la historia   b. las noticias optimistas   c. la extinción de animales

4. a. por los veranos   b. por el crecimiento de   c. observando el sol
                                   los árboles

5. a. la actividad humana   b. el nivel del mar   c. la composición del hielo

15-23   Nuestro planeta. Some students are not only concerned about the environment, but they actually take action. Such is the case of Gisela and Ramón. First listen to the conversation for the gist, then read the following statements and indicate who expressed each idea: Gisela or Ramón.

	GISELA	RAMÓN
1. Los estudiantes deben hacer algo para mejorar el medio ambiente.		
2. Los estudiantes no tienen poder para conseguir cambios importantes.		
3. La Asociación Estudiantil colaborará con el proyecto de reciclaje (*recycling*).		
4. Necesitan medios de transporte para que el proyecto tenga éxito.		
5. En la cafetería hay muchas cosas que se pueden reciclar.		
6. Los primeros anuncios van a estar en la cafetería.		

15-24   Un futuro diferente. Older generations often say that they would have never anticipated the advances they have witnessed in their lifetime. Have you ever imagined what the future will bring? Look at the following chart and anticipate some novelties we could have in the areas listed. Then listen to the sentences and indicate the area of life to which each refers.

	LA ALIMENTACIÓN	EL TIEMPO LIBRE	LA EDUCACIÓN
1.			
2.			
3.			
4.			
5.			
6.			

15-25   Las ciudades del futuro. Read the statements below. Then listen to the conversation between Emilia and Camilo regarding an article Emilia read. Indicate whether the following statements are true (**Cierto**) or false (**Falso**). Finally, correct the false statements.

		CIERTO	FALSO
1.	En las ciudades del futuro habrá menos personas. _____		
2.	Las ciudades usarán energía atómica. _____		
3.	Los edificios de las ciudades del futuro van a ser muy altos. _____		
4.	Habrá ciudades en el mar y en el espacio. _____		
5.	Los helicópteros conectarán unas ciudades con otras. _____		
6.	Los coches usarán un tipo especial de combustible (*fuel*). _____		

EXPLICACIÓN Y EXPANSIÓN

1. The imperfect subjunctive

15-26   El primer turista del espacio. Space tourism is already becoming a reality. The first Mexican space tourist is now in space, and your roommate has seen him on a television interview from the space station. Listen to your roommate as he tells you what this tourist said. Then complete the man's actual statements, using the present tense, as in the model. Note that some sentences will require a verb in the subjunctive.

MODELO: You hear: Agradeció que los astronautas la trataran tan bien.
           You write: Quiero dar las gracias a los astronautas porque me *tratan* muy
                        bien.

1. Hay algo sorprendente: la Tierra _____ azul.

2. La sensación más extraña es que mi cuerpo no _____ peso.

3. Es importante que los astronautas _____ mucha preparación.

4. Es necesario que _____ más programas espaciales.

5. Quiero que otras personas _____ esta experiencia.

15-27   Consejos para un viaje al espacio. You were so fascinated by the idea of space tourism that you decided to do it too. Before going on your space trip, you called the man who went before you and asked for advice. Listen to his suggestions and then tell your friends what he said to you.

MODELO: You hear: Sea valiente.
           You say and write: *Me dijo que fuera valiente.*

1. _____

2. _____

3. _____

4. _____

5. _____

15-28   ¡Un extraterrestre en la estación espacial! Your trip was quite extraordinary: you even had a visit from an extraterrestrial creature! After it left, the other tourists gave their impressions. You were more suspicious than they were. Listen to what the others say and repeat their statements, both orally and in writing, changing them to reflect your doubts: **Habla como si...**

MODELO: You hear: Parece que es muy simpático.
           You say and write: *Habla como si fuera muy simpático.*

1. _____

2. _____

3. _____

4. _____

5. _____

2. *If* clauses

15-29   Imaginando un futuro mejor. Many young people are optimistic about the future and hope life improves greatly. Listen to some of the hypotheses these people make and select a logical consequence from among the options on the right.

1. _____   a. Tendríamos más tiempo libre.

2. _____   b. Nuestro planeta no tendría tanta basura.

3. _____   c. No habría problemas de tráfico en las ciudades.

4. _____   d. El aire y el agua estarían más limpios.

5. _____   e. Menos personas morirían.

15-30   Y usted, ¿qué haría? How would you take advantage of future possibilities? Listen to the questions and respond, both orally and in writing.

1. _____

2. _____

3. _____

4. _____

5. _____

3. *Se* for unplanned occurrences

15-31   **¿A propósito o accidental?** You are going to hear about things that have happened lately to some people. Some of these things were done on purpose whereas others were accidental. Listen carefully to the narration of these events and select whether they were done on purpose (**a propósito**) or accidentally (**accidentalmente**).

	A PROPÓSITO	ACCIDENTALMENTE
1.		
2.		
3.		
4.		

15-32   **¡Qué mala suerte!** You and your friends are having one of those days when everything seems to go wrong. Listen to Miguel as he goes over what happened to everybody, and select who was affected by each event.

	A MIGUEL	A TI	A JAVIER	A JAVIER Y A TI	A JAVIER Y DARÍO
1.					
2.					
3.					
4.					
5.					
6.					

15-33   **Durante el examen.** Unfortunately the worst was not over: your bad luck remained for your exam. Listen as Miguel tells you what happened to him during the exam. Then tell him what happened to you by using the cues you see.

MODELO: You hear: Se me olvidaron los verbos.
           You see: escribir mi nombre.
           You say and write: *Y a mí se me olvidó escribir mi nombre.*

1. el papel _____

2. la calculadora _____

3. los cuadernos _____

4. la computadora _____

5. las tareas _____

MOSAICOS

 15-34   La realidad virtual. Advances in technology are happening so fast that sometimes it is hard to keep up. Listen to Héctor talk about virtual reality with his grandmother. Then indicate whether the following statements are true (**Cierto**) or false (**Falso**). Finally, correct the false statements.

	CIERTO	FALSO
1. Según Héctor, la realidad virtual es como estar en un lugar que parece real pero no lo es. _____		
2. La abuela quiere visitar un lugar que ya no existe. _____		
3. Para tener una experiencia con realidad virtual, se necesita un cibercasco (*cyberhelmet*). _____		
4. En la realidad virtual se pueden ver y oír cosas pero no tocarlas. _____		
5. La abuela piensa que, seguramente, la realidad virtual es mejor que un libro. _____		
6. Los pilotos y médicos se divierten con la realidad virtual en su tiempo libre. _____		

Notas

Notas

Notas

Notas

Notas

Notas

Notas

Notas

Notas

Notas

Notas

Notas